# *Biology: A Critical-Thinking Approach*

## Anton E. Lawson

*Teacher's Guide*

**Addison-Wesley Publishing Company**
Menlo Park, California • Reading, Massachusetts • New York
Don Mills, Ontario • Wokingham, England • Amsterdam • Bonn
Paris • Milan • Madrid • Sydney • Singapore • Tokyo
Seoul • Taipei • Mexico City • San Juan

Participants:

The following teachers have participated in trial testing of *Biology: A Critical Thinking Approach* and have provided several critical comments and recommendations. This has contributed substantially to the development of the program.

Ronald Adams

Alfred Andrews

John Arlee

Steven Armstrong

David Barner

Kathryn Blattman

Margaret Burton

Scott Centanni

Richard Cherry

Clyde Christensen

Raymond Collins

Kenneth Costenson

Roy Doyle

William Erlenmeyer

Barry Feldman

Marcia Fischer

Richard Forshier

Margarita Gannos

Bill Gilsinger

Scott Greenhalgh

Kenneth Grubbs

Sarojnie Jagernauth

Bart James

Robert Johnson

Jorgi Katsenes

Larry Kellerman

Thomas Kirsch

Wendy Longston

Gene Maison

Barbara Ewan McGaughey

Richard Merenkow

Joe Miller

Roger Olander

Brad Olsen

David Pile

Paul Plummer

Caroline Purser

Dwight Rawlings

Barbara Ruff

Deb Schlice

Jan Snyder

Marilyn South

Dennis Stadel

Janet Stein

Windy Rose Stelmach-Thomas

Paul Tennyson

Edward Thompson

Jan Tiede

David Tollefson

Jacqueline Tooley

Michael Trimble

Robert Turley

James Ware

John Wescr

William Worsnop

Editorial and Production: Navta Associates, Inc.
This book is published by Innovative Learning™, an imprint of Addison-Wesley's Alternative Publishing Group.

This book is printed
on recycled paper.

# Table of Contents

## Preface to the Teacher

The following curriculum has been designed for use in high-school biology courses. The curriculum uses the learning-cycle method of instruction that consists of three phases—exploration, term introduction, and concept application. The learning cycle provides students freedom to inquire into biological phenomena, stimulates their interest and curiosity, and allows them to discover key patterns of regularity in those phenomena. This in turn allows important biological theories and terms to be introduced and applied in an orderly fashion. An emphasis is placed on active student participation in the knowledge construction process, thereby maximizing the likelihood that instruction will result not only in specific biological knowledge but also in an understanding of the nature of the investigative process and of the creative- and critical-thinking skills and values used in that process.

I am extremely grateful to Frank Collea and Charles Puglia of the National Science Foundation and to the foundation itself for providing the encouragement and funds for the initial phases of this project. We also wish to express thanks to Jack Renner, Robert Karplus, Chester Lawson, Ralph Lewis, and the many former students of BIO 480: Methods of Teaching High-School Biology at Arizona State University, as well as the staffs of the Science Curriculum Improvement Study and the Biological Sciences Curriculum Study for their many helpful ideas and suggestions and their pioneering work in the field of biological sciences curriculum development.

Last, but most certainly not least, we wish to thank Penny Pandelisav, Amy Rosenhaus, Janet Gould, and Jennifer Ashley for their excellent help in editing and typing both the preliminary and final versions of the manuscript.

## Program Goals

In 1961, the Educational Policies Commission of the United States drafted a document entitled *The Central Purpose of American Education* (National Education Association of the United States, 1961). In that document, the commission identified the central objective of education in America. That objective, in their words, is "freedom of the mind." It is their belief that no person is born free; thus, schools must foster intellectual skills required for this essential freedom.

A free mind is one that can think and choose. According to the Educational Policies Commission, rational abilities exist, which if acquired, constitute the free mind. These abilities allow one to apply reason and the available evidence to ideas, attitudes, and actions, and to better pursue whatever goals he or she may have.

In 1966, the Educational Policies Commission, recognizing the key role that could be played by science education in the development of the ability to think, published a second document, entitled *Education and the Spirit of Science* (National Education Association of the United States, 1966). In that document, they emphasized science not so much as a body of accumulated knowledge but as a way of thinking, a spirit of rational inquiry driven by a belief in its efficiency and by a restless curiosity to know and to understand. They also emphasized that this mode of thought, this spirit, relates to questions people usually ask and answer for reasons that they may think are totally nonscientific—religious, aesthetic, humanistic, literary. Thus, the spirit of science infuses many forms of scholarship besides science itself.

Although it was recognized that no particular scientist may fully exemplify the spirit of science nor may his or her work be totally objective, it is clear that the following key values or "patterns of creative and critical reasoning" underlie science as an enterprise.

1. Longing to know and to understand
2. Questioning of all things
3. Search for data and their meaning
4. Demand for verification
5. Respect for logic
6. Consideration of premises
7. Consideration of consequences

This list, by its nature, insists that students are not indoctrinated to think or act a certain way. Rather, it insists that they acquire the ability to make up their own minds—to develop freedom of the mind—and to learn to make their own decisions based on reason and evidence. In this sense, the values of science are the most complete expression of one of the deepest human values—the belief in human dignity. Consequently, these values are part and parcel of any true science but, more basically, of rational thought, and they apply not only in science but in every area of life where decisions must be made.

More recently the American Association for the Advancement of Science (*Science for All Americans*, 1989) echoed the importance of scientific knowledge and scientific ways of thinking within their goal of scientific literacy for all Americans. In their words, a scientific person "uses scientific knowledge and scientific ways of thinking for individual and social purposes" (p. 11). More specifically they state: "Scientific habits of mind can help people in every walk of life to deal sensibly with problems that often involve evidence, quantitative considerations, logical arguments, and uncertainty; without the ability to think critically and independently, citizens are easy prey to dogmatists, flimflam artists, and purveyors of simple solutions to complex problems" (p. 13). Regrettably, a review of the current state of affairs in the United States led AAAS to conclude that most Americans are not scientifically literate.

To achieve scientific literacy, the AAAS advocates a teaching/learning approach that starts with questions about nature, engages students actively, concentrates on the collection and use of evidence, does not separate knowing from finding out, and de-emphasizes the memorization of technical vocabulary. This theme of inquiry and de-emphasis of meaningless memorization is also evident in the words of the National Research Council's Commission of Life Science (1990). In their recent book entitled *Fulfilling the Promise: Biology Education in the Nation's Schools*, the commission states:

> We need a much leaner biology course that is constructed from a small number of general principles that can serve as scaffolding on which students will be able to build further knowledge. . . Concepts must be mastered through inquiry not memorization of words. The number of new words introduced must be kept to an absolute minimum (p. 21).

The present course has been designed to achieve scientific literacy in the way advocated by the Education Policies Commission, the AAAS, and by the Life Science Commission. Because creative and critical thinking skills, scientific knowledge, and values develop best through attempts to explore and explain nature, the laboratory and field experiences in this course emphasize biology as an investigative process and in so doing will help students become scientifically literate.

## Creative- and Critical-Thinking Skills

Creative- and critical-thinking skills essential to the accurate description and explanation of events in all aspects of life can be divided into the following seven categories:

1. Describing nature accurately

2. Sensing and stating causal questions about nature

3. Recognizing, generating, and stating alternative hypotheses and theories

4. Generating logical predictions

5. Planning and conducting controlled experiments to test hypotheses

6. Collecting, organizing, and analyzing relevant experimental and correlational data

7. Drawing and applying reasonable conclusions

Some of the above skills are creative, while others are critical. Still others involve both creative and critical aspects of scientific thinking. We are defining a skill as "the ability to do something well." Skilled performance includes knowing what to do, when to do it, and how to do it. In other words, being skilled at something involves knowing a set of procedures, knowing when to apply those procedures, and being proficient at executing those procedures. The general skills listed above can be delimited further into the following subskills:

---

1.00     Describing nature accurately
  1.10    Describing objects in terms of observable characteristics
  1.20    Seriating objects in terms of observable characteristics
  1.30    Classifying objects in terms of observable characteristics
  1.40    Describing, seriating, classifying, and measuring objects in terms of such variables as amount, length, area, weight, volume, and density
  1.50    Identifying variable and constant characteristics of groups of objects
     1.51    Identifying continuous and discontinuous variable characteristics and naming specific values of those characteristics
     1.52    Measuring, recording, and graphing the frequency of occurrence of certain values of characteristics in a sample of objects
     1.53    Determining the average, median, and modal values of the frequency distribution in 1.52
  1.60    Recognizing the difference between a sample and a population and identifying ways of obtaining a random (unbiased) sample
     1.61    Making predictions concerning the probability of occurrence of specific population characteristics based on the frequency of occurrence of those characteristics in a random sample
2.00     Sensing and stating causal questions about nature
  2.10    Recognizing a causal question from observations of nature or in the context of a paragraph or article
  2.20    Distinguishing between an observation and a question
  2.30    Recognizing a question even when it is stated in expository form rather than in interrogatory form
  2.40    Distinguishing a question from a possible answer to a question (hypothesis) even when the hypothesis is presented in interrogatory form
  2.50    Distinguishing between descriptive and causal questions

---

3.00    Recognizing, generating, and stating alternative hypotheses (causal explanations) and theories

   3.10    Distinguishing a hypothesis from a question

   3.20    Differentiating between a statement that describes an observation or generalizes from the observation and a statement that is a hypothesis (causal explanation) for the observation

   3.30    Recognizing the tentativeness of a hypothesis or theory

   3.40    Distinguishing between a tentative explanation for a phenomenon (hypothesis) and a term used merely to label the phenomenon

   3.50    Generating systematically all possible combinations of created hypotheses

4.00    Generating logical predictions

   4.10    Differentiating between hypotheses and predictions

5.00    Planning and conducting controlled experiments to test hypotheses

   5.10    Selecting reasonable alternative hypotheses to test

   5.20    Differentiating between an uncontrolled observation and an experiment involving controls

   5.30    Recognizing that only one independent factor in an experiment should be varied

      5.31    Recognizing the independent variable factor and the dependent variable factor(s)

      5.32    Recognizing the factors being held constant in the partial controls

   5.40    Recognizing experimental and technical problems inherent in experimental designs

   5.50    Criticizing faulty experiments when

      5.51    the experimental design was such that it could not yield an answer to the question

      5.52    the experiment was not designed to test the specific hypotheses stated

      5.53    the method of collecting the data was unreliable

      5.54    the data were not accurate

      5.55    the data were insufficient in number

      5.56    proper controls were not included

6.00    Collecting, organizing, and analyzing relevant experimental and correlational data

   6.10    Recognizing the existence of errors in measurement

   6.20    Recognizing when the precision of measurement given is warranted by the nature of the question

   6.30    Organizing and analyzing data

      6.31    Constructing tables and frequency graphs

      6.32    Measuring, recording, and graphing the values of two variables on a single graph

      6.33    Constructing a contingency table of discontinuous variables

   6.40    Seeing elements in common to several items of data

   6.50    Recognizing prevailing tendencies and trends in data and in extrapolating and interpolating

| | |
|---|---|
| 6.60 | Applying quantitative notions of probability, proportion, percent, and correlation to natural phenomena; recognizing when variables are related additively or multiplicatively; and setting up simple quantitative equations describing these relationships |
| 6.61 | Recognizing direct, inverse, or no relationship between variables |
| 6.62 | Recognizing that when two things vary together, the relationship may be coincidental, not causal |
| 6.63 | Recognizing additional evidence needed to establish cause and effect (see 6.62) |
| 7.00 | Drawing and applying reasonable conclusions |
| 7.10 | Evaluating relevancy of data and drawing conclusions through a comparison of actual results with predicted results |
| 7.11 | Differentiating between direct and indirect evidence |
| 7.12 | Recognizing data that are unrelated to the hypothesis |
| 7.13 | Recognizing data that support a hypothesis |
| 7.14 | Recognizing data that do not support a hypothesis |
| 7.15 | Combining both supporting and contradicting evidence from a variety of sources to weigh the likely truth or falsity of hypotheses |
| 7.16 | Postponing judgment if no evidence or insufficient evidence exists |
| 7.17 | Recognizing the tentativeness inherent in all scientific conclusions |
| 7.20 | Applying conclusions to new situations |
| 7.21 | Refraining from applying conclusions to new situations that are not closely analogous to the experimental situation |
| 7.22 | Being aware of the tentativeness of conclusions about new situations even when a close parallel exists between the two situations |
| 7.23 | Recognizing the assumptions that must be made in applying a conclusion to a new situation |

These skills function in concert in the mind of the creative and critical thinker as he or she learns about the world. They include key steps and the key words *If, and, then,* and *therefore* as depicted in Figure 1. The skills are, in essence, learning tools essential for success and even for survival. Hence, if you help students improve their use of these creative and critical thinking skills, you have helped them become more intelligent and have helped them "learn how to learn."

Acquiring these skills involves psychological and developmental considerations; therefore, one cannot expect them to be acquired as a consequence of brief instructional intervention. Because they are intimately related to one another in the overall process of question asking and answering, they cannot be taught in isolation from each other or from the phenomena (content) of science, which serves to pose relevant questions and to provide the necessary motivation to engage in the process in the first place. In this sense, the content of science is crucial because it allows questions to be raised, alternative ideas to be created and argued about, and evidence to be gathered in their test. It is through the examination of students' alternative conceptions that have been acquired spontaneously through their own personal attempts to understand nature that arguments and the need for evidence arises, which in turn provides the opportunity for students to 1) become dissatisfied with prior unscientific conceptions and develop more appropriate scientific conceptions and 2) abstract the forms of logical argumentation used in the process and thus acquire the creative and critical thinking skills listed previously.

Thus, real inquiries into specific content enable thinking skills to develop. Importantly, however, which specific content one uses does not matter provided it is developmentally appropriate, is used to provoke questioning, and stimulates the creation and testing of hypotheses. In science, one cannot teach to one objective at a time, just as one cannot demand understanding in a short period of time. All effective science instruction has at least two objectives: 1) to help students acquire creative and critical thinking skills, and 2) to help them understand the causes of fundamentally important natural phenomena. Neither is achieved easily or quickly.

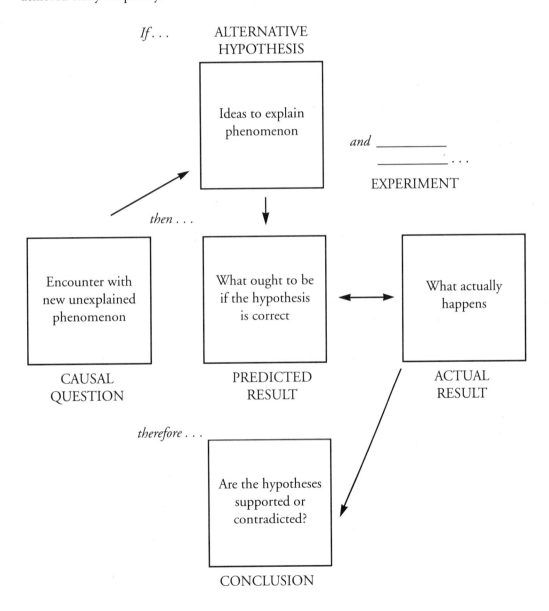

## The Nature of Hypotheses

Most high-school students do not have a clear understanding of the role of hypotheses in science. Because hypotheses play such a crucial role in science and in this curriculum, obtaining a clear understanding is absolutely essential. To start, it will be helpful to state what hypotheses are *not*. They are not merely educated guesses. Creating hypotheses does require some background knowledge and an element of guessing, but not all educated guesses are hypotheses.

Suppose, for example, that you taste a green apple and discover it sour. After tasting a second, third, and fourth green apple, you find them also sour. So, from this "education" you "guess" that all green apples are sour, and on the basis of this you predict that the next green apple you taste will also be sour. Does your educated guess that "all green apples are sour" constitute a hypothesis? No. It is not. It is merely a generalization (an induction) based on limited experience. Is the educated guess that "the next green apple will be sour" a hypothesis? Again, no. Instead, it is better referred to as a *prediction*.

The American College Dictionary defines the word *hypothesis* as "a proposition or set of propositions proposed as an explanation for some specific group of phenomena." Further, the same dictionary defines the word *explain* as "to make clear the cause or reason of; account for." Thus, a hypothesis is defined as "a proposed explanation, a tentative cause for some specific observation"—in this case, a tentative cause for the sourness of the green apples. Perhaps the apples lack sugar molecules. Perhaps they contain an excess of "sour" molecules. Can you think of any other alternative hypotheses?

Philosophers use the term *abduction* to refer to the process of creating hypotheses; for example, abduction consists of studying the facts and devising an explanation for them. Obviously, doing so requires some education and some guessing, but it is guessing about causes, the guesses coming not from logical induction or deduction but from the creative process of abduction. The guesses are made by sensing ways in which the current situation is somehow analogous to other situations in the past such that you can borrow ideas from those situations and apply them as hypotheses to the present situation.

Finally, good scientists do not merely state one possible cause but state as many alternative possibilities as they can think of. Then they set out to devise ways of testing the alternatives by deducing their logical consequences and comparing these with evidence, as previously depicted in Figure 1.

## Appropriate Content to Stimulate Thinking

The structure of biology consists not only of its methods of inquiry but of its theories as well. The term *theory* will be used to refer to a set of general statements that function together to explain a phenomenon or set of related phenomena. A theory may or may not represent an adequate explanation. Many theories of the past seemed adequate at the time but subsequently have been rejected or modified. Nevertheless, they remain theories. To determine whether a theory is a "good" one, its general statements must be tested as discussed above. It is by no means an understatement to say that the central purpose of modern biology is to construct comprehensive and satisfactory theories about life.

Perhaps the best way to provide you with a sense of how the term *theory* is used is to offer a few examples. Below are the major statements (often referred to as postulates) of two major theories of biology that are relevant to the investigations in this curriculum.

### Postulates of the Theory of Natural Selection

*(To explain how organisms adapt to their environments)*

1. Populations of organisms have the tendency and the potential to increase at a geometric rate.

2. In the short run, the number of individuals in a population remains fairly constant because the conditions of life are limited.

3. Individuals in a population are not all the same; they have variations (variable characteristics).

4. A struggle for survival exists so that individuals having favorable characteristics will survive and produce more offspring than those with unfavorable characteristics.

5. Some of the characteristics responsible for differential survival and reproduction are passed from parent to offspring (they are heritable). Hence, there is a natural selection for certain favorable characteristics.

6. The environments of many organisms have been changing throughout geologic time.

7. Natural selection causes the accumulation of favorable characteristics and the loss of unfavorable characteristics to the extent that new species may arise.

### Postulates of Gregor Mendel's Theory of Inheritance and of Classical Gene Theory

*(To explain how characteristics are passed from parent to offspring)*

1. Inherited characteristics are determined by particles called *factors* (genes).

2. Factors are passed from parent to offspring in the gametes.

3. Individuals have at least one pair of factors for each characteristic in each cell except the gametes.

4. During gamete formation, paired factors separate. A gamete receives one factor of each pair.

5. The chances are equal that a gamete will receive either one of the factors of a pair.

6. In the case of two or more pairs of factors the factors of each pair assort independently to the gametes.

7. Factors of a pair that are separated in the gametes recombine randomly during fertilization.

8. Sometimes one factor of a pair dominates the other factor so that it alone controls the characteristic (dominance).

The above are Mendel's postulates. The postulates of classical gene theory consist of Mendel's postulates plus the following:

9. Genes are arranged linearly in one or more groups (chromosomes); that is, the genes are linked.

10. Genes of a pair (alleles) occupy the same loci on the chromosomes of a homologous pair.

11. When chromosomes pair in meiosis, they may exchange portions; that is, crossing over may occur.

12. That frequency of crossing over between two genes on nonallelic pairs is directly proportional to the distance between them.

Major postulates of the theories introduced are included in the Background Information for the Teacher sections of this manual. In addition to the two theories mentioned above, learning cycles allow you to introduce key postulates of the following theories:

- Kinetic-Molecular Theory
- A Theory of Life
- A Theory of Biological Organization and Emergent Properties
- A Theory of Biological Classification
- Mendel's Theory of Inheritance
- Harvey's Theory of Circulation and a Theory of Heart Regulation
- Theories of Behavior
- Cell Theory
- A Theory of Cellular Fermentation and Respiration
- A Theory of Cell Replication
- Theories of Sexual Reproduction and Meiosis
- A Theory of Embryological Development
- General Metabolic Theory
- A Theory of Molecular Movement
- Watson and Crick's Theory of DNA Structure and Replication
- A Theory of Gene Action
- A Theory of Photosynthesis
- A Theory of Water Rise in Plants
- A Theory of Population Growth and Crash
- Theories of Population Regulation
- A Theory of Ecosystem Dynamics
- A Theory of Succession
- A Theory of the Origin of Life on Earth
- Organic Evolution Theory
- Darwin's Theory of Natural Selection
- A Synthetic Theory of Evolution

## The Learning-Cycle Method of Teaching

Suppose you are asked to develop a laboratory to study the heart rate of *Daphnia*. Which of the following procedures would you select as most effective?

(a)  Provide the students with live daphnia, thermometers, depression slides, and compound microscopes. Have the students count the number of heartbeats per minute of daphnia at three different temperatures; 5°, 20°, and 35°C. Ask them to plot the number of heartbeats versus the temperature on a sheet of graph paper.

(b)  Provide the students with live daphnia, thermometers, depression slides, and compound microscopes. Ask the students to find out whether different temperatures influence the rate of heartbeat and to explain how variables could account for the differences observed.

(c)  Explain to the students that temperature has a general effect on the metabolism of invertebrates. Higher temperature speeds up metabolic activity, and lower temperature slows down metabolic activity. One rule states that metabolic rate doubles for every 10° increase in temperature. A cold-blooded animal like daphnia is influenced directly by the environmental temperature. Now have your students go to the laboratory and use live daphnia to verify that what you have explained is correct.

(d)  Provide students with live daphnia, a hot plate, dexedrin solution, 5% alcohol solution, light source, rulers, thermometers, slides, pH paper, balances, graph paper, microscopes, stirring device, and ice cubes. Ask them to investigate the influence of environmental changes on the heartbeat of *Daphnia* and to search for quantitative relationships among the variables.

Certainly the resources available to you and the preparation of your students will influence your choice. Compare my comments below with yours.

(a)  This approach may be effective for students who are somewhat inexperienced in the process of scientific inquiry, as it is fairly directive yet does not spoil student motivation by telling them what they are going to find out. For more experienced students, however, it may be too directive, as it limits the scope of inquiry to only one variable (temperature) and fails to justify the selection of three temperatures (why are only three temperatures selected? why were 5°, 20°, and 35°C selected?).

(b)  This approach is very much like the previous one because it focuses on the effect of a single variable, although it does so without specifying which temperatures to use. This increased nondirectiveness is a strength: It is more apt to cause students to think about what they are doing because it forces them to make their own decisions. If improved skill in decision making is a goal, then some nondirectiveness is essential.

(c)  This approach has little to recommend it because it tells the students what they will find. This has two extremely unfortunate consequences. First, it shifts the motivation for the activity away from satisfying one's curiosity about nature to satisfying the teacher. Second, it shifts the source of authority about what is correct or incorrect from its natural place in data to an authority figure, namely the teacher. In science, one tests ideas in the empirical world, not in armchairs.

(d)  Clearly, this is the most nondirective, open-ended of the approaches. It does what approaches (a) and (b) do and more. For the inexperienced student, this nondirectiveness would be difficult to cope with without helpful procedure hints. If frustration is a problem, these hints can be provided to small groups of students working together, or the entire class can be stopped to discuss ideas of ways to get started. For experienced students, this approach is recommended highly, as it allows for a variety of paths of investigation that give considerable opportunity to think and to make decisions about what to investigate and how best to investigate it.

The recommended approach in (d) and the somewhat more directive approaches in (a) and (b) are examples of exploratory activities on which later conceptual understandings can be built. Exploration represents the first phase of a three-phase learning cycle based on current theories of learning and designed to encourage the development of creative and critical thinking skills. The three phases of the entire learning cycle are exploration, term introduction, and concept application.

During exploration, the students learn through their own actions and reactions in a new situation. In this phase, they explore new materials and new ideas with minimal guidance. The new experience should raise questions or complexities that they cannot resolve with their accustomed patterns of reasoning. It should lead also to the identification of a pattern of regularity in the phenomena (e.g., heart rate increases with temperature). Approaches (a) and (b) also are considered explorations although they are not as likely as approach (d) to encourage reflective thought.

The second phase, term introduction, starts with the introduction of a new term or terms, such as *metabolism, cold-blooded,* or *poikilotherm,* that are used to refer to the patterns discovered during exploration. The term(s) may be introduced by the teacher, the textbook, a film, or another medium. This step should always follow exploration and should relate directly to the pattern discovered during the exploration activity. The lecture in alternative (c) could be part of a term-introduction session following laboratory activities like (d). Students should be encouraged to identify as much of a new pattern as possible before it is revealed to the class, but expecting students to discover all of the complex patterns of modern biology is unrealistic.

In the last phase of the learning cycle, concept application, students apply the new term and/or reasoning pattern to additional examples. After the introduction of *cold-bloodedness,* for instance, concept application might be concerned with determination of the type of metabolism of other invertebrates or vertebrates, such as mice or humans.

The concept-application phase is necessary to extend the range of applicability of the new concept. Without a number and variety of applications, the concept's meaning will remain restricted to the examples used during its definition. Many students may fail to abstract it from its concrete examples or to generalize it to other situations. In addition, application activities aid students whose conceptual reorganization takes place more slowly than average or who did not adequately relate the teacher's original explanation to their experiences.

Note that this phase is referred to as *concept application,* while the previous phase was labeled *term introduction.* A concept is defined as "a mental pattern (a pattern in one's mind) that is linked to a verbal label (a term)." Thus, a concept is the pattern plus the term. We can introduce terms, but the students must perceive the pattern themselves. Exploration provides the opportunity for the students to discover the pattern. Term introduction provides you with the opportunity to introduce the term and provides students the opportunities to link the pattern with the term (develop the concept). Finally, concept application allows students to discover applications (and nonapplications) of the concept in new contexts.

Exploration, term introduction, and concept application are phases in a learning cycle. Exploratory sessions frequently require the application of prior concepts while creating a need for your introduction of the new terms. Term-introduction sessions frequently lead to questions best answered by giving students opportunities to work on their own to discover applications of the new concept. Concept-application activities can provide opportunities to use terms introduced earlier, and they can permit students to explore a new pattern. Diagrammatically, the learning cycle can be represented this way:

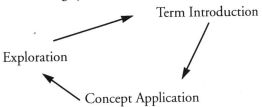

## Three Types of Learning Cycles

Each learning cycle in the present curriculum has been classified as one of three types—descriptive, empirical-abductive, and hypothetical-deductive. The essential difference among the three types of learning cycles is the degree to which students either gather data in a purely descriptive fashion (not guided by explicit hypotheses they wish to test) or actually set out to test hypotheses in a controlled fashion. The three types of learning cycles therefore represent three points along a continuum from descriptive to experimental science. They obviously place differing demands on students' initiative, knowledge, and reasoning skills. In terms of student reasoning, descriptive learning cycles require only descriptive skills, while hypothetical-deductive learning cycles demand use of hypothetical-deductive skills (assuming the students receive little or no help from the teacher). Empirical-abductive learning cycles are intermediate and involve reasoning that is of intermediate difficulty and complexity.

In descriptive learning cycles, students discover and describe an empirical pattern within a specific context (exploration), the teacher gives it a name (term introduction), and the pattern is then identified in additional contexts (concept application). This type of learning cycle is called *descriptive* because the students and teacher merely are describing what they observe without attempting to create hypotheses to explain their observations. Descriptive learning cycles answer the question, *What?*, but do not raise the causal question, *Why?*

In empirical-abductive learning cycles, students again discover and describe an empirical pattern in a specific context (exploration), but they go farther by proposing possible causes for that pattern. This requires the use of abduction to create hypotheses (term introduction). The hypotheses may be introduced by the students, the teacher, or both. With the teacher's guidance, the students then sift through the data gathered during the exploration phase to see whether the hypothesized causes are consistent with those data and other known phenomena (concept application). In other words, observations are made in a descriptive fashion, but this type of learning cycle goes farther to introduce and initially test a cause(s), hence the name *empirical-abductive*.

The third type of learning cycle, hypothetical-deductive, is initiated with the statement of a causal question to which students are asked to propose possible answers (hypotheses). Students' time is then devoted to deducing the logical consequences of these hypotheses and to explicitly designing and conducting experiments to test them (exploration). The analysis of experimental results allows for some hypotheses to be rejected and others retained, and for terms to be introduced (term introduction). Finally, the relevant concepts and reasoning patterns that are involved and discussed may be applied in other situations at a later time (concept application). The explicit creation and testing of hypotheses through a comparison of logical deductions with empirical results is required in this type of learning cycle, hence the name *hypothetical-deductive*.

The following steps are used in preparing and using the three types of learning cycles.

1.  Descriptive Learning Cycles
    a.  The teacher selects some empirically derived concept he or she wishes to teach.
    b.  The teacher identifies some phenomenon that involves the pattern on which the concept is based.
    c.  Exploration Phase: The students explore the phenomenon and attempt to discover and describe the pattern.
    d.  Term-Introduction Phase: The students report the data they have gathered, and they and/or the teacher describe the pattern; the teacher then introduces a term to refer to the pattern.
    e.  Concept-Application Phase: Additional phenomena are discussed and/or explored that involve the same concept.

2.  Empirical-Abductive Learning Cycles
    a.  The teacher selects some concept he or she wishes to teach.
    b.  The teacher identifies some phenomenon that involves the pattern on which the concept is based.
    c.  Exploration Phase: The teacher raises a descriptive question.
    d.  Students gather data to answer the descriptive question.
    e.  Data to answer the descriptive question are put on the board.
    f.  The descriptive question is answered, and the causal question is raised.
    g.  Hypotheses are advanced to answer the causal question, and the already gathered data are examined for their initial test.
    h.  Term-Introduction Phase: Terms are introduced that relate to the explored phenomenon and hypothesized explanation.
    i.  Concept-Application Phase: Additional phenomena are discussed or explored that involve the same concept(s).

3.  Hypothetical-Deductive Learning Cycles
    a.  The teacher selects some concept or reasoning pattern he or she wishes to teach.
    b.  The teacher identifies some phenomenon that involves the pattern on which the concept is based.
    c.  Exploration Phase: The students explore a phenomenon that raises the causal question, or the teacher raises the causal question.
    d.  In a class discussion, hypotheses are advanced, and either students are told to work in groups to deduce implications and to design experiments or this step is done in a class discussion.
    e.  The students conduct the experiments.
    f.  Term-Introduction Phase: Data are compared and analyzed, terms are introduced, and conclusions are drawn.

g. Concept-Application Phase: Additional phenomena are discussed or explored that involve the same concepts.

## Objectives and Use of the Reasoning Modules

Every effort has been made to design the learning cycles to foster the development of the creative and critical skills listed previously. To this end, you will notice the inclusion of six Reasoning Modules in the student manual. These provide students with discussion of and exercises in the use of six key patterns of scientific reasoning. The reasoning patterns introduced are probabilistic reasoning, correlational reasoning, causal reasoning, the isolation and control of variables, hypothetical-deductive reasoning, and proportional reasoning. The learning cycle immediately preceding each Reasoning Module requires use of the reasoning pattern discussed in the subsequent module and will allow you to introduce the reasoning pattern in question. Because only some of your students will comprehend fully the introduced reasoning pattern, reading the module and working the problems will be necessary for most students to be able to use the reasoning pattern. Subsequent learning cycles also will require use of the reasoning patterns and will provide students with additional opportunities to become skilled in their use.

## Measuring Scientific-Thinking Skills

A 12-item test of scientific-thinking skills is included for your use. You may want to pretest your students at the start of the school year and posttest them at the end of the school year to measure progress in the development of scientific-thinking skills. The pretest scores can also be used to alert you to students who may need extra attention and to students who are likely to become the class leaders. Some teachers have used the scores to form lab teams so that each team has a more skilled thinker to assist those who are initially less skilled.

Responses to each of the 12 items should be scored as correct or incorrect. To be considered correct, the student should select the correct answer and provide a reasonable explanation. Of course some explanations, other than those given above, can be reasonable and can be scored as correct. Total scores of 0–4 indicate the use of descriptive-level thinking, or *concrete-operational* thinking in terms of Jean Piaget's theory of intellectual development. Scores of 5–8 are transitional, and scores of 9–12 indicate the use of hypothetical-deductive level thinking (Piaget's *formal-operational* stage).

# CLASSROOM TEST OF SCIENTIFIC REASONING

(Revised Pencil-Paper Edition)
November 1987

by Anton E. Lawson
Arizona State University

Directions to Students:

## DO NOT OPEN THIS BOOKLET UNTIL YOU ARE TOLD TO DO SO!!

This is a test of your ability to apply aspects of scientific and mathematical reasoning to analyze a situation to make a prediction or solve a problem. In some tests you will be asked to show your work and/or explain your answer. Try to answer as completely as you can in the spaces provided. On some items these explanations are more important than your actual answer. When the item lists answers, circle the best answer and explain your selection. **If you do not fully understand what is being asked in an item, please ask the test administrator for clarification.**

## CLASSROOM TEST OF SCIENTIFIC REASONING

**Item 1.** Suppose you are given two clay balls of equal size and shape. The two balls also weigh the same. One of the balls is flattened into a pancake-shaped piece. Which of these statements is correct?

    **a.** The ball weighs more than the pancake-shaped piece.

    **b.** The two pieces weigh the same.

    **c.** The pancake-shaped piece weighs more than the ball.

Please explain your selection.

**Item 2.** At the right are drawings of two cylinders that are filled to the same level with water. The cylinders are identical in size and shape. Also shown at the right are two marbles, one made of glass and one made of steel. The marbles are the same size but the steel one is much heavier than the glass one.

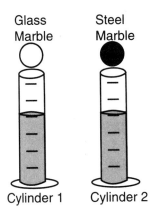

    When the glass marble is put into Cylinder 1, it sinks to the bottom and the water level rises to the 6th mark. If we put the steel marble into Cylinder 2, the water will rise

    **a.** to a lower level than it did in Cylinder 1.

    **b.** to a higher level than it did in Cylinder 1.

    **c.** to the same level as it did in Cylinder 1.

Please explain your selection.

**Item 3.** At the right are drawings of a wide and a narrow cylinder. The cylinders have equally spaced marks on them. Water is poured into the wide cylinder up to the 4th mark (see A).

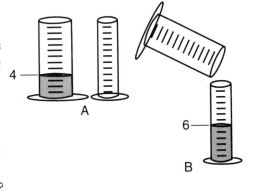

    This water rises to the 6th mark when poured into the narrow cylinder (see B). Water is now poured into the *wide* cylinder up to the 6th mark. How high would this water rise if it were poured into the empty narrow cylinder?

Please show (or explain) how you arrived at your answer.

**Item 4.** Water is now poured into the narrow cylinder (refer back to Item 3) up to the 11th mark. How high would this water rise if it were poured into the empty wide cylinder?

Answer: _____

Please show (or explain) how you arrived at your answer.

_____

_____

_____

_____

**Item 5.** At the right are drawings of three strings hanging from a bar. The three strings have metal weights attached to their ends. String 1 and String 3 are the same length. String 2 is shorter. A 10-unit weight is attached to the end of String 1. A 10-unit weight is also attached to the end of String 2. A 5-unit weight is attached to the end of String 3. The strings (and their attached weights) can be swung back and forth, and the time it takes to make a complete swing can be timed. Suppose you want to find out whether length of string has an effect on the time it takes to swing back and forth. Which strings would you use to find out?

Answer: _____

Please explain why you chose those strings.

_____

_____

_____

_____

**Item 6.** Suppose you want to find out whether the amount of weight attached to the end of a string has an effect on the time it takes for a string to swing back and forth. Which of the strings in Item 5 above would you use to find out?

Answer: _____

Please explain why you chose those strings.

_____

_____

_____

_____

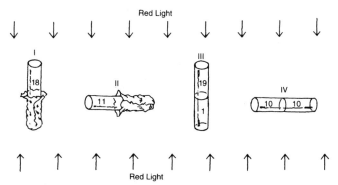

**Item 7.** Twenty flies are placed in each of four glass tubes. The tubes are sealed. Tubes I and II are partially covered with black paper; Tubes III and IV are not covered. The tubes are suspended in midair. Then they are exposed to red light for five minutes. The number of flies in the uncovered part of Tubes I and II is shown in the drawing. The number of flies in each half of Tubes III and IV is also indicated.

This experiment shows that flies respond to (*respond* means to go to or away from)
   **a.** red light but not gravity.
   **b.** gravity but not red light.
   **c.** both red light and gravity.
   **d.** neither red light nor gravity.

Please explain your selection.

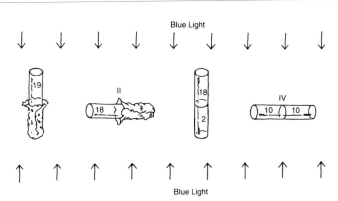

Item 8. In a second experiment, blue light was used instead of red. The results are shown in the drawing.

These data show that flies respond to (*respond* means to go to or away from)

   **a.** blue light but not gravity.
   **b.** gravity but not blue light.
   **c.** both blue light and gravity.
   **d.** neither blue light nor gravity.

Please explain your selection.

**Item 9.** Six square pieces of wood are put into a cloth bag and mixed about. The six pieces are identical in size and shape; however, three pieces are red and three are yellow. Suppose someone reaches into the bag (without looking) and pulls out one piece. What are the chances that the piece is red?

Answer: _____

Please show (or explain) how you arrived at your answer.

_____

_____

_____

_____

**Item 10.** Three red square pieces of wood, four yellow square pieces, and five blue square pieces are put into a cloth bag. Four red round pieces, two yellow round pieces, and three blue round pieces are also put into the bag. All the pieces are then mixed about. Suppose someone reaches into the bag (without looking and without feeling for a particular-shaped piece) and pulls out one piece. What are the chances that the piece is a red or blue circle?

Answer: _____

Please show (or explain) how you arrived at your answer.

_____

_____

_____

_____

**Item 11.** The drawing to the right shows a device with four buttons, numbered *1, 2, 3,* and *4,* and a light bulb. The bulb will light up when the correct button or combination of buttons are pushed at the same time. Your problem is to figure out which button or buttons must be pushed at the same time to make the bulb light up. Make a list of all the individual buttons or combinations of buttons you would need to push to figure out how to make the bulb light up.

_____  _____  _____   _____  _____  _____

_____  _____  _____   _____  _____  _____

_____  _____  _____   _____  _____  _____

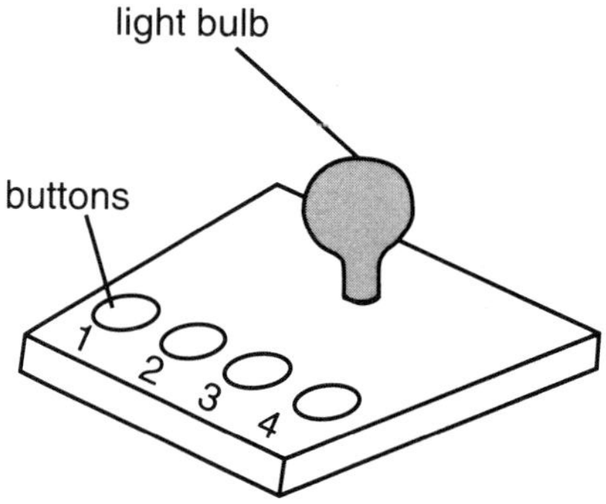

**Item 12.** Look at the fish below that were caught by a fisherman. The fisherman noticed that some of the fish were big and some were small. Also, some had wide stripes and some had narrow stripes. This made the fisherman wonder if there was a link between the size of the fish and the width of their stripes.

Do you think there is a relation between the size of the fish and the width of thier stripes?

**a.** yes

**b.** no

Please explain your choice.

_____

_____

_____

_____

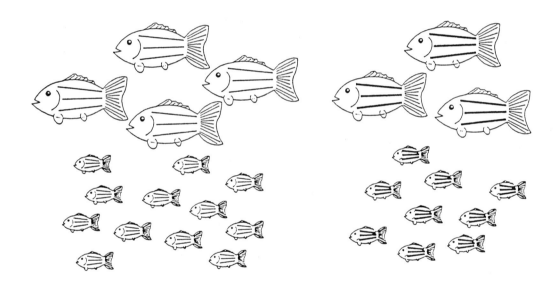

## Answers and Thinking Patterns Assessed

1. (b). The two pieces weigh the same because no clay has been added or taken away. (Conservation of weight)

2. (c). The water will rise to the same level in both cylinders, because the marbles have the same volume and thus displace the same amount of water. (Conservation of displaced volume)

3. The water will rise to the 9th mark. The relationship is proportional: $\%=\%$. (Proportional thinking)

4. The water will rise to 7 ⅓ marks in the wide cylinder. The same proportional relationship holds as in item 3 above: $\%={}^{7.33}\!/_{11}$. (Advanced proportional thinking)

5. Strings 1 and 2 should be used. They vary in length but not in weight; therefore, any observed difference in time would be due to the length variation. (Identification and control of variables)

6. Strings 1 and 3 should be used. They vary in weight but not in length; therefore, any observed difference in time would be due to weight variation. (Identification and control of variables)

7. (b). Tube III shows a response to gravity, as the majority of flies (¹⁹⁄₂₀) are at the top even though the amount of red light is the same at either end. A comparison of tubes II and IV reveals no significant difference in fly distribution (i.e., 11 to 9 versus 10 to 10); therefore, the amount of red light appears to have no effect on the flies. (Isolation and control of variables; probabilistic thinking)

8. (c). Tube III shows a response to gravity, as in item 7. A comparison of tubes II and IV reveals a significant difference in fly distibution that is not likely to be due to chance alone (i.e., 18 to 2 versus 10 to 10); therefore, the amount of blue light appears to have an effect on the flies. (Isolation and control of variables; probabilistic thinking)

9. ³⁄₆, or ½. Three out of six, or one out of two, of the pieces are red. (Probabilistic and proportional thinking)

10. Seven out of the 21 pieces are red or blue circles, so the chances are 7 out of 21, or 1 out of 3. (Probabilistic and proportional thinking)

11. 1, 2, 3, 4, 12, 13, 14, 23, 24, 34, 123, 124, 134, 234, 1234. There are 15 different combinations. (Combinatorial thinking)

12. (b, no). There appears to be no link (correlation) between fish size (large/small) and stripe width (wide/narrow) because the ratio of wide to narrow stripe is the same on both sizes of fish (3 to 4 among the large fish, and 9 to 12—or 3 to 4—among the small fish). For there to be a relation there would need to be, for example, mostly wide stripes on the large fish and mostly small stripes on the small fish, or vice versa. (Correlational thinking)

## Sequencing Topics

The most common sequence of topics in introductory biology courses is to start with the smallest units of organization—atoms, molecules, cells—work up through tissues, organs, organisms, and finally end the year with the ecological topics of populations, communities, and ecosystems. Although this is common and makes a good deal of sense from the point of view of the subject-matter expert (the teacher and textbook author), it makes little sense from the point of view of the novice (the learner). The expert, who already understands the interrelationships among the various levels of organization, sees clearly how chemistry fits into the larger picture, but the novice does not. The novice loses sight of the forest for the trees. Thus, at the start of such a course, the students justifiably ask, "Why do we have to know all this stuff about atoms and molecules? We thought this was supposed to be a biology course!" To which the teacher replies, "Just learn it; you will need it later." To which I reply, "If it's needed later, then teach it later."

Accordingly, following the initial candle-burning lab that introduces students to basic elements of inquiry and key postulates of kinetic molecular theory, the present sequence of topics starts with the familiar and proceeds to the unfamiliar, introducing chemical phenomena only when needed to understand the biological questions under investigation. Thus, the investigations start at the organism level. Students first learn about such topics as classification schemes, behavior, and animal anatomy and physiology. They then work their way down to the cellular and molecular levels in the normal investigative pattern of starting with the "whole" prior to differentiation of its parts. Following investigations of such molecular phenomena as osmosis, diffusion, and enzymatic reactions, they go back to the organismic level and investigate plant anatomy and physiology prior to working their way up through the population, community, and ecosystem levels. The final topics—ecosystem interactions and evolution through natural selection—serve to tie together the previous investigations and provide a coherent framework for future study in the biological sciences.

Clearly, some room is available for resequencing; however, you should make changes only after careful consideration of the present sequence and your own students' backgrounds.

## The Textbook

The textbook should play little or no role in class activities; the major emphasis should be on student investigation, data analysis, and teacher term introduction. Textbook readings done prior to the exploration phase of the learning cycle may not be comprehended, or worse, they may preempt student inquiry. Although I do not advocate the exclusion of textbooks from the curriculum, I strongly urge that text reading assignments be made only after the explorations and after terms have been introduced orally and defined. In other words, textbook readings should occur during the concept-application phase of the learning cycle. The readings then can serve to reinforce, refine, or enlarge the meanings of the phenomena previously explored and the terms introduced. Textbook comprehension for most students is much greater under these circumstances.

The textbook emphasizes two major themes. The first theme is that science results in the production of theories and that these theories consist of sets of postulates. The second theme is that the postulates must be tested by comparing the results of experiments and observations to the deduced consequences of the postulates. For students to become skilled in the use of this pattern of scientific thinking, it is extremely important that students have many opportunities to use this pattern in the lab and to read about its use in various contexts. Also, the Questions for Reflection at the end of each chapter are intended to provoke students to think deeply about the issues raised. Deep processing encourages divergent thinking and the retention of key ideas rather than the memorization of trivial facts. Because the text focuses on key concepts, theories, and thinking patterns and omits many unnecessary facts and terms, it can remain relatively short without losing important concepts.

## Class Discussions

Conversation among students or between teacher and students is an important part of the learning process. While participating in experiments, students spontaneously exchange observations and ideas with one another. During term-introduction sessions, you illustrate and define a new term. When gathering feedback, you may address a question to a particular student. On other occasions, discussions in which the students report on their experimental results, compare observations, and sometimes challenge one another's findings should take place. Many students should participate in these discussions, and the teacher should avoid controlling the topic or the pace. Encourage the students to comment to one another, without calling on specific individuals to recite in turn.

If you call attention to disagreement between two findings, you invite evaluative comments and suggestions, which may lead to further meaningful inquiries. Announcing that one student is right and another is wrong rarely leads to further inquiry experiences. Instead, such action encourages students to ask you, as the authority figure, for the answers; it reduces their commitment to independent investigation, which is fundamental to an understanding of science.

The questions you ask and the way in which you ask them will affect the students' work and attitudes. Note the difference between "What did we study yesterday?" and "What did you find out yesterday?" Though both questions call for review of a previous activity, the former only seeks an answer already in the teacher's mind. The latter inquires into a student's own experience.

A question that aims for a predetermined answer is called *convergent* because of its specific goal. Most questions in multiple-choice tests are of this nature (as are many questions asked by some teachers). A question that allows a variety of answers is called *divergent* because it may lead in many directions. Provocative-discussion questions are usually of this nature.

Suit your questions to your purpose. If you wish to gather feedback about understanding or recall of a certain fact, ask a convergent question. Often this is best done individually, perhaps while small-group work is in progress. When you are looking for a specific answer, make this clear to the students.

If you wish to spark discussion, ask a divergent question and then sit back while several students propose answers. If the students continue their discussion without your leadership, so much the better.

Determine which of the following two questions is divergent and which is convergent: *What caused the plant to die? What might have caused the plant to die?* The first question calls for a specific answer; thus, it is convergent. The student either knows the cause or does not; thus, it does not require any thinking, only recall or guessing the answer already in the teacher's mind. The second question is divergent as it has many potential answers. It opens up the door to student thinking and hypothesis creation. It opens the door to science itself.

In order for inquiry to occur in your classroom, divergent questions must be the norm.

One further important point must be made. After you have asked a divergent question, be patient and allow plenty of time for student thinking. Most teachers wait less than a few seconds before going on or answering their own questions. This practice inhibits thinking.

## Helping Students Create Hypotheses

You may have found that getting students to propose specific hypotheses is not easy. Teachers sometimes remark, "But my students just do not think." The learning cycles in this curriculum have been designed with this in mind and generally will provoke students' hypothesis creation with little special effort on your part. Nevertheless, here are some important tips to follow if difficulty arises.

- Make certain the causal question is clear. Write the question(s) on the board. Even though you may have repeated it several times, some students still may not have heard.

- Do not ask for one hypothesis. This implies that only one "correct" answer exists. Instead, ask for alternative hypotheses: What might be some reasons for what was observed? Empirical-abductive learning cycles are designed to have students make observations and to gather data prior to proposing hypotheses. The exploration phase usually provides several "hints" and provokes considerable thinking.

- Call on specific students by name. This alerts other students that they too may be called on, so they had better try to think of some ideas.

- Do not respond differently to the "correct" hypothesis if and when it is advanced. Instead, treat it as just another possibility and continue asking for alternatives. This gives the students the correct message that you, the teacher, are not the arbitrator of what is correct or incorrect. Rather, a hypothesis must be tested prior to making that judgment.

- Keep in mind that you are also an investigator, so you also may advance hypotheses. Generally, it is best to offer hypotheses that students can test and find to be incorrect; however, if no one comes up with the "correct" answer, then you should. If you get into the habit of advancing a combination of "correct" and "incorrect" hypotheses, students will learn to treat your ideas just like theirs—that is, as ideas to be tested.

- In hypothetical-deductive learning cycles, students are asked to propose alternative hypotheses before data are collected. In some hypothetical-deductive cycles, alternative hypotheses are suggested in the introductory material. In others, enough information is provided to elicit ideas most of the time. If difficulty remains, briefly describe the data-collection process and ask students to predict what they think might happen. Because students often have intuitions about possible outcomes, this question will spark further discussion. After students have indicated what they think will happen, ask them *why* they think it will happen. The answer to their question, of course, is a hypothesis. When you find two students with opposite predictions and alternative hypotheses, you have found precisely what you are looking for. Now the class can continue on to the experiment to test the alternatives.

- Accept all sincere hypotheses as reasonable even though they may seem implausible to you. A positive teacher response encourages additional thought, while a negative one may stop future participation.

- Make sure your quizzes and tests require use of the process skills used in creating and testing hypotheses. Although this may cause some initial student frustration, you must not give in and require just the "facts" on evaluations. Doing so would give the students the wrong message that the facts are more important than the processes. This view prohibits future participation in the process.

## Correcting "Wrong" Conclusions

When you open up the teaching process to real inquiries, the possibility exists that students will not discover the "correct" answers. For some teachers, this possibility poses more of a concern than for others. Certainly, I do not advocate teaching students incorrect conclusions. In reality, the learning cycles seldom lead to this problem as students gather data in groups and ample opportunity exists for debunking incorrect data-collection procedures and conclusions. Thus, if "correctness" lies in the data and in one's interpretation of data (where scientists claim it does), then little danger exists for students to venture off with incorrect ideas, especially if you are willing to repeat the data-collection process when results are particularly mixed. Further, if you emphasize the tentativeness of all conclusions in science, the danger will be reduced further.

It is better to have the students leave believing in the primacy of the process rather than having the teacher or text reveal the "correct" answer, for doing so may reduce motivation for future inquiries. Students may well ask, "If (s)he was going to tell us the correct answer, why did we bother going through all the trouble to get our own?" Nevertheless, if you judge that students have arrived at some incorrect conclusion that they simply cannot live with, you might consider introducing the correct answer as follows: "You have carefully explored the issue and tentatively concluded such and such. Biologists interested in this problem have done considerably more research on the question, and on the basis of this research, they now believe . . ." This approach allows you to present the correct answer, it reemphasizes the notion that answers come from research, and it does not seriously undermine students' own research efforts.

## Classroom Control, Seating Arrangements, and Motivation

Classroom control is an important concern of every teacher. Obviously, during the exploration phase of the learning cycle, the teacher is no longer the focus of student attention. Rather, attention is on the phenomenon and on cooperative group interactions. Your job becomes one of moving about the classroom from one group of students seated together to another to provide helpful suggestions and/or to ask probing questions. To some, this approach may appear to lead to a loss of classroom control. In reality, however, good exploration activities that have been properly introduced increase student interest and motivation, and thus greatly reduce classroom control problems. No longer are you purveyor of information; you become a fellow investigator of interesting questions and phenomena. Student motivation shifts from an extrinsic desire for a good grade, which only some students view as possible or even desirable, to an intrinsic one of satisfying one's curiosity about nature.

Although explorations and many concept-application activities require cooperative group work, having students seated next to or facing one another is not the most effective arrangement when you want to lead discussions and/or introduce new terms (during the term-introduction phase of the learning cycle). Rather, when you want attention focused on group-generated data or on yourself, students should be seated in rows facing forward. This arrangement reduces unwanted and potentially disruptive student interactions. Of course, row seating should also be used during examinations or any other time you want students to work independently.

In other words, you should select the seating arrangement to match the nature of the classroom activity. A classroom with lab tables in the back and row seating in the front is ideal. Such an arrangement allows one to have the best of both worlds—highly motivating group explorations and orderly discussions.

## "Covering" Content

Virtually every experienced teacher, when first introduced to the learning cycle, agrees with its emphasis on creative and critical thinking but has one question: Will I be able to cover enough content? The answer is an emphatic YES.

First, you must keep in mind that when one uses the lecture-textbook method, very little of what is "covered" is actually understood and retained. The learning cycle facilitates retention and transfer of reasoning skills and content.

Second, most nationally distributed standardized achievement tests, such as the Iowa Tests of Educational Development, the Scholastic Aptitude Tests, the ACT Test of Critical Thinking, and the National Association of Biology Teachers Achievement Test, emphasize reasoning over specific content. Therefore, learning-cycle students will outperform lecture-textbook students on these tests. If your district or state has developed its own "fact-oriented" achievement test, work to have it changed to be more in line with the national goals of education and these standardized tests.

Third, the present curriculum introduces and focuses on major theories in biology. The major theories serve as conceptual frameworks for the acquisition and retention of information. Approaches that do not emphasize major theories do not provide such frameworks. Thus, although it may appear somewhat paradoxical, the learning-cycle approach may actually "cover" fewer facts and terms, but it "uncovers" considerably more biology. Some teachers using the learning cycle have even found that their students outperform lecture-textbook students on tests over content that they have not even covered.

## Scheduling the Learning Cycles

Because some learning cycles require extended periods for data gathering, which on any one day may require only a few minutes of class time, you often will need to initiate new learning cycles prior to finishing others. It is not uncommon to have two or three learning cycles in progress at any one time. You might think this would cause student confusion, but it is less a cause of confusion than it is an opportunity to provide syntheses of related subject matter. To ensure that class time is used fully, it is helpful to reserve a place on the board in which you list the day's activities. When students become familiar with this approach, they often will read the board and go right to work without your having to say anything at all. The chart below provides a suggested scheduling of the learning cycles for the entire year.

| Schedule of Learning Cycles and Reasoning Modules | | | | | | | | | | | | | | | |
| --- | --- | --- | --- | --- | --- | --- | --- | --- | --- | --- | --- | --- | --- | --- | --- |
| Weeks | | | | | | | | | | | | | | | |
| Investigation | 1 | 2 | 3 | 4 | 5 | 6 | 7 | 8 | 9 | 10 | 11 | 12 | 13 | 14 | 15 | 16 |
| 1 | | | | | | | | | | | | | | | |
| 2 | | | | | | | | | | | | | | | |
| 3 | | | | | | | | | | | | | | | |
| Module 1 | | | | | | | | | | | | | | | |
| 4 | | | | | | | | | | | | | | | |
| Module 2 | | | | | | | | | | | | | | | |
| 5 | | | | | | | | | | | | | | | |
| 6 | | | | | | | | | | | | | | | |
| 7 | | | | | | | | | | | | | | | |
| Module 3 | | | | | | | | | | | | | | | |
| 8 | | | | | | | | | | | | | | | |
| 9 | | | | | | | | | | | | | | | |
| 10 | | | | | | | | | | | | | | | |
| 11 | | | | | | | | | | | | | | | |
| 12 | | | | | | | | | | | | | | | |
| Module 4 | | | | | | | | | | | | | | | |
| 13 | | | | | | | | | | | | | | | |
| Module 5 | | | | | | | | | | | | | | | |
| 14 | | | | | | | | | | | | | | | |
| 15 | | | | | | | | | | | | | | | |
| 16 | | | | | | | | | | | | | | | |
| 17 | | | | | | | | | | | | | | | |
| 18 | | | | | | | | | | | | | | | |

| Investigation | Schedule of Learning Cycles and Reasoning Modules Weeks | | | | | | | | | | | | | | |
|---|---|---|---|---|---|---|---|---|---|---|---|---|---|---|---|
| | 17 | 18 | 19 | 20 | 21 | 22 | 23 | 24 | 25 | 26 | 27 | 28 | 29 | 31 | 32 |
| 19 | | | | | | | | | | | | | | | |
| 20 | | | | | | | | | | | | | | | |
| Module 6 | | | | | | | | | | | | | | | |
| 21 | | | | | | | | | | | | | | | |
| 22 | | | | | | | | | | | | | | | |
| 23 | | | | | | | | | | | | | | | |
| 24 | | | | | | | | | | | | | | | |
| 25 | | | | | | | | | | | | | | | |
| 26 | | | | | | | | | | | | | | | |
| 27 | | | | | | | | | | | | | | | |
| 28 | | | | | | | | | | | | | | | |
| 29 | | | | | | | | | | | | | | | |
| 30 | | | | | | | | | | | | | | | |
| 31 | | | | | | | | | | | | | | | |
| 32 | | | | | | | | | | | | | | | |
| 33 | | | | | | | | | | | | | | | |
| 34 | | | | | | | | | | | | | | | |
| 35 | | | | | | | | | | | | | | | |
| 36 | | | | | | | | | | | | | | | |
| 37 | | | | | | | | | | | | | | | |
| 38 | | | | | | | | | | | | | | | |

## A Theory of Instruction

The following list represents the major postulates of the theory of instruction on which the present curriculum is based. The postulates summarize the major ideas that were used to develop the curriculum and will serve as a guide for its use.

1. Children and adolescents acquire beliefs about natural phenomena, some of which are incompatible with presently accepted scientific theory.

2. Some of these alternative beliefs may be instruction-resistant impediments to the acquisition of scientifically valid concepts and theories.

3. The replacement of alternative beliefs requires students to move through a phase in which a conflict exists between the alternative belief and the scientific explanation and provokes a state of mental "disequilibrium."

4. The improvement of critical-thinking skills arises from situations in which students are engaged in exchanges of contradictory beliefs, where arguments are advanced and evidence is sought to resolve the contradiction.

5. Argumentation provides experiences from which particular forms of argumentation (patterns of critical thinking) may be abstracted.

6. The learning cycle is a method of instruction that consists of three phases—exploration, term introduction, and concept application.

7. Use of the learning cycle provides the opportunity for students to reveal prior beliefs and to argue and test them, thus becoming "disequilibrated" and acquiring more scientifically valid beliefs and improved critical thinking skills.

8. The three types of learning cycles (descriptive, empirical-abductive, hypothetical-deductive) are not equally effective at producing disequilibrium and improved reasoning.

9. The essential difference among the three types of learning cycles is the degree to which students either gather data in a purely descriptive fashion or initially set out to explicitly test alternative beliefs (hypotheses).

10. Descriptive learning cycles are designed to have students observe a small part of the world, discover a pattern, name it, and seek the pattern elsewhere. Only descriptive reasoning patterns are required, and little or no disequilibrium occurs.

11. Empirical-abductive learning cycles require students to describe and explain a phenomenon, thus allowing for the generation of alternative explanations, argumentation, disequilibrium, and improved use of hypothetical-deductive reasoning patterns.

12. Hypothetical-deductive learning cycles require the immediate and explicit statement of alternative beliefs or hypotheses to explain a phenomenon and require hypothetical-deductive reasoning patterns in the test of the alternatives.

## Safety in the Science Laboratory

Safety in a laboratory situation is of prime importance in every classroom. Following safety guidelines and precautions can minimize laboratory dangers. Good safety habits should be developed and demonstrated by both teacher and students. The following safety guidelines and precautions will help establish safety regulations and procedures in the classroom.

### Safety Symbols

When appropriate, each investigation provides safety cautions and symbols to alert students to any potential hazards. Safety precautions appear in boldface throughout the investigation as a reminder to students. An explanation of these symbols appears in the front of the student lab manual.

### Classroom Organization

All classroom laboratories should be equipped with fully charged fire extinguishers, one or more fire blankets, a first-aid kit, an eyewash station, and a smoke alarm. Students should be aware of the locations of all safety equipment as well as how to use the equipment properly.

The laboratory should be arranged in such a way that equipment and supplies are clearly labeled and easily accessible. Furniture and equipment should be organized in wide, clear aisles to minimize accidents. Supply stations should be set up at various points around the laboratory so students do not crowd into one area when gathering supplies. Make sure students keep all work areas clean. Have them remove any unnecessary books, papers, and equipment from lab tables or counters.

### Classroom Safety

**Pre-lab discussions** Begin all laboratory investigations with a discussion of safety procedures. Demonstrate the proper use of the materials to be used. Wear safety goggles during activities that involve potential hazards to the eyes. Laboratory aprons also should be worn. Caution students to never taste or eat any substances or chemicals. Review the procedure with students. Caution them to follow the steps in the laboratory investigation in the order they are presented.

**Glassware** Broken, cracked, or chipped glassware should not be handled with bare hands. Use heavy gloves and a dustpan for removal. Provide a container marked BROKEN GLASS for disposal. Use only heat-resistant glass in the laboratory. Caution students to use tongs when handling hot glassware.

**Chemicals** Chemicals should be properly labeled, dated, and stored. Read all caution labels and follow directions carefully. Avoid keeping strong acids in the classroom. When diluting an acid, always add the acid to the water. When using corrosive liquids and/or vapors, use a fume hood. When students are required to note odors and fumes, have them waft the fume toward their noses. They should never inhale fumes directly. Warn students of any chemicals that are flammable.

**Heat and flames** Use hot plates or a water bath whenever possible. Never allow papers or other flammable substances anywhere near flames. Make sure students tie back hair and loose clothing when near flames. Do not use a flame in an open draft. Keep an emergency supply of water and sand nearby to extinguish fires. Never use water to extinguish a fire from a leaking alcohol lamp; use sand or baking soda. The open end of a test tube being heated should always be pointed away from students. Be sure all hot plates and other burners are turned off when not in use.

**Storage and disposal** Chemicals should be properly labeled and stored in a locked area that is accessible only to authorized persons. Chemicals should be protected from contamination from the outside environment. Dissecting instruments should be stored in a locked area. At the end of an investigation, inventory should be taken to insure all materials have been returned. Always dispose of unused portions of chemicals. Never return unused chemicals to their unused containers. At the end of each investigation, make sure students have returned all equipment and disposed of broken glassware and chemicals properly. Provide separate containers for paper, glassware, and chemical waste. Students should wash their hands with soap and water when the investigation is completed.

**Animals in the Classroom** Small, caged mammals can give dangerous bites that could possibly lead to rabies. Do not allow students to handle any animal roughly or to anger the animal to the point that it will bite. If a bite occurs that draws blood, you should notify the local police or Board of Health, since the animal may have to be placed under surveillance.

If an animal seems sick or listless, remove it from the classroom as soon as possible.

Avoid all poisonous snakes. Do not allow students to handle bats or even to bring them into the classroom.

**Bacteria cultures** Bacteria and molds will grow and multiply in any stagnant materials, especially if they are allowed to remain undisturbed for several days. It is unlikely that they will be dangerous, but be sure to get rid of such cultures as soon as possible. Wash containers and hands with hot water and soap. In addition, caution students never to put their hands into their mouths after handling any lab specimens and to wash their hands as soon as possible.

**Electricity** All activities that involve experimentation with electricity recommend the use of only small cells and batteries, which are harmless. However, students should be cautioned about the dangers of house current, which is the source of power for lamps, hot plates, and other appliances that will be used from time to time. Wires and plugs for those devices should be in good condition and should not be allowed to get wet. None of the electrical setups that call for other than house current should ever be plugged into house current.

## Biology Materials List

The following materials will be needed for the student laboratory exercises. You will need to refer to the individual labs for specific quantities. Materials followed by an asterisk are optional.

**A**
acetate, colored
acetone, 5 mL
alcohol (ethanol)
alcohol burner
alcohol, ethyl
algae culture
aluminum pan
ammonia
animals, dead, and animal products (e.g., smelt, cricket, mealworm, bologna, hamburger)
antiseptic solution
artificial sweetener

**B**
balance
bamboo shavings
beakers, 50 mL, 250 mL
beans, brown and white
Benedict's solution
binoculars
Biuret reagent
bottle, small, with lid or stopper
brine shrimp eggs
bromthymol blue
bucket
butcher paper

**C**
candles, birthday
cardboard
cardboard box
carrot slice
cellophane, colored
cellophane tape
cereal, bran
chalk
cheesecloth
chromatography paper
chicken egg, unincubated
    incubated: 48 and 72 hours,
    and 4, 5, and 10 days

clay, modeling
clock with second hand
coleus
colored pencils or markers
construction paper
containers, potting*
containers, sprouting
copper sulfate solution
cork
corn, Indian ear
corn plants (green and albino)
corn seeds (6 albino, 6 normal)
corn syrup
coupled gear systems
covered cabinet or drawer
coverslips, microscope
cracker
crayons
Cuisenaire® rods
culture dish
cutting surface
cylinders, open at one end

**D**
dechlorinated water
dialysis tubing
dice, pair
dissecting needle
dissecting probles
dissection kit
drain tray
dropper

**E**
elodea
egg carton
environmental variables, other sources of

**F**
fertilizer*
film loop, *The Galapagos Tortoises*
flowers, variety
food coloring, Schilling red
foods, various

forceps
fossil kit containing representative fossils
    from 6 rock layers of Grand Canyon
frog, preserved
fruits, variety
**G**
germinating seeds
glass stirring rods
glucose solution
glue
graduated cylinder
graph paper
gravel
grow lights
**H**
hand lens
heat source
heating pads
honey
hornwort
hot plate
human skeleton, diagram of
hydrogen peroxide
**I**
ice
index cards
iodine
isopods
**J**
jars, various sizes
**L**
labels
leaf, kalanchoe
leaves from 3 different plants
leaves, spinach
lens paper
light source
liver, raw
lunch meat
**M**
marking pens
matches
mealworms
meterstick
meter tape
methyl cellulose

metric ruler
microscope, compound
microscope, dissecting
mortar and pestle
**N**
notebooks or clipboards with data table
**O**
onion root tip slide
**P**
paper bags
paper roll
paper towels
paper, colored
paper, white
patterned fabric, 8 pieces of
pencils, wax
pepper, bell
perfume
petri dish
petroleum jelly
pH paper
pictures of fossils from fossil kit
pipe cleaners
planaria
plant cuttings*
plant pigment extract
plants or plant products (e.g., banana,
    lettuce, apple, pear, leaf, bread)
plants, small*
plastic bags
plastic sandwich bags
poking stick
pond, temporary
post with bolt and wing nut
potato
powder
**R**
razor blade
razor blade, new single-edged
red blood cells
references on pond life
refrigerator (cold source)
rivets
rope (transect)
rubber bands

S
safety goggles
sand, fine
salt
scale, metric
scalpel
scissors
screw eye
seeds
shells, assorted
shovels
show box
simulation area
skulls, 10 different vertebrate species
slide projector
slides, animal cells
slides, microscope
slides, plant cells
slides, prepared
   meiotic sequence, whitefish or ascaris
sling
snake skin
soaked seeds, variety
sodium bicarbonate solution, 0.25%
sodium chloride solution
sodium hydroxide
soil, potting*
splints, wood
spot plates
starch suspension, 1% and 5%
step blocks or stairs
splints, wood
straws
string
stirring rods
stopper, cork
stoppers, one-hole rubber
string
sugar
synthetic sponge
syringes
T
tape, masking
test-tube caps
test-tube clamps
test-tube rack

test tube, screw-top
test tubes, various sizes
thermometers
timer
tomato
tubes, S-shaped glass
tubing, rubber
twist ties
U
unknown object (wrapped in foil)
V
vials
vial stands
vinegar
W
water, day-old tap
water, distilled
water, fresh tap
water, pond
water, salt
water, sugar
water, with mud
waterproof marker
wax, paraffin
Whirlybirds®
wire loops
wrap, plastic
Y
yarn
yeast cultures in test tubes
yeast, baker's

## Suppliers List

Arbor Scientific
P.O. Box 2750
924 N. Main St.
Ann Arbor, MI 48106
(313) 663-3733, (800) 367-6695

Cadillac Plastic and Chemical Company
2625A East University Srive
Phoenix, AZ 85034

Carolina Biological
Powell Laboratories Division
Gladstone, OR 97027
(800) 547-1783

Carolina Biological Supply Co.
2700 York Rd.
Burlington, NC 27215
(919) 584-0381, (800) 334-5551

Central Scientific Co. (CENCO)
11222 Melrose Ave.
Franklin Park, IL 60131
(312) 452-0150, (800) 262-3626

Creative Dimensions
P.O. Box 1393
Belllingham, WA 98227

Delta Biologicals
P.O. Box 26666
Tuscon, AZ 85726-6666
(800) 824-6778

Edmund Scientific Co.
101 E. Gloucester Pike
Barrington, NJ 08007
(609) 547-3488

Fisher Scientific Co.
Educational Materials Division
4901 W. LeMoyne St.
Chicago, IL 60651
(800) 621-4769

Frey Scientific Co.
905 Hickory Ln.
Mansfield, OH 44905
(419) 589-9905

Grau-Hill Scientific Corporation
6501 Elvas Ave.
Sacramento, CA 95819
(916) 455-5258

Hach Company
P.O. Cox 389
Loveland, CO 80539
(800) 525-5940, (303) 669-3050

Hubbard Scientific Co.
P.O. Box 104
1946 Raymond Dr.
Northbrook, IL 60062
(312) 272-7810, (800) 323-8368

Invicta Plastics Ltd.
200 Fifth Avenue
New York, NY 10010

Lab-Aids, Inc.
249 Trade Zone Dr.
Ronkonkoma, NY 11779
(516) 737-1133

Learning Alternatives
P.O. Box 219
Vienna, OH 44473
(800) HANDS -ON

Nasco
901 Janesville Ave.
Fort Atkinson, WI 53538
(414) 563-2446, (800) 558-9595

Sargent-Welch Scientific Co.
7300 N. Linder Ave.
Skokie, IL 60077
(312) 677-0600

Science Kit and Boreal Labs
777 E. Park Dr.
Tonawanda, NY 14150
(800) 828-7777, (716) 874-6020

Ward's Natural Science Establishment, Inc.
5100 West Henrietta Rd.
P.O. Box 92912
Rochester, NY 14692-9012
(800) 962-2660, (716) 359-2502

# Introduction to Inquiry

## Investigation 1 — *What Caused the Water to Rise?*

## Synopsis

Students invert a cylinder over a candle burning in a pan of water. They observe that the flame soon goes out and water rises into the cylinder. They then repeat the procedure in several ways and attempt to explain their observations. Testing of these explanations leads to new explanations and increased understanding of combustion, air pressure, and the nature of scientific inquiry. This is an empirical-abductive learning cycle.

## Suggested Time

Two class periods

## Background Information for the Teacher

The primary purpose of this first learning cycle is to involve students personally in the use of science in an attempt to answer two questions that arise from firsthand observations.

A burning candle is held upright by a small piece of clay in a pan of water. Shortly after a cylinder is inverted over the candle and placed into the water, the candle flame goes out and water rises in the cylinder. These observations raise two major causal questions: *Why did the flame go out?* and *Why did the water rise?* The generally accepted answer to the first question is that the flame "consumed" oxygen in the cylinder to a level too low to sustain combustion, thus causing the flame to die. The generally accepted answer to the second question is that the flame heated the air in the cylinder, causing it to expand and causing some to escape out the bottom. When the flame went out, the remaining air then cooled and contracted, creating a partial vacuum. This partial vacuum then was replaced by water rising into the cylinder until the air pressure pushing on the surface of water outside was equal to the air pressure pushing on the water surface inside.

This learning cycle is an excellent way to introduce students to science as a hypothesis-creation-and-testing enterprise because the hypotheses they invariably generate to answer the questions can be shown experimentally to be inadequate and therefore must be modified through the use of both creative and critical thought processes and data gathering and analysis.

Students' initial beliefs generally center around a theory that states that oxygen is "used up," creating a partial vacuum that "sucks" water into the cylinder. They fail to realize that when oxygen is "burned," it combines with carbon, producing $CO_2$ rather than being destroyed (hence no partial vacuum can be created in this way). They also fail to understand that a vacuum cannot "suck" anything. Rather, the force that causes the water to rise is a push from the relatively greater number of air molecules hitting the water surface outside the cylinder.

The experiments and discussions provide you with an opportunity not only to attempt to modify these misconceptions by introducing more satisfactory models of combustion and air pressure but also, more important, to introduce science as an intellectually stimulating and challenging way of trying to describe and explain nature.

What follows is a list of major postulates of a theory of air pressure that can be used collectively to explain the water rise in the cylinder.

1.  Air is composed of tiny particles (atoms and combinations of atoms, called molecules).

2.  The particles move and can strike other particles and transfer some or all of their motion (kinetic energy) to the other particles.

3.  An energy source, such as a flame, consists of rapidly moving particles that can transfer some of their motion to nearby particles through collisions.

4.  The temperature of a gas is a measure of the amount of motion of its particles (the more motion the greater the temperature).

5.  The term *air pressure* refers to the force exerted on a surface by the collisions of air particles (more particles at higher velocities equals greater air pressure).

## Teaching Tips

### *Exploration*

1.  To initiate this lesson, let the students obtain the materials and get started on their own. Challenge them first to see what happens and then to vary several "things" (e.g., the number of candles, amount of water, type of cylinder) to see what effect if any each has.

2.  If you let the students start on their own, you probably will have to stop them after about 15 to 30 minutes for a discussion of their observations and ideas.

3.  During the discussion, observations and ideas should be listed on the board. The most obvious questions are *Why did the flame go out?* and *Why did the water rise?* The most likely explanation to the second question is that because the oxygen was "burned up," the water rose to replace the oxygen that was lost.

    Lead the students to realize that this explanation (hypothesis) leads to the prediction (expectation) that varying the number of burning candles will not affect the level of water rise. Four candles, for instance, would burn up the available oxygen faster and go out sooner than one candle, but they would not burn up more oxygen.

4.  Have the students do this experiment and report their results. The results, of course, will show that the water level is affected by the number of candles (the more candles, the higher the water level). Their hypothesis, therefore, has been contradicted. At this point, you should emphasize the need for an alternative explanation and ask students to propose one. This may be an excellent time for the bell to ring; if no one has a good alternative, you can challenge them to think up a new explanation as their homework assignment.

5.  If someone does propose the "correct" explanation (the heated air escaped out the bottom, etc.), do not immediately tell the class it is correct. Rather, treat it as just another explanation to be tested. Ask students to think of a way to test the explanation. They should realize that the explanation leads to the prediction that bubbles should be seen escaping out the bottom of the cylinder. (Note that it also leads to the prediction that the number of candles will affect the level of water rise because more candles will heat more air, therefore more will escape, which in turn will be replaced by more water. Although it is true that one candle burning over a long period of time will release as much energy as three candles burning only a short time, it will not raise the temperature of the air in the cylinder as much because its energy is dissipated rather quickly to the air outside the cylinder.) Have

the students repeat the experiment to see whether bubbles appear. If no one proposes the "correct" explanation, propose it yourself. But make sure that you do not give the students the impression that this is the correct explanation. Rather, it is simply an idea you had that should be tested along with any other ideas that are generated. The conclusion that it is correct should come only after data have been gathered that are consistent with the predictions derived from the proposed explanation.

### Term Introduction

6.  After such data have been gathered, carefully repeat your explanation of the phenomena, introducing the term *air pressure* and a molecular model of gases that assumes air to be composed of moving particles that have weight and can bounce into objects (such as water) and push them out of the way. You may wish to discuss the common misconception of "suction" in this context. The molecular model implies that suction (as a force that can suck up water) does not exist (the water is being pushed into the cylinder by moving particles of air rather than being sucked by some nonexistent force).

### Concept Application

7.  To allow students to apply the molecular model of gases and the concept of air pressure to new situations, provide each group a piece of rubber tubing, a syringe, a beaker, and a pan of water. Instruct them to invert the beaker into the pan of water and to fill it with water in that position with the mouth of the beaker submerged. Students probably will make futile efforts to force water through the tube into the beaker before discovering that they must extract the air through the tube.

8.  As a homework assignment, challenge the students to find a way to insert a peeled hard-boiled egg into a bottle with an opening that is smaller in diameter than the egg. They must not touch the egg after it has been placed on the opening. After a piece of burning paper has been dropped into the bottle or after a small amount of water in the bottle has been heated, it is only necessary to place the smaller end of the egg over the opening of the bottle to form a seal. The egg will be forced into the bottle by the greater air pressure outside as the air inside cools. **CAUTION: Warn students not to heat the bottle excessively, as it may crack.**

9.  Pour about 10 mL of water into an empty aluminum soda can, and heat the water to boiling over a Bunsen burner or hot plate. Holding the can with tongs, quickly invert the can and submerge it in cool water. The can will collapse quickly with a "pop." Challenge students to explain their observations, using the molecular model of gases and the concept of air pressure.

10. Applications of the thinking skills of observation and hypothesis-creation-and-testing will come in subsequent learning cycles.

11. Chapters 1 and 2 of the textbook should be assigned reading.

| Scientific Terms | Thinking Skills |
|---|---|
| air pressure | accurately describe nature |
| molecular theory of gases | state causal questions |
| combustion | create alternative hypotheses |
| kinetic energy | generate logical predictions |
| | plan and conduct experiments |
| | organize and analyze data |
| | draw and apply conclusions |

## Sample Test Questions

Doing science involves raising questions, creating hypotheses, designing and conducting experiments, generating predictions, gathering and analyzing data, and drawing conclusions. These terms are defined as follows:

### KEY:

A. hypothesis:  a tentative explanation put forth to be tested

B. experiment:  a manipulation of nature to allow hypotheses to be tested

C. prediction:  a statement of an expected result of an experiment

D. data:  the observed result of an experiment

E. conclusion:  a statement concerning the relative "correctness" or "incorrectness" of the hypothesis tested

*Items 1–10 refer to certain parts of the paragraphs that are italicized. Each italicized portion is an item. Identify each item with a response from the key.*

When we put the cylinder over the burning candle, the candle went out and water rose in the cylinder. We wondered why the candle went out and why the water rose. At first, we thought that 1) *the water rose because the candle burned up the oxygen.* 2) *The reason the candle went out was because the oxygen was used up.*

If the water rose because the oxygen was used up, then 3) *the water should rise to the same level* 4) *when we use one candle and when we use three candles.* More candles may use up the oxygen faster, but they cannot use up more than just one candle uses. We discovered that 5) *the water rose higher when more candles were used,* so we decided that 6) *our idea was probably wrong.*

Suzy then suggested that the water rises because 7) *some of the air has been heated and has escaped out the bottom.* She said that 8) *more candles should make the water rise higher because they heat more air, so more air will escape.* 9) *We also saw bubbles coming out the bottom of the cylinder,* so 10) *we thought that maybe Suzy's idea was right.*

## Answers

| 1. A | 3. C | 5. D | 7. C | 9. D |
|---|---|---|---|---|
| 2. A | 4. B | 6. E | 8. C | 10. E |

# Characteristics of Living Things •
# Biological Classification

## Investigation 2  *How Are Living Things Classified?*

## Synopsis

Students observe 25 unlabeled objects (both living and nonliving) and attempt to group them based on observable characteristics. Characteristics of living things as well as the concepts of hierarchical classification and the levels of kingdom, phylum, class, order, family, genus, and species are introduced. Students then apply these ideas in keying out a variety of additional objects. This is a descriptive learning cycle.

## Suggested Time

Four class periods

## Background Information for the Teacher

Living things (organisms) are distinguished from nonliving things primarily by their ability to grow, reproduce, die, respond to stimuli, and exchange materials with their environment. Biologists classify living things into hierarchical categories based on the presence or absence of specific characteristics. A commonly used scheme subdivides organisms into five major groups called kingdoms: Moneran Kingdom (primarily single-celled prokaryotes), Protist Kingdom (single-celled eukaryotes), Fungal Kingdom (multicellular organisms that directly absorb nutrients), Plant Kingdom (multicellular organisms that carry out photosynthesis), and Animal Kingdom (multicellular organisms that ingest nutrients). The five kingdoms then are subdivided into phyla, which in turn are subdivided into classes and so on down to the species level. A species can be viewed as a specific kind of organism. Two organisms are operationally defined as being of the same species (of the same kind) if, when mated to each other, they are capable of reproducing fertile offspring. Dichotomous (either-or) branching "keys" have been developed by biologists to allow one to identify unknown organisms on the basis of observable characteristics.

The purpose of this learning cycle is to introduce students to characteristics of living things, ways of classifying living things, an operational definition of species, and ways of using keys to name organisms. The learning cycle also will provide experience with the reasoning patterns associated with identifying variable and constant characteristics and with generating and using class-subclass relationships (classification schemes).

The learning cycle deals essentially with a theory of life and a theory of biological classification.

## Major Postulates of the Theory of Life

1. A variety of objects exist on Earth. These objects are of two basic types—living and nonliving. Living objects are called *organisms.*

2. All organisms possess the following characteristics not shared by nonliving objects: They are chemically complex and highly organized; they use energy, develop, and reproduce; they are capable of change over generations; and they contain a set of instructions in

their genes that direct their activities.

3. Some objects, such as viruses, are intermediate between living and nonliving objects because they possess some but not all of the above characteristics.

## Major Postulates of the Theory of Biological Classification

1. Ideally, a biological classification represents the evolutionary development of the species considered.

2. A species is one "kind" of organism, operationally defined as "a group of organisms with enough similarities to allow the production of fertile offspring."

3. Groups of species can be arranged in a hierarchy with single species (sometimes subspecies) at the base and the largest groups (the kingdoms) at the top.

4. The more characteristics shared by two groups, the more closely they are related and the closer they are to their common ancestor.

## Advance Preparation

Materials should include unlabeled specimens from each kingdom, including microscopic organisms, a few nonliving objects (e.g., crystals, an interesting rock, a fossil, a piece of rubber hose submerged in water in a bottle), and some unfamiliar specimens (tapeworms, roundworms, a sponge) to keep interest high.

## Teaching Tips

### Exploration

1. Prior to having students observe the specimens, define the term characteristic (a distinctive feature or property), and have students list several characteristics of an object in the classroom (e.g., the teacher). Encourage them to play the role of a naturalist in the 1700s observing the objects for the first time.

2. During the time students are listing characteristics and are attempting to determine whether the object is or was once alive, offer assistance whenever needed but do not tell students the names of the objects.

### Term Introduction

3. Following student observations, allow them 10 to 20 minutes to struggle to invent a classification method before you introduce the notion of hierarchical classification during a class discussion. To do this, start with a category of "all objects" listed at the top of the chalkboard. Ask students to name a characteristic that could be used to divide all of the objects into two groups (e.g., microscopic vs. macroscopic). Have them now suggest another characteristic to subdivide each of these two groups (e.g., appendages vs. no appendages, single cell vs. multicellular, etc.). The drawing on the board should appear something like this:

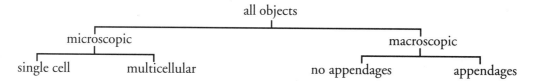

Introduce the terms *variable, value,* and *constant,* giving examples from students' observations, and allow time for the students to complete their classification hierarchies.

4. After groups of students have developed classification hierarchies, have several hierarchies put on the board for discussion. Although no one scheme is correct, students may be able to identify strengths and weaknesses of a number of the schemes. Make certain that the schemes are based on characteristics, not on category names. If, for example, students have divided specimens into plant and animal groups, point out that this is wrong unless they can state the characteristic or set of characteristics that separate plants from animals. A discussion of these characteristics, as well as those that separate living from nonliving, should ensue.

5. At this point, the terms *kingdom, phylum, class, order, family, genus,* and *species* may be introduced to refer to levels within their hierarchies. Operationally define *species,* and point out characteristics biologists use to classify organisms into kingdoms. If students still are interested in learning the names of the original specimens, they also could be introduced at this time.

### Concept Application

6. To further extend the idea of classification, you may wish to have students use a variety of published keys to identify the genus and species names of some specimens.

7. You also may want to have your students develop a key for the plants on your campus and/or develop a classification system and key for such common objects as a collection of washers, nuts, bolts, and screws.

8. Chapters 3, 4, and 5 of the textbook should be assigned reading.

| **Biological Terms** | **Thinking Skills** |
|---|---|
| organisms<br>hierarchical classification<br>characteristics of living things<br>kingdom, phylum, class, order, family,<br>    genus, species | accurately describe nature |

## Sample Test Questions

1. On the next page are pictures of eight bugs. In what ways do they clearly vary? What characteristics appear to be constants? Generate a hierarchical classification scheme that places each bug into its own category.

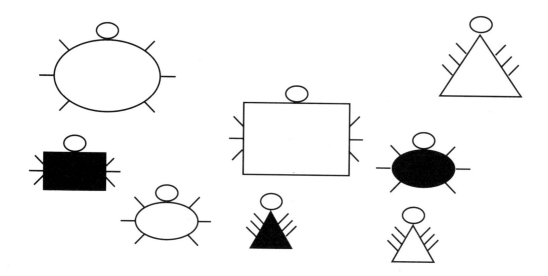

2. In the modern scheme of classification of living things, protozoa are to phylum as dog is to
   a. genus.    b. species.    c. order.    d. class.

3. Suppose you find two dead birds on the beach and both are new to you. One has long narrow legs with no webbing on its feet; the other has short powerful legs with its feet well-webbed. What would you suspect regarding the habits of these birds?
   a. They both are probably swimmers because they were found on the beach.
   b. The long-legged bird probably roosts in trees.
   c. The web-footed bird is probably a good swimmer.
   d. They both are poorly adapted because they are dead.
   e. b and c

4. Which of these categories of classification contains organisms that are most closely related?
   a. family    b. class    c. order    d. genus

*The next six items are based on the following table. (Hint: Fill in the blank spaces before answering the items.)*

|          | Organism I   | Organism II | Organism III | Organism IV |
|----------|--------------|-------------|--------------|-------------|
| **Phylum**  | Arthropoda   |             |              |             |
| **Class**   | Hexopoda     |             |              |             |
| **Order**   | Lepidoptera  | Lepidoptera |              |             |
| **Family**  | Tortricidae  | Psychidae   | Tortricidae  | Tortricidae |
| **Genus**   | *Archips*    | *Solenobia* | *Archips*    | *Eulia*     |
| **Species** | *rosana*     | *walshella* | *fervidana*  | *pinatubana* |

5. Which two organisms are most closely related?
   a. I and II
   b. I and III
   c. I and IV
   d. II and III
   e. II and IV
   f. III and IV

6. Which organism is the most distantly related to organism IV?
   a. I        b. II        c. III        d. All are equally related.

7. Which organism(s) belong(s) to Phylum Arthropods?
   a. I
   b. I, II, and IV
   c. I and IV
   d. I and IV
   e. I, II, III, and IV

8. Which organisms belong to Class Hexapods?
   a. I and III
   b. I and IV
   c. I, II, and IV
   d. I and IV
   e. I, II, III, and IV

9. Which organisms belong to the same family?
   a. I and III
   b. I and IV
   c. III and IV
   d. I, III, and IV
   e. I, II, III, and IV

10. Which of these organisms would have an internal skeleton?
    a. II, III, and IV
    b. all of them
    c. none of them
    d. Insufficient information is given.

## Answers

| | | |
|---|---|---|
| 2. B | 5. B | 8. E |
| 3. C | 6. B | 9. D |
| 4. D | 7. E | 10. C |

# Normal Variation • Mendelian Genetics

## Investigation 3    *How Do Characteristics Vary?*

## Synopsis

Students measure and graph observable variations in shells and colors of corn kernels and discover patterns in that variation. The question of what causes those patterns is raised, and postulates of Mendelian genetics are introduced to explain why the patterns occur. This is an empirical-abductive learning cycle.

## Suggested Time

Two class periods

## Background Information for the Teacher

Observable characteristics are the product of an organism's genetics and environment. When continuous varying characteristics of a population, such as height or weight, are plotted on a frequency graph, the values often distribute themselves in a "bell-shaped" or normal distribution. This pattern can be explained partially by assuming that the characteristic under consideration is determined by multiple pairs of genes that are passed from parents to offspring, with each gene independently combining with others in a random fashion, much like the sum of the numbers on two dice rolled on a table.

Observed patterns of either-or characteristics, such as gender, handedness, and tongue-rolling ability, can be explained by assuming that the offspring characteristic is determined by a single pair of genes (or very few genes) that somehow combine their effects in the offspring (blending inheritance), or in some cases, one gene of the pair may dominate the other to produce its effect as though the other gene were not present. Combinations of dominant and recessive gene pairs result in simple ratios of offspring characteristics (e.g., 1:1, 3:1, 1:2:1) that depend on the precise combination of dominant and recessive genes.

Gregor Mendel usually is credited with inventing these concepts of inheritance. They can be summarized by the following.

## Postulates of Gregor Mendel's Theory of Inheritance

1.  Inherited characteristics are determined by particles called *genes*.

2.  Genes are passed from parent to offspring in the gametes (egg and sperm).

3.  Individuals have at least one pair of genes for each characteristic in each cell except in the gametes.

4.  During gamete formation, paired genes separate. A gamete receives one gene of each pair.

5.  The chances are equal that a gamete will receive either one of the genes of a pair.

6.  In the case of two or more pairs of genes, the genes of each pair assort independently to the gametes.

7.  Gene pairs that are separated in the gametes recombine randomly during fertilization.

8.  Sometimes one gene of a pair dominates the other gene so that the first gene alone controls the characteristic (dominance).

You may wish to provide these eight postulates to your students at the conclusion of the term introduction phase as a summary of the major ideas. Do not introduce them prior to that time, as doing so would restrict students' thinking and detract from the naturally motivating exploratory nature of the activity.

Note that the next activity, Reasoning Module 1, concerns the concept of probability. Investigation 3 introduces the concept of probability in the context of dice-rolling and genetics. Most students, however, will not understand probability sufficiently well to solve genetic problems. Therefore, you should complete Reasoning Module 1 prior to assigning the genetics problems at the conclusion of this investigation.

## Advance Preparation

Assorted shells are available from Delta Education, P. O. Box 915, Hudson, NH 03051-0915, (800) 258-1302, FAX (603) 880-6520.

Genetic corn is available from Carolina Biological, Powell Laboratories Division, Gladstone, OR 97027, (800) 547-1733, FAX (503) 656-4208, or from Carolina's headquarters at 2700 York Road, Burlington, NC 27215, (800) 334-5551, FAX (919) 584-3399. Ears of corn with 3:1, 1:1, and 1:2:1 ratios of colored kernels should be purchased. The labels must be removed before the ears are given to the students. You may wish to provide students with pieces of masking tape to help them keep track of which rows are counted, especially if they are interrupted.

## Teaching Tips

### Exploration

1. Use the introduction from the student manual as a basis for introducing the lesson. Then have each group of three to four students obtain a bag of 300 to 400 shells of eight to ten species.

2. Although students may need suggestions on what sorts of shell characteristics to measure (e.g., length, width, number of ribs, shades of color), encourage groups to select different characteristics. You may need to go over definitions and methods of calculating or identifying the mean, median, mode, and range of their distribution. Or you may decide to omit this step or assign it later, perhaps as a homework assignment.

### Term Introduction

3. After the graphs have been drawn, have each group choose one member to tape its graph to the board so that all the graphs can be seen and discussed. Ask students to state how the graphs are similar and different. Is a similar pattern displayed by most of the graphs? Students should note that most graphs show few shells with values at the extremes of the range but many near the middle of the range.

   When this pattern is noted, tell students that this pattern is referred to as a normal distribution because it is what normally occurs. Write the term *normal distribution* on the board. Ask students to think of other characteristics that might show normal distributions when similarly graphed.

4. Now pose the next question: What might cause values to be distributed normally? Allow students to suggest alternative explanations. These should be written on the board. Ideas may center around environmental effects, or a student may suggest a genetic cause.

Graphs that do not show normal distributions also should be discussed. Have the students speculate on why these abnormal patterns emerged. Do not press for agreed-on explanations at this point. Go on to procedure step 11, and ask students to think about how this activity of rolling dice might be related to the shell distributions.

5. After the dice activity is completed, have one graph from each group placed on the board. In a class discussion, compare graphs and note the similarity in pattern. Again, a normal distribution will be seen. Ask how the dice-rolling activity seems to be related to the shell situation.

6. Go on to procedure step 12. Compare data, and ask students how the corn, dice, and shell situations appear similar and different.

7. To introduce the general postulates and terms involved in Mendelian theory and to help explain the observed data patterns, ask students to imagine that one of the dice represents the female egg. Imagine that the numbers on the die represent factors or "genes" that somehow dictate observable characteristics in offspring—the values of those characteristics being determined by the sum of the numbers shown in the combined egg and sperm. If one imagines that six possible "types" of sperm and six possible "types" of eggs (1, 2, 3, 4, 5, 6) exist, then 36 total combinations of sperm and egg types are possible: one combination totaling 2 (1 + 1 = 2), two combinations totaling 3 (1 + 2 = 3; 2 + 1 = 3), three combinations totaling 4 (1 + 3 = 4; 2 + 2 = 4; 3 + 1 = 4), four combinations totaling 5, and so on. It helps if you draw the six hypothesized sperm and the six hypothesized eggs on the board. Use arrows from the sperm to the eggs to represent possible combinations. Plot these combinations on a frequency graph to show the class that a normal distribution results, just as was the case for the shells. Thus, if we assume genes exist and behave the same as dice, then we have a theory to account for the normal distribution. The terms *dominant, recessive,* and *blending inheritance,* and the idea of fewer possible "types" of genes, can be introduced now to explain the observed ratios of color of corn kernels (e.g., 3:1, 1:2:1). The terms *allele, genotype,* and *phenotype* may be introduced too.

### Concept Application

8. Patterns of inheritance for blood typing and inheritance in other organisms should be discussed (e.g., pea plants, chickens, cattle), and Reasoning Module 1, which introduces basic concepts of probability, should be completed prior to your requiring students to solve the genetics problems that appear as Study Questions at the end of this learning cycle.

9. Chapter 6 of the textbook should be assigned reading.

---

| **Biological Terms** | **Thinking Skills** |
|---|---|
| normal variation | accurately describe nature |
| genes | state casual questions |
| independent assortment | create alternative hypotheses |
| random recombination | generate logical predictions |
| genotype | organize and analyze data |
| phenotype | draw and apply conclusions |
| dominant | |
| recessive | |
| blending inheritance | |
| allele | |

## Sample Test Questions

1. Human identical twins raised in different environments differ somewhat in intelligence. This shows that
   a. heredity is more important than environment.
   b. environment is more important than heredity.
   c. environment affects the expression of certain genes.
   d. heredity controls the environment.

2. Suppose a cross were made between two black, rough-haired guinea pigs, and the resultant offspring included six with black, rough hair and one with white, rough hair. From this information, it can be assumed that
   a. one of the parents carried genes for white hair.
   b. both parents carried genes for white hair.
   c. a mutation had occurred.
   d. white hair is a dominant trait.

3. "A" represents the gene for a dominant trait, and "a" is its recessive allele. If Aa mates with aa,
   a. all offspring will be of the dominant phenotype.
   b. all offspring will be of the recessive phenotype.
   c. 50% of the offspring will be of the recessive phenotype.
   d. 75% of the offspring will be of the dominant phenotype.

4. Hornless is dominant over horned in cattle. A farmer has a herd of hornless cattle. A horned calf is born from time to time in his herd. What is the reason for this?
   a. All are homozygous hornless.          c. A mutation is taking place.
   b. Some cattle are heterozygous.          d. Hornless is a sex-linked characteristic.

5. A tossed dime comes up heads six times straight. What is the probability of it coming up tails on the seventh toss?
   a. 100%          b. 60%          c. 50%          d. 40%

6. Two coins are tossed simultaneously 40 times. About how many times would both come up tails?
   a. 10          b. 20          c. 25          d. 30

*The next six items are based on the following information:*

A set of triplets, two of which were known to be identical, were separated at birth and were brought up under very different circumstances. The following data were recorded for them at the age of 19.

|  | Tom | Dick | Harry |
|---|---|---|---|
| **Height** | 6'2" | 6'2" | 5'11" |
| **Weight** | 185 lbs | 193 lbs | 215 lbs |
| **Blood Type** | Type O | Type AB | Type O |
| **IQ** | 138 | 142 | 125 |

7. Which of the boys are identical?
   a. Tom and Dick only
   b. Tom and Harry only
   c. Dick and Harry only
   d. Tom, Dick, and Harry

8. Which characteristic was most important in answering the above question?
   a. height     b. weight     c. blood type     d. IQ

9. If the three boys were reunited and then attempted to locate their parents, which clue would be provided about the blood types of the parents?
   a. One parent was type A, the other type B.
   b. Both parents were type AB.
   c. One parent was type A, the other type AB.
   d. One parent was type O, the other type AB.

10. Both parents were known to be right-handed (R) (assume that right-handedness is dominant to left-handedness). Tom is left-handed (r). What were the probable genotypes of the parents?
    a. RR × rr     b. RR × RR     c. Rr × Rr     d. rr × rr

11. What is the probability that Dick is left-handed?
    a. $1/1$     b. $3/4$     c. $1/2$     d. $1/4$

12. What is the probability that Dick is right-handed?
    a. $1/1$     b. $3/4$     c. $1/2$     d. $1/4$

## Answers

1. C
2. B
3. C
4. B
5. C
6. A

7. B
8. C
9. A
10. C
11. D
12. B

# Probabilistic Reasoning

## Reasoning Module 1 *Probability*

## Synopsis

Students sample beans out of a sack and estimate the number of brown beans in the sack, based on their sample ratios. The terms *sample, population,* and *probability* are then introduced, and a number of problems are presented as the concepts are applied in a variety of contexts.

## Suggested Time

One class period

## Background Information

Basic to understanding nature is the linking of events with causes. Humans quite naturally assume that things happen for a reason. Unfortunately, the identification of cause-effect relationships is hindered by our inability to observe directly all of the possible events that may serve as causes of an observed effect. In many instances, the best one can do is estimate the "chances," or probability, of the occurrence of an event, given a general description of the conditions leading up to it. Thus, if we know that rain has fallen on the 4th of March on nine of the past ten years in Salem, Oregon, we can estimate that the probability of rain on the next 4th of March is fairly high ($\%_{10}$) even if we know nothing about the conditions that actually conspire to cause rain.

The probability of occurrence of an event is given as follows:

$$\text{Probability} = \frac{\text{Number of desired events}}{\text{Total number of possible events}}$$

Estimation of probability is easy in cases in which one actually can count the total possible events and the number of desired events (e.g., the probability of rolling a 3 on a fair die is $\frac{1}{6}$ because one 3 out of six possible numbers could turn up). In cases in which counting is not possible, the best that one can do is extrapolate from some known sample of data to an unknown situation, as was done above to arrive at an estimate of the chances of rain on the 4th of March in Salem, Oregon.

The purpose of this reasoning module is to provide students with an opportunity to better understand ideas of probability and their relationship to cause-effect prior to attempting to solve genetics problems, which require such understanding.

## Advance Preparation

Fifteen sacks of beans should be prepared in advance for a class of 30 students. Each sack should contain exactly 100 beans. About 50 (but not exactly 50) of the beans should be brown and about 50 should be white. The ratio should not depart from $\frac{50}{50}$ more than about $\frac{45}{55}$ or $\frac{55}{45}$.

## Teaching Tips

1. To introduce the lesson, you may wish to toss a coin in front of the students and ask them to state the chances the coin will come up heads. Correct answers will be 1:1, 50%, 1 out of 2, 50 out of 100. Point out the reasons for the answers and their similarities and differences.

2. You may wish to introduce the term *probability* at this time and define it as "the ratio of the number of desired events over the total number of possible events," or this definition may be presented after the students have read the second essay.

3. Allow students time to read the essays, to do the activity, to plot their graphs, and to work the Study Questions. Unfinished Study Questions may be done as homework if necessary.

4. The Brain Bender is intended as a challenge to the abler students. The problem requires making a number of reasonable assumptions about the volume of the haystack, the chances of finding a needle in a smaller haystack—say, 3 cubic meters—and adjusting your estimate based on the relative sizes of the two haystacks. A similar strategy of making reasonable assumptions can be used to estimate the number of piano tuners in Phoenix without looking in the phone book (How many pianos do you know of on your block? How often does a piano need to be tuned? How long does it take to tune a piano? How many similar blocks are in Phoenix?).

---

### Biological Terms

sample
population
ratio/percent
bias/random

### Thinking Skills

probabilistic reasoning

---

# Correlation • Cause and Effect

## Investigation 4 *Which Characteristics Are Linked?*

## Synopsis

Students note or measure and record their gender, handedness, eyedness, quickness, height, weight, tongue-rolling ability, and arm span. The teacher then introduces ways of graphing and analyzing data to identify relationships between variables and introduces the term *correlation* to refer to a situation in which the values of two variables covary. This is a descriptive learning cycle.

## Suggested Time

One class period to collect data; two additional class periods to share and plot data and introduce methods of data analysis

## Background Information for the Teacher

Much of science deals with the identification and measurement of *variables* (characteristics that vary) and their values. When the values of two variables increase simultaneously—such as the thickness of the coating on neuron axons and the speed of transmission of electrical impulses down those axons, or the number of hours one studies for an exam and the number of questions one correctly answers on that exam—we say that two variables covary and a correlation exists between them. Correlations may be *direct* (the values of both variables increase) or *inverse* (the values of one variable increases, while those of the other decrease). Consider, for example, the inverse correlation that exists between the speed at which you drive an automobile and the distance you can travel.

The identification of correlations is a central task of scientific investigation because correlations suggest the possibility of causality. They do not, however, indicate which variable is the cause or which is the effect. In fact, the correlation may be caused by another, as yet unidentified, "intervening" variable. Nevertheless, the identification of correlations is an important step toward understanding.

The present learning cycle allows students to measure and record the values for a number of *continuous variables* (values that vary along a continuum, such as height and weight) and *dichotomous variables* (values that are discrete and essentially discontinuous, such as eyedness, gender, and handedness). The learning cycle then allows you to introduce a means of graphing the values of continuous variables to identify whether a correlation exists, and it allows you to introduce the use of contingency tables to deal with dichotomous data. Students then use these techniques to discover correlations between the variables they have measured.

Because the concept of correlation is such a difficult one for many students, Reasoning Module 2 follows this investigation. It allows students additional practice in analyzing data for correlations. Have your students complete Reasoning Module 2 prior to your assigning the Study Questions in this investigation and prior to evaluating them on these ideas.

## Advance Preparation

Punch holes in the 3-by-5-inch cards. Make photocopies of the rows of zeros as needed.

## Teaching Tips

### Exploration

1.  To introduce the exploration, you may wish to summarize the points made in the student manual introduction and to provide a few additional examples. Do not, however, introduce the term *correlation* at this time or spend any time discussing techniques for data analysis. These issues will be discussed in some detail after the students have gathered data and are appropriately motivated.

2.  To get students started in their data collection, you will need to mention each variable briefly and to tell students how to measure and record its values. Be sensitive toward how some students view themselves by not insisting that height and/or weight be measured.

3.  Following data collection, each student must obtain data from the rest of the class to complete the data table. This can be accomplished by having each student read his or her data aloud while others copy down the data, or each student can copy his or her data onto a class data table to be reproduced and distributed by you to each student the next day. If the class is relatively small, you may wish to supplement the class data with data from other classes. More data make it easier to identify trends.

### Term Introduction

4.  Select two continuous variables that might be linked (e.g., height, weight, arm span), and plot the values of these variables on a graph on the board. Students should plot the data in their manuals along with you. The graphs should appear like the one shown below.

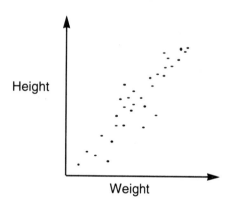

5.  Ask students to look at the graph and to see whether they can identify a pattern within the data. Students should report that, in general, the taller people tend to be heavier because the points tend to go from lower left to upper right. You may wish to draw a line through the points to reflect this trend, as shown on the top of page 19.

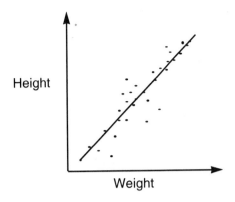

6. Introduce the term *correlation* by stating that the two variables appear to be "linked," their values vary together, covary, or are "co" related, and we say the variables themselves are correlated. A correlation exists between them.

7. To introduce the use of contingency tables to analyze data, divide the graph into four sections at the median value of each variable and label each section as shown:

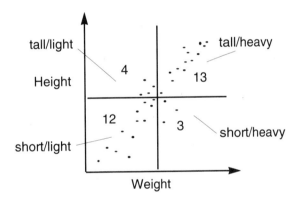

8. Count the number of persons in each section, and record this number in a contingency table drawn on the board.

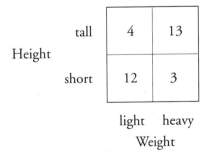

9. Point out that the majority of students ($^{25}\!/_{32}$) are either tall and heavy (13) or short and light (12), while the minority ($^{7}\!/_{32}$) are either tall and light (4) or short and heavy (3). In other words, 25 of the students fit the pattern of correlation, while only 7 "exceptions" are found in this pattern. In actuality, some of these exceptions should not be considered exceptions as they may lie very close to the line.

10. Have students now use these methods to do procedure steps 12–14 as homework.

### Concept Application

11. Expect considerable student difficulty in data analysis, as a complex aspect of scientific reasoning (correlational reasoning) is required, and few of your students will come to class skilled in using this reasoning pattern. For this reason, Reasoning Module 3 is provided to help students better understand and use this important reasoning pattern.

| **Biological Terms** | **Thinking Skills** |
|---|---|
| correlation (covariation) | accurately describe nature |
| contingency tables | organize and analyze data |

## Sample Test Questions

1. The graph below depicts the relationship between height and the time it took a sample of runners to run a race.

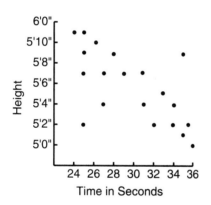

a. Construct a contingency table of the data by dichotomizing each variable at its median value.

b. Suppose someone states that a correlation exists between height and time. How many people in the table support this statement? How many people are exceptions to the statement?

c. Do you think a correlation exists? Explain.

d. If a correlation exists, is it direct or inverse?

2. In an experiment to determine the way salmon find their way to their home stream, a biologist captured fish from the North Branch and South Bend rivers (see diagram on the next page). He blocked the noses of some of the fish from each river (the experimental group) and did nothing to the remaining fish (the control group). He tagged all the captured fish and released them below the fork where the two rivers join. He recaptured the fish as they swam back up into the North Branch or South Bend rivers. The biologist's data are on the next page.

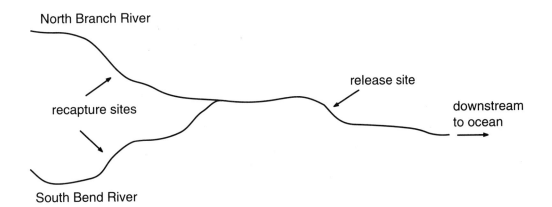

|  | **Control Group**<br>**Recapture Site** | |  |  | **Experimental Group**<br>**Recapture Site** | |
|  |  |  |  |  |  |  |
|  | South<br>Bend | North<br>Branch |  |  | South<br>Bend | North<br>Branch |
| South<br>Bend | 22 | 3 |  | South<br>Bend | 12 | 13 |
| North<br>Branch | 8 | 23 |  | North<br>Branch | 11 | 14 |

**Capture Site** (left); **Capture Site** (right)

- a. What hypothesis is the biologist testing?
- b. What is the independent variable in his experiment?
- c. What is the dependent variable?
- d. Do the data support his hypothesis? Explain (be specific).

3. A newspaper article reported the following information with respect to amounts of carbon monoxide in the air and the incidence of lung cancer. Brownsville (population 200,000) was found to have a high amount of carbon monoxide in the air, and during the past year 6,000 people died of lung cancer. Walnut Bay (population 300,000) was found to have small amounts of carbon monoxide in the air, and 9,000 people died of lung cancer. Do the data indicate a correlation between amount of carbon monoxide in the air and the occurrence of lung cancer? Justify your answer.

4. Read the newspaper article, and answer the following items.

# Cholesterol, heart-ill link is affirmed

The Associated Press

SANTA FE, N.M. — A 25-year study of 1,969 men has shown a direct link between increased cholesterol in the diet and an increased risk of a fatal heart attack, researchers said Thursday.

Many previous studies have shown that too much cholesterol in the blood raises the risk of dying of a heart attack, but this is the first study to show convincingly that cholesterol in the diet can raise blood cholesterol and in turn increase the likelihood of death of heart attacks.

Furthermore, the study may explain why the incidence of heart disease is falling in the United States, said the study's author, Richard Shekelle of the University of Texas School of Public Health in Houston.

The men Shekelle studied, workers at a Western Electric Co. plant in Chicago, had a median intake of 737 milligrams of cholesterol per day when the study began.

Average cholesterol consumption in Americans is now about 400 or 450 milligrams per day, Shekelle said.

"Our data are consistent with the idea that this decline in the intake of cholesterol over the past 25 years may have contributed to the observed decline in coronary heart disease," Shekelle told the American Heart Association. The association's figures show a 20 percent drop in coronary heart disease during the past decade.

Shekelle said the study, done with Jeremiah Stamler of Northwestern University in Chicago, provides the most convincing demonstration so far that dietary cholesterol increases the risk of death of heart disease.

In the study, men who consumed more than 500 milligrams of cholesterol per day had a 22 percent higher risk of dying of a heart attack than did men whose cholesterol intake was low enough to rank them in the bottom fifth of the group.

Shekelle and Stamler began following the Western Electric workers in 1957 and 1958. In 1981, the researchers reported a link between dietary cholesterol and fatal heart attacks.

Since then, he said, they have been combing the data to be sure that those men who consumed higher cholesterol did not have other dietary abnormalities that were contributing to the increased risk of fatal heart attacks.

The link persisted when they discounted the effects of known risk factors, such as high blood pressure, smoking, alcohol consumption, and family history of heart disease.

a. What two variables are presumed to be correlated in this article?

b. What evidence is offered to support the hypothesis that cholesterol causes heart attacks?

c. Does the article indicate how cholesterol causes heart attacks? If yes, how? If not, what mechanism(s) can you think of?

d. What other variables are suggested as contributors to heart disease?

## Answers

1. a.

| | | Fast—less than 30 seconds | Slow—more than 20 seconds |
|---|---|---|---|
| **Height** | Tall–greater than 5'6" | 8 | 2 |
| | Short–less than 5'6" | 2 | 8 |

Time

b. 16 support it; 4 are exceptions

c. Yes, a correlation exists. Most of the tall people (8/10) ran the race in less than 30 seconds, while most of the short people (8/10) took over 30 seconds.

d. The correlation is inverse—the taller the person, the less the time.

2.  **a.** The fish locate their home stream by smell.
    **b.** ability to smell
    **c.** ability to locate home stream or recapture site
    **d.** Yes, because only about 50% of the fish that could not smell found the correct stream (12 + 14 = 26 out of 49 = 53%), while most of the fish that could smell found the correct stream (22 + 23 = 45 out of 56 = 80%).

3.

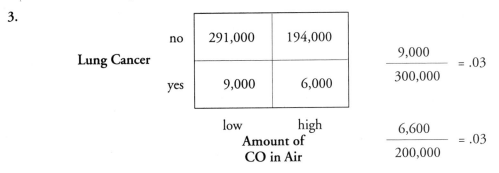

No, because the probability of getting lung cancer is the same (.03) in both cities.

4.  **a.** amount of cholesterol in diet and risk of fatal heart attack
    **b.** First evidence is that a drop of median intake of cholesterol from 737 milligrams per day to 400–550 milligrams per day is accompanied by a 20% drop in coronary heart disease. The second evidence is that a study of men who consumed more than 500 milligrams of cholesterol per day had a 22% higher risk of a fatal heart attack than men whose intake ranked them in the bottom fifth of the group. The third evidence is that this correlation persisted when effects of other known risk factors were eliminated.
    **c.** no; Maybe the cholesterol in the blood sticks on the sides of the blood vessels going to the heart and keeps it from getting blood and needed oxygen as the heart muscle dies.
    **d.** high blood pressure, smoking, alcohol consumption, and family history (genetic factors?)

# Correlational Reasoning

## Synopsis

Students examine samples of cards showing faces of students that have varying eye and hair color. They sort the faces according to observed characteristics and attempt to determine whether a correlation exists between the characteristics.

## Suggested Time

Two class periods, plus homework time to finish Study Questions

## Background Information

The establishment of relationships between variables is basic to prediction and scientific explanation. Correlational reasoning—the reasoning processes one uses in determining the strength of mutual or reciprocal relationship between variables—is therefore a fundamental aspect of scientific reasoning.

Suppose, for instance, that a scientist is interested in finding out whether a correlation exists between the body weight of rats and the presence of substance X in their blood. The establishment of a correlation requires an initial recognition of the four possible associations: a) heavy weight and presence of substance X, b) heavy weight and absence of substance X, c) light weight and presence of substance X, and d) light weight and absence of substance X. When variables can be dichotomized like this, one may construct a $2 \times 2$ association table of the sort used to compute simple contingencies.

Organization of Data to Exhibit Possible Correlation

|  | Heavy Weight | Light Weight |
|---|---|---|
| Presence of Substance X (pill) | a | c |
| Absence of Substance X (no pill) | b | d |

High-school students vary considerably in their ability to use correlational reasoning to analyze such data. In brief, however, it is clear that for most students correlational reasoning skills are poorly developed. The following types of responses have been observed when high-school students were individually administered tasks requiring correlational reasoning. The following examples are from a table in which a = 3, b = 7, c = 8, and d = 2.

Category NR: No relation between cell frequencies is considered.

NR-1    The subject does not accept the possibility of a relationship in view of the disconfirming cases: "No, some rats who are fat didn't have pills, and some rats who are skinny did have pills."

NR-2    The subject describes various events qualitatively: "I don't know, because there are some rats of each kind."

NR-3    The subject describes various events quantitatively: "I think no connection exists. Seven fat rats had no pills and three had pills; two thin rats had no pills and eight had pills."

Category TC: The number of events in two cells is compared.

TC-1    The subject compares two cells with a common attribute: "The pill made them fat because seven fat rats had no pills and only two skinny rats had no pills."

Category FC: The numbers of events in all four cells are used to make two comparisons.

FC-1    The subject compares the events in two pairs of cells: "There are more fat rats without pills than with, and more thin rats with pills than without."

FC-2    The subject combines two cells having one common attribute, compares one cell with the total, and then does the same with the other pair of cells: "The majority of no-pill rats are fat, and the majority of pill rats are skinny."

Category CO: Correlation is described by a quantitative comparison using all four cells.

CO-1    The subject identifies and/or compares two ratios: "More fat rats have pills by 7:3, and more thin rats have no pills by 8:2."

CO-2    The subject identifies and/or compares two percentages: "Without pills, the rats are more likely to be fat, 78%; with pills, the rats are more likely to be thin, 73%."

CO-3    The subject compares the number of confirming cases (b + c) to the number of disconfirming cases (a + d): "The pill has a weight-loss effect because of the eight thin rats with pills and the seven fat rats with no pills (b + c). These five rats (a + d) are exceptions. So about 75% of the time it worked as a diet pill."

Because so few students spontaneously respond with Category CO responses, which indicate use of correlational reasoning, this reasoning module initially presents data in a very simple and familiar context and gradually works students through increasingly complex situations to help them better analyze data for possible correlational relationships.

## Advance Preparation

Packets A through F containing the faces of the students described in the second essay of the student manual need to be prepared in advance. The faces may be hand-drawn in colored markers on index cards, or four-color pictures of faces may be cut from magazines. The contents of each packet should be:

| Packet A | 10 faces with brown hair and blue eyes |
|---|---|
|  | 10 faces with blond hair and blue eyes |
| Packet B | 12 faces with blond hair and brown eyes |
|  | 8 faces with blond hair and blue eyes |
| Packet C | 10 faces with brown hair and brown eyes |
|  | 10 faces with blond hair and blue eyes |
| Packet D | 10 faces with brown hair and blue eyes |
|  | 10 faces with blond hair and brown eyes |

Packet E     9 faces with brown hair and brown eyes

9 faces with blond hair and blue eyes

1 face with brown hair and blue eyes

1 face with blond hair and brown eyes

Packet F     5 faces with brown hair and brown eyes

5 faces with blond hair and blue eyes

5 faces with brown hair and blue eyes

5 faces with blond hair and brown eyes

## Teaching Tips

1. This module should follow Investigation 4, *Which Characteristics Are Linked?*, which introduces the term *correlation*. The module represents a concept application activity for correlational reasoning. You may wish to introduce the module by briefly discussing the introductory paragraphs of the student manual.

2. Have students work in groups of two to three in sorting the cards in Packets A-F.

3. Assign as homework any problems that were not completed in class, and spend as much time as student interest will allow in discussion of problem solutions.

4. Keep in mind that correlational reasoning is a difficult reasoning pattern for many students, so do not expect mastery at this time. Subsequent learning cycles provide additional opportunities for students to examine data for possible correlations. These opportunities will be necessary for many students to become skilled.

5. Include at least one item on class exams that requires correlational reasoning, and give partial credit to students who show some insight. In other words, ask students to explain their answers, and base your scoring largely on the adequacy of their explanations.

---

### Thinking Skills

identifying variables and constants
sorting and classifying
probabilistic reasoning
correlational reasoning

---

# Skull Structure and Function

## Investigation 5    *What Can Be Learned From Skulls?*

## Synopsis

Students observe a variety of vertebrate skulls and attempt to identify each animal, its habitat, and what it eats. Through class discussion, the relationships between skull characteristics and implied functions are explored, and the terms *herbivore, omnivore, carnivore, nocturnal, diurnal,* and *niche* are introduced. This is a descriptive learning cycle.

## Suggested Time

Two class periods

## Background Information for the Teacher

Vertebrate skulls reveal adaptations for specific functions. Large eye sockets, for example, accommodate large eyes needed for nocturnal activity. Eye sockets located on the sides of the head imply a similar positioning of the eyes for the good peripheral vision needed by prey animals, whereas a more frontal location implies good depth perception needed by predatory animals. Teeth also reveal adaptations. The teeth of herbivores are relatively flat for the grinding of plant material, while the teeth of carnivores are more pointed and sharp for the grasping and tearing of flesh.

The purpose of this learning cycle is to provide students with an opportunity to observe skull characteristics and infer facts about the animal's food source and habitat (place where it lives) and to improve their ability to support or refute ideas through use of evidence and logical argumentation.

## Advance Preparation

A variety of skulls may be obtained from your state game and fish department or from biological supply houses. The activity works best if a diversity of familiar and unfamiliar vertebrates are used (e.g., small monkey, tortoise, seal, bear, cat, bird, dog, fox, horse, snake, garpike, beaver). Plastic replicas are satisfactory and are considerably less expensive.

Place a different skull at each of ten numbered stations.

## Teaching Tips

### Exploration

1. To introduce the lesson, you may want to remind students of the work of paleontologists, who are able to infer many things about the lifestyle and habitat of ancient animals from only a few fossil bones. Ask them for any examples of this sort of work that they may know of and what might be some of the clues paleontologists use to draw their inferences. Tell students that the investigation will challenge them to draw inferences about the lifestyles and habitats of a variety of vertebrates whose skulls are located throughout the room. Specific questions they should consider are *What type of food does this animal eat (plants, animals, or both)?* and *What evidence exists for that inference (number, shape, size, location of teeth)? Is this animal active during the day, at night, or both?*

*What is the evidence (size, location of eye sockets)? Is the animal a predator or prey? Why (eyes front for depth perception indicates a predator, eyes to the side for peripheral vision indicates prey)?* Make sure only to raise the questions during the introduction. Do not mention specific characteristics and inferences, such as sharp teeth imply "meat-eater," or eyes in front suggest "predator." Let the students discover these on their own. If they are not proposed, you may mention them later during the term-introduction discussion.

### Term Introduction

2. After students have gathered data on each skull, assign each group to report their observations and inferences for one of the skulls. Start the discussion by having one group hold up the first skull and report their ideas, inferences, and evidence. Argumentation among students should be encouraged. You even may wish to play the role of devil's advocate in some instances to encourage students to think more critically about their conclusions and the alternatives. Then have the next group report on the second skull, and so on.

3. As the discussion begins to center on teeth, put the words the students use to describe them (tearing, crushing, grinding) on the board.

4. These teeth types will suggest function. Discuss this relationship. At the appropriate time, introduce the terms *herbivore, carnivore, omnivore,* and *niche,* defining *niche* as "an organism's role (function) within its habitat." Introduce the terms by stating the definitions first. Then state the term. For example, "This animal has sharp teeth for tearing and no flat teeth for grinding. This implies that it eats only animals. An animal that eats other animals is called a *carnivore.* An animal that eats only plants is called a *herbivore.*"

5. Student attention to eye sockets will allow you to introduce the terms *nocturnal* and *diurnal* (e.g., "This animal has large eye sockets, which implies that it has large eyes for night vision. An animal that is active during the night is called nocturnal.").

### Concept Application

6. Provide opportunities for students to examine a variety of bones (bird bones, fish bones, etc.), in addition to skulls, and to make inferences from their structure about their functions.

| **Biological Terms** | **Thinking Skills** |
| --- | --- |
| nocturnal | accurately describe nature |
| herbivore | create alternative hypotheses |
| carnivore | draw and apply conclusions |
| omnivore | |
| niche | |
| diurnal | |

## Sample Test Questions

*Items 1–9 refer to the drawing of the skull. Determine the type of conclusion made, using the following key. Explain your answers in the space provided on the right.*

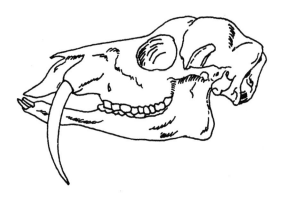

### Key

A. Justifiable conclusion based on direct observation

B. Justifiable conclusion based on inference

C. Nonjustifiable conclusion

1. Animal has grinding-type teeth.
2. Animal is a herbivore.
3. Animal does not use tusk for eating purposes.
4. Animal has relatively large eye orbits.
5. Sense of sight is important for this animal.
6. Animal is nocturnal.
7. Animal has lower intelligence than a monkey.
8. This is a male.
9. This is a mammal.

## Answers

| | | |
|---|---|---|
| 1. A | 4. A | 7. B |
| 2. B | 5. B | 8. C |
| 3. B | 6. B | 9. B |

# Homeostasis • Heart Function

| Investigation 6 | *What Causes Changes in Heart Rate?* |

## Synopsis

Students experiment to identify variables that influence respiration and heart rate, such as exercise, rebreathing air, and temperature. Data are analyzed in a class discussion, and the terms *homeostasis, feedback,* and *chemical regulation* are introduced, followed by a discussion of other homeostatic mechanisms. This is an empirical-abductive learning cycle.

## Suggested Time

Three class periods

## Background Information for the Teacher

This learning cycle explores the effect of exercise, temperature, deep breathing (hyperventilation), and rebreathing of air on the heart rate of students. In general, heart rate increases with exercise and rebreathing air, and decreases with hyperventilation and low temperatures.

Exercise and rebreathing air presumably increase heart rate due to an increase in waste $CO_2$ given off by active muscle cells or the inability of $CO_2$ gas to diffuse out of the lungs. Most of the $CO_2$ carried by the blood is transported as bicarbonate ions ($HCO_3^-$). Bicarbonate ions are produced because $CO_2$ tends to combine with water to produce carbonic acid:

$$CO_2 + H_2O \rightarrow H_2CO_3$$

In the blood, carbonic acid tends to dissociate into hydrogen ions ($H^+$) and bicarbonate ions ($HCO_3^-$).

$$H_2CO_3 \rightarrow H^+ + HCO_3^-$$

This reaction lowers the pH of the blood. The drop in pH is sensed by cells in the aortic arch and carotid sinus that send electrical signals to the cardioaccelerator center in the brain stem. The center then relays signals back to the heart muscle that cause it to increase its rate of beating. This increase will, of course, pump blood more rapidly, allowing $CO_2$ to be unloaded more rapidly by the lungs. Drops in $CO_2$ level, for example due to hyperventilation, will have the reverse effect via the cardioinhibitory center. Regulation of heart rate in this way is an excellent example of a homeostatic mechanism.

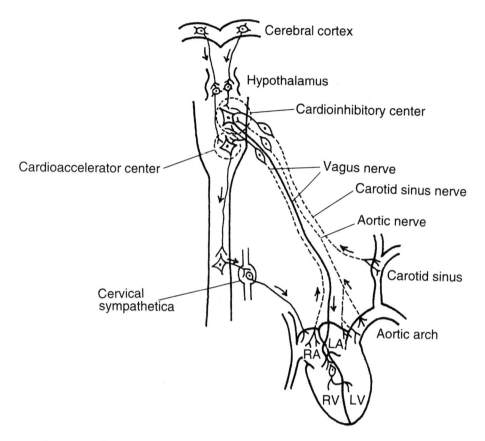

The cause of the decrease in heart rate with decreasing temperature (e.g., putting an arm in an ice bath) is more problematic. One possible explanation goes something like this: Lower temperature causes a constriction of blood vessels in the arm (a response to cold temperatures to keep core body temperature up). Constriction of blood vessels increases blood pressure, which is sensed in the carotid sinus and aortic arch. Signals then are sent to the brain, which returns inhibitory signals back to the heart to decrease the heart rate, which lowers the blood pressure back to its original level.

Of course, students do not generate data that bear on the validity of these theories of homeostatic regulation; nevertheless, the data they do gather allow you to raise the question and to begin to think about what sorts of physiological mechanisms might be involved. You may decide to propose these mechanisms as a possible answer, but you need not do so. It is a huge jump from the student data to these mechanisms, as the students really are unable to generate specific data in their support. If you do choose to introduce these mechanisms, make it clear to your students that the mechanisms are "theoretical" in the sense that they cannot be observed directly. Instead, they have been imagined to exist, and they lead to logical predictions that have been observed. Hence, the imagined explanations have been supported by evidence.

## Advance Preparation

Obtain ice cubes.

## Teaching Tips

### *Exploration*

1. After students determine their resting pulse rates, record these on the board and discuss possible reasons for student variation. If you make a quick plot of *pulse rate versus frequency* on the board, the data most likely will be distributed normally. Asking students to recall the name of such a distribution represents a good application for the concept of normal distribution. Have students derive the mean heart rate for the class. Pulse rates should be reported as beats per minute. You may wish to count beats for a 15-second interval and simply multiply by 4 to obtain beats per minute.

2. Ask for students' ideas of what variables may influence pulse rate. They may suggest exercise, temperature, illness, drugs, food, fright, stress, smoking, lack of air, and so on. Accept all of these as reasonable possibilities, and indicate that the class will have an opportunity to test some of them. If the terms *independent variable* and *dependent variable* have been introduced previously, they can be applied in this new context (concept application). For example, amount of physical activity is an independent variable, and pulse rate is the dependent variable. When a student predicts, for example, that physical activity will increase pulse rate, ask why. Although the student may not have a well-thought-out reason, a brief discussion of ideas at the outset is a good way to get the students thinking about possible causes.

3. You are encouraged to let students design ways of testing their own ideas about ways to influence heart rate as long as they stay well within the limits of classroom safety. These ideas should come from the class discussion and a look through the materials list. The following procedures may be suggested to students if they have difficulty getting started. Keep in mind, however, that giving students procedures to follow robs them of an opportunity for independent thinking and will encourage a continued dependence on you for guidance.

### STATION 1    Effect of Exercise

a. Obtain resting heart rate for 1 minute.

b. Record.

c. Walk rapidly up and down a flight of stairs 4 times.

d. Obtain heart rate and record.

e. Keep monitoring heart rate each minute until it reaches normal.

### STATION 2    Effect of Decreased Temperature

a. Obtain resting heart rate for 1 minute.

b. Put hand up to forearm in icy cold water.

c. Leave for 3 to 5 minutes.

d. Remove hand and take heart rate.

e. Record each minute until it reaches normal.

STATION 3    **Effect of Increased Temperature**

a. Record resting heart rate.

b. Wrap arm in heating pad or dip in hot water for 4 minutes.

c. Record heart rate.

d. Keep monitoring heart rate each minute until it reaches normal.

STATION 4    **Effect of Deep Breathing**

a. Record resting heart rate.

b. Sit in a chair and hyperventilate for 5 minutes or until you become dizzy. Hyperventilation is when you take deep breathes continuously. **CAUTION: Watch students carefully at this station; hyperventilation for an extended period can cause fainting. Students should stop as soon as they feel slightly dizzy.**

c. Record heart rate.

d. Keep monitoring heart rate each minute until it reaches normal.

STATION 5    **Effect of Rebreathing Air**

a. Record resting heart rate.

b. Breathe into paper bag. **CAUTION: Watch students carefully at this station; rebreathing air for an extended period can cause fainting. Students should stop as soon as they feel slightly dizzy.**

c. Record heart rate.

d. Keep monitoring each minute until it reaches normal.

4. **CAUTION: Before students gather data, check for students with such potentially dangerous conditions as asthma, and limit their participation if appropriate to do so.** After students have gathered data, collect results on the board in a table. You may wish first to list the variables tested. Write an *I* (for increase), *D* (for decrease), or *N* (for no change) next to the variable for each student's result. Select a student or students to summarize the main trends in the data, as not all students will obtain precisely the same results. These differences may provoke a discussion of differences in procedures and the need to eliminate these differences (control variables) to obtain more consistent results. Some data may need to be retaken.

### *Term Introduction*

5. Ask students to discuss their results and their possible explanations (hypotheses) of the different rates recorded. Students may have discovered that heart rate may be increased by exercise, holding their breath, or breathing into a bag, and decreased by hyperventilation and lower temperatures. They have learned from previous explorations that carbon dioxide is produced at the cellular level by respiration. A significant fact that they will not know without your assistance is that some areas in the circulatory system are highly sensitive to pH changes brought about by carbon dioxide. It is not a deficiency of oxygen but an excess of carbon dioxide in the blood that triggers increased heart rate and breathing rate.

6. In discussing how the delicate balance between heart rate and level of carbon dioxide in the blood is maintained, you may introduce the terms *homeostasis, negative feedback*, and *chemical regulation*. These mechanisms can explain changes due to changes in $CO_2$ levels, but they will not explain any changes due to changes in temperature. Students may wish to speculate on the mechanism involved, and you may wish to discuss the homeostatic mechanism of temperature regulation in mammals and reptiles.

7. Because this activity clearly involves questions, hypotheses, predictions, results, and tentative conclusions, you may wish to have students explicitly identify these elements in their thinking to reinforce these aspects of scientific reasoning.

### Concept Application

8. Investigations 19, 31, 32, 33, and 34 allow students to explore regulatory systems in other biological contexts.

9. Chapter 7 of the textbook should be assigned reading.

| **Biological Terms** | **Thinking Skills** |
| --- | --- |
| homeostasis | accurately describe nature |
| negative feedback | state causal questions |
| chemical regulation | create alternative hypotheses |
| | plan and conduct experiments |
| | generate logical predictions |
| | organize and analyze data |
| | draw and apply conclusions |

## Sample Test Questions

*The following 12 items are based on the following data and key. Use the data to classify the statements.*

### KEY

A.  A hypothesis consistent with the results

B.  A hypothesis contradicted by the results

C.  A statement of the results

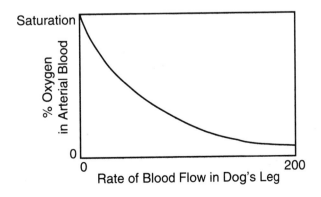

1. A correlation exists between the oxygen level in the blood and the rate of blood flow.

2. Lack of oxygen causes contraction of blood vessels and thus reduces blood flow.

3. Lack of oxygen causes an increase in size of blood vessels.

4. Greater amounts of oxygen in the blood bring about a marked increase in blood flow by increasing heart rate.

5. Decreasing oxygen increases heart rate.

6. Increased breathing rate causes an increase in oxygen level and thus a decrease in blood flow.

7. The rate of blood flow in the dog's leg is lowest at near 100% saturation.

8. As the oxygen level in the blood drops, the rate of flow increases.

9. Capillaries contract when the percentage of oxygen is high.

10. Rate of blood flow is inversely correlated with the amount of oxygen in the blood.

11. Increased exercise causes blood flow to increase.

12. Smoking decreases the blood's ability to carry oxygen, so it will cause blood flow to increase.

## Answers

| | |
|---|---|
| 1. C | 7. C |
| 2. B | 8. C |
| 3. A | 9. A |
| 4. B | 10. C |
| 5. A | 11. A |
| 6. A | 12. A |

# Animal Behavior

## Investigation 7  *In What Ways Can Isopods Sense Their Environment?*

## Synopsis

Students observe the responses of individual isopods to a variety of stimuli, and design and conduct experiments with a larger number of isopods to draw general conclusions about their behavior. Through discussion and analysis of student data, the terms *stimulus*, *response*, *taxis*, *innate behavior*, *learned behavior*, *learning*, and *reasoning* are introduced. This is a hypothetical-deductive learning cycle.

## Suggested Time

Three class periods

## Background Information for the Teacher

Isopods are small gray "bugs" that are members of the class Crustacea. Isopods are abundant in damp soil under rotting logs, in flower beds, or wherever wet, decomposing plant material exists. They are excellent animals for laboratory observations and experimentation; they are easy to collect, maintain, and manipulate; and they respond rapidly to a variety of stimuli, such as light intensity, heat, moisture, touch, and various chemical substances.

Observed responses suggest that isopods have sense receptors for these stimuli even though the sense receptors are generally not visible to the naked eye. Evidence for a sense of sight, for instance, comes from experiments in which a number of isopods (e.g., ten) are placed in the center of a box darkened on one end. A repeated movement of most of the isopods toward the darkened end (all other things being equal) is supportive of the hypothesis that isopods can indeed sense differences in light intensity.

An experiment of the type just described demonstrates a critical issue in scientific investigation—that of replication and generalization of results. Simply because one, two, or a few isopods move toward the dark does not "prove" that the darkness is actually "preferred" or that isopods can sense differences in light intensity. Their movements simply might be random, or perhaps isopods play follow-the-leader and the leader's movements are random. Or perhaps the dark end was cooler than the light end and the isopods were reacting to temperature difference, not light difference.

How can these problems be overcome? In point of fact, they cannot be overcome completely. This is why proof lies beyond the realm of scientific investigation. The problems nevertheless can be minimized—first by being careful to ensure that only one factor varies from one end of the box to the other (perform a controlled experiment) and second by repeating the experiment sufficient times to allow one to be reasonably sure that the experimental results depart significantly from the predicted 50-50% chance movements of isopods to the light and dark ends, assuming that they cannot "see." You most likely will have to raise these issues with your students because most students will not have an appreciation of their importance.

In terms of specific types of behaviors exhibited by the isopods, consider the figure on page 38, which compares dominant modes of behavior across various groups of organisms.

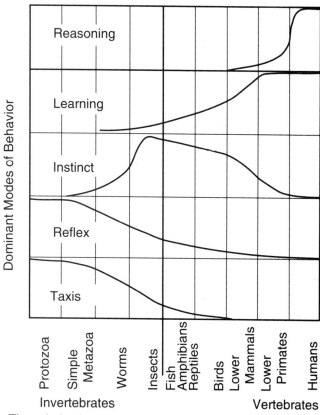

Dominant Modes of Behavior

Reasoning

Learning

Instinct

Reflex

Taxis

Protozoa | Simple Metazoa | Worms | Insects | Fish Amphibians Reptiles | Birds | Lower Mammals | Lower Primates | Humans

Invertebrates     Vertebrates

The relative importance of different modes
of behavior in various groups of animals.    From Keeton, W.T., *Biological Science.* New York: Norton

A taxis is defined as "a simple continuously oriented movement either toward or away from a stimulus," such as the continuous movement of a planarian toward a light source (a positive photo taxis). Taxes dominate in protozoa, simple metazoa, and worms, yet play little or no role in vertebrates. A reflex is defined as "a simple and essentially automatic response to a stimulus," such as the pulling away of your finger from a hot surface or the sequence of orienting movements of a paramecium away from a bubble of $CO_2$. Reflexes tend to dominate the behavior of invertebrates but are of decreasing importance in vertebrates. An instinct is defined as "a behavioral pattern acquired genetically." Instincts tend to dominate in the insects. Learning, defined as "behavioral patterns acquired through experience," begins to dominate in the lower vertebrates and dominates in the primates. Finally, reasoning, defined as "the act of reflecting on prior experience to allow the modification of old behavior patterns or the invention of new behavior patterns," is evidenced in lower mammals and dominates in humans.

An interesting issue that can be addressed following the exploration of isopod behavior in this lab is the classification of their behaviors into one or more of these categories. Clearly, taxes and reflexes can be observed, but which behaviors may be due to instinct or learning? Students may wish to discuss the issue and perhaps design experiments to determine whether isopods are capable of learning.

You may wish also to introduce the term *anthropomorphism* (attributing human characteristics to nonhuman beings and things, e.g., birds feed their young because they "love" them, a worm wiggles on a hook because it is in "pain," isopods move to the cool end of the box because they do not "like" to be hot) and point out the shortcoming in trying to interpret nonhuman behaviors in this way.

## Advance Preparation

Collect or purchase isopods prior to beginning the learning cycle. Students can be asked to help.

Isopods can be kept in loosely covered jars. Place damp soil in the jar; cover isopods with damp paper towels and/or damp plant material.

You may expand the materials list to include other stimuli that you think appropriate.

## Teaching Tips

### Exploration

1. Each group should start with at least five isopods. More will be needed for procedure step 3.

2. Emphasize the importance of reasonable care and respect when working with living organisms.

3. After about 15 to 20 minutes of student exploration (procedure step 2), you may wish to hold a class discussion. Ask students to report their findings thus far. Read step 3 with the class, and ask students for ideas about how they may conduct experiments to obtain quantitative data to answer one or more of the questions posed (*Can isopods see? Can isopods hear? Do they communicate?*). Students may need to be reminded that results must be repeatable prior to drawing firm conclusions. They most likely will have to try to replicate their initial findings either by increasing the number of isopods per trial or by using more trials. Good experimental design involves important ideas of probability and the control of variables that many of the students may not understand well. A discussion of these topics in the context of a simple experiment, such as testing isopods' reaction to amount of light (e.g., with a light at one end of the box and the other end covered in the dark, placing ten isopods in the center to see which way they go) should help students realize the need for 1) using lots of isopods or repeating the trials (to overshadow the random responses of "unusual isopods") and 2) controlling all independent variables except the one being tested (to isolate its effect from the possible effects of additional variables).

### Term Introduction

4. You may wish to initiate this phase of the learning cycle by having one member of a few or all groups (time permitting) orally present their question, hypothesis (if they have one), prediction (expected results), actual results, and conclusion. Expect some confusion; many students are unfamiliar with this hypothetical-deductive mode of experimentation and will have particular difficulty differentiating between hypotheses and predictions. Introduce relevant terms when students present data or conclusions. For example, if students report that the isopods tend to move toward moisture, the terms *taxis, reflex,* and *innate* and *learned behavior* may be introduced and defined. You may wish to draw the figure from the background information onto the board (or make a transparency) and briefly discuss it. Students then can be challenged to try to classify the observed behavior as one of these types or to specify what additional research would be needed to tell.

The discussion may range to other types of organisms. For example, how might one determine whether a bird's nest-building behavior is learned or innate? Or consider a mother quail accompanied by her chicks: The mother clucks out a soft alarm, and the chicks scatter in all directions, running only a short distance and then stopping and remaining motionless. This is a brilliant strategy because the chicks' colors and markings blend with the desert floor, and running more than a short distance would only make them more conspicuous. Is this behavior innate or learned? How could we find out?

### Concept Application

5. Subsequent learning cycles will provide a number of additional opportunities to apply such concepts of experimental design as probability and controlling variables. You may wish to have your students do the additional activity with planaria to extend their understanding of taxes, reflexes, and innate and learned behavior.

6. Chapter 7 of the textbook should be assigned reading.

---

### Biological Terms

stimulus/response
taxis
reflex
instinct
innate behavior
learned behavior
reasoning

### Thinking Skills

accurately describe nature
state causal questions
create alternative hypotheses
generate logical predictions
plan and conduct experiments
organize and analyze data
draw and apply conclusions

---

## Sample Test Questions

*The next six items are based on the following data and diagrams.*

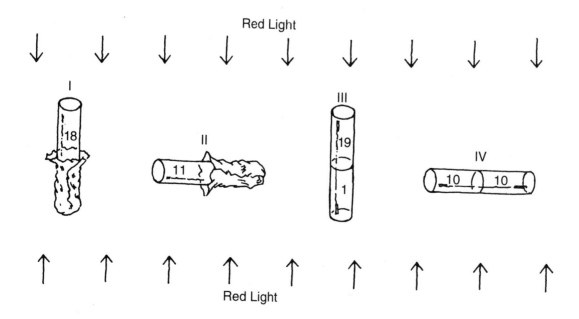

Twenty flies are placed into each of four glass tubes. The tubes are sealed. Tubes I and II are covered with foil; Tubes III and IV are not covered. The tubes are placed as shown. Then they are exposed to red light for 5 minutes. The number of flies in the uncovered part of each tube is shown in the drawing.

1.  This experiment shows that flies respond to
    a.  red light but not to gravity.
    b.  gravity but not to red light.
    c.  both red light and gravity.
    d.  neither red light nor gravity

In a second experiment, blue light was used instead of red. The results are shown in the drawing.

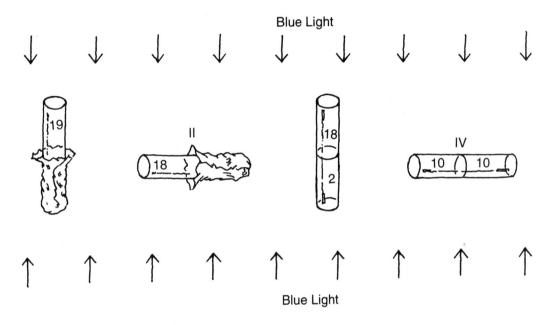

2.  These data show that flies respond to
    a.  blue light but not to gravity.
    b.  gravity but not to blue light.
    c.  both blue light and gravity.
    d.  neither blue light nor gravity.

3.  From both experiments, one can conclude that flies react to
    a.  red light but not to blue light.
    b.  blue light but not to red light.
    c.  both blue and red light.
    d.  neither blue nor red light.

4.  Which tubes served as controls for the light variable?
    a.  I and II        b.  II and III        c.  III and IV        d.  IV and I

5.  Which tubes served as controls for the gravity variable?
    a.  II and IV       b.  II and III        c.  III and IV        d.  V and I

6. These experiments tested the flies' responses to
   a. red light only.
   b. blue light only.
   c. gravity and blue light only.
   d. red and blue light and gravity.

*The next 13 items refer to the italicized parts of the following paragraphs. Each part in italics is an item. Identify each item with a response from the Key.*

**KEY**

A. Hypothesis (possible answer to the causal question)

B. Result of experiment

C. Question

D. Prediction (expected result of the experiment)

7) *Some animals have the ability to change color.* 8) *How do animals change color?* 9) *When a catfish is placed into an aquarium that has a black bottom and sides, the fish becomes black in a few days.* 10) *When the same fish is transferred to a tank that has a white bottom and sides, it becomes very pale, almost white.* 11) *Perhaps it has some type of color receptor in its skin.* 12) *Or perhaps the sense receptor that is responsible for this is located in the eyes.*

If the sensitivity were due to stimulation of the eyes, 13) *blinding should inhibit the ability to change color.* 14) *Blinded fish were unable to respond to changes in the background color,* but light intensity does not seem to be the whole answer.

If light intensity were the only stimulus, 15) *fish in a dark tank under bright light would become lighter, and fish in a white tank under dim light would become darker.* This would happen because more light would be reflected from a brightly lighted, dark tank than from a dimly lighted, white one.

But this was not the case. 16) *The fish turned white even in a very dimly lighted, white tank. They turned dark in a brightly lighted, dark one.*

In the next phase of the experiment, the amount of direct light and reflected light was varied. This experiment showed that 17) *the darkness of the fish was proportional to the ratio of direct light to reflected light.*

This suggested that 18) *more than one receptor was involved in the mechanism of adjustment.* Glass lenses were fitted over the fish's eyes. 19) *When the lower half of each lens was blackened, shielding the eyes from the bottom and walls of the tank, the fish became dark even on a white background. When the upper half was blackened, concealing direct light, the fish became pale even when placed in a black aquarium.*

## Answers

| | | | |
|---|---|---|---|
| 1. B | 6. D | 11. A | 16. B |
| 2. C | 7. B | 12. A | 17. B |
| 3. B | 8. C | 13. D | 18. A |
| 4. C | 9. B | 14. B | 19. B |
| 5. A | 10. B | 15. D | |

# Causality

## Reasoning Module 3 *Causal Relationships*

## Synopsis

Students are introduced to a method of determining when events are likely to be due to chance or to a specific cause by simulating the results of an experiment with mealworms in a box.

## Suggested Time

Two class periods

## Background Information

To establish that a single event, A, is the cause of a specific effect, B, one has to establish that A precedes B in time and that only A can produce B. For all practical purposes, doing this is impossible because of our inability to isolate cause A from all other possible causes. Nevertheless, experimental techniques do exist that allow one to be reasonably certain that one event is the cause of another.

Consider the case of the four mealworms in a box with a light at one end (see p. 37 of the student manual). Observation of the box reveals that three out of every four mealworms have moved away from the light and are resting at the darker end of the box. Does this imply that the light caused them to move? How can we be sure that some other factor was not the cause? You might suggest doing something to be certain that the only difference between the two ends of the box is the amount of light. This is a good idea, but the problem is that one can never be certain that the amount of light is the only variable. This unknown factor sometimes is referred to as random noise or "chance"; the mealworms may have moved away from the light due to some unknown reason or reasons. The question then becomes, *Did the mealworms move because of the light or because of "chance"?*

To answer this question, we need to know the likelihood that this particular event can occur due to chance alone (not due to the light). If the likelihood is relatively small, we can be relatively certain that the light is the cause. If the likelihood is relatively large, the light is probably not the cause. For a method of determining this likelihood, see page 8 of the student manual. The diagram shows that the result will occur 4 out of 16 times, or 25% of the time, due to chance alone; therefore, if you conclude that light was the cause, you stand a 25% chance of being wrong.

This Reasoning Module introduces students to this type of reasoning and provides a number of Study Questions to test their understanding. This is a difficult Reasoning Module because it requires aspects of combinatorial reasoning, probabilistic reasoning, and the control of variables—all scientifically advanced skills. You therefore should expect some confusion and should be alert to other opportunities for students to apply this type of reasoning in subsequent learning cycles.

## Advance Preparation

Have the sacks with the cardboard mealworms ready for use with the second essay. Each sack should contain four cardboard mealworms. Each mealworm should have two sides, one marked *L* for light, and one marked *D* for dark. Each group of two students should get a sack.

## Teaching Tips

1.  Briefly discuss the introductory material, and then have students work in groups of two or three to do the activities in the two essays.

2.  Assign the second set of Study Questions as homework, and plan to spend an entire class period discussing them. You no doubt will have to demonstrate use of the branching diagram in a number of contexts before students become comfortable with its use.

| Biological Terms | Thinking Skills |
|---|---|
| causality | isolation and control of variables |
| probability | combinatorial reasoning |
| | probabilistic reasoning |

# Vertebrate Organ Systems

## Investigation 8    *What Is Inside a Frog?*

## Synopsis

Students dissect frogs, examine internal structures, and create hypotheses concerning their functions. After students have removed, examined, drawn, and proposed hypotheses concerning the functioning of digestive organs, the teacher directs attention to overall length, organ sequence and positioning, and differential inner lining through the digestive tract, and introduces the term *digestive system* and the names of the organs observed. Students then examine organs of the respiratory, circulatory, and urogenital systems. Analogous systems in such other vertebrates as humans are discussed. This is an empirical-abductive learning cycle.

## Suggested Time

Four class periods

## Background Information for the Teacher

The dissection of a frog reveals organs and systems of organs typical of vertebrates. Observable organs include the trachea, lungs, liver, esophagus, stomach, small and large intestines, spleen, pancreas, gallbladder, heart, veins, arteries, muscles, brain, and nerves. You may wish to consult a text or dissection manual for diagrams of major organs and organ systems and their functions. The major purpose of the activity is to enable students to discover internal organs and systems and to propose alternative hypotheses about possible organ functions based on the size, shape, location, and attachments of the observed structures.

You may wish to have students dissect other animals, such as worms, fetal pigs, or clams. These dissections can be accomplished in much the same way as this frog dissection. Information obtained from earlier dissections can and should be used for comparison with later dissections.

## Teaching Tips

### Exploration

1. Avoid giving students labeled diagrams at the start. The idea is to explore the internal structures and to try to figure out their functions by observing their structure, colors, textures, sizes, shapes, locations, and points of attachment. Names come later during term introduction.

2. Because few specific instructions are given to students in their manual, circulate among lab groups to provide suggestions if needed. Feel free to stop the dissection at any point to discuss what students have done thus far, to note difficulties, and to provide suggestions to reduce possible confusion.

3. After students have cut through the ventral surface, the first organ they will encounter is the liver. After points of attachment have been noted and the organ removed, students will have little difficulty in finding, examining, and removing organs of the digestive system. The major respiratory and circulatory organs, as well as those of the urogenital system, are also easily located once other organs have been removed.

### Term Introduction

4.  After procedure step 10, assemble the class for a discussion to introduce terms related to the digestive system. Do this by having several students draw their observed structures on the board. Point out similarities and differences in the drawings, and try to arrive at a single fairly complete drawing. At this point, ask students whether they know the names of the structures and the possible functions. Label the structures with their appropriate names (stomach, esophagus, large intestine, etc.). Discuss students' ideas about the functions of the various organs. Ask what evidence they have to support the proposed functions. Do the shapes of the structures and their locations provide evidence? What other evidence could be gathered?

5.  Now that students have an initial insight into the workings of a system, have them begin their dissection of the respiratory, circulatory, and urogenital systems.

6.  On completion of each phase of the dissection, the class should be brought together again to put drawings on the board, to compare the drawings, and to introduce organ names of the respiratory, circulatory, and urogenital systems. Hypothesized organ functions and how one or more of them could be tested should be discussed as well.

### Concept Application

7.  Text readings, films, diagrams, and further discussions can be used to relate to other vertebrates the ideas introduced here.

| **Biological Terms** | **Thinking Skills** |
| --- | --- |
| organ | accurately describe nature |
| system | state causal questions |
| digestive system | create alternative hypotheses |
| respiratory system | |
| circulatory system | |
| urogenital system | |

## Sample Test Questions

The two hypotheses below are alternative explanations of the control of pancreatic secretion into the intestine.

I:  Nerves stimulate the pancreas to secrete its enzymes into the intestine.

II:  A hormone in the blood causes the pancreas to secrete its enzymes into the intestine.

### KEY

A.  Supports hypothesis I only

B.  Supports hypothesis II only

C.  Supports both hypotheses

Use the key above to classify each of the following experiments as they relate to the hypotheses.

1.  The pancreas is stimulated when food enters the small intestine of a normal animal.

2. When a nerve leading to the pancreas is stimulated, the pancreas secretes enzymes.

3. When the nerves leading to the pancreas are cut and weak acid is placed into the intestine, the pancreas secretes enzymes.

4. If no food is in the stomach or intestine of a normal animal, the pancreas will not secrete enzymes.

5. The circulatory systems of two frogs are connected. Food is placed into the intestine of one frog. The pancreas in both frogs secretes enzymes.

6. If the nerves leading to the pancreas of a hungry frog are cut, no enzymes are secreted by the pancreas.

7. The blood from the intestine of an animal was prevented from reaching its pancreas. When the nerve leading to the pancreas was stimulated, the pancreas secreted enzymes.

8. An animal that attaches to the side of a fish and sucks the fish's blood for food probably would have
   a. a long digestive tract with many blind pouches.
   b. a short, simple digestive tract.
   c. no digestive tract.
   d. a digestive tract unlike that of any known animal.

9. Which is the best definition of a system?
   a. a network of interrelating components in which each works predominantly to its own benefit
   b. many units, having the same function, that cooperate to multiply the effects of their service
   c. interrelating components that work together to provide a service
   d. an organ's function whereby the organ is made up of many subunits; for example, the lung is made of numerous alveoli
   e. related components that cooperate for the benefit of one; for example, the blood vessels all cooperate to provide blood to the heart

10. The fact that the small intestine has an inner surface with many folds and is supplied with a rich supply of blood suggests that an important function is to
   a. produce chemicals used in digestion.
   b. support the body.
   c. absorb food into the bloodstream.
   d. transfer food from the stomach to the large intestine.
   e. receive signals from the brain to coordinate digestion.

## Answers

1. C
2. A
3. B
4. C
5. C
6. A
7. A
8. B
9. C
10. C

# Cell Structure

| Investigation 9 | *What Do Living and Nonliving Things Look Like Under the Microscope?* |

## Synopsis

Students view living, once-living, and never-living objects under the microscope to look for similarities and differences. Students' drawings are compared and discussed. The compartmental structure of living and once-living things are noted and given the name *cells*. Such structures as *cell wall* and *nucleus* also are named. This is a descriptive learning cycle.

## Suggested Time

Three class periods

## Background Information for the Teacher

Living things (organisms), as opposed to nonliving things, are composed of one or more small compartments called cells. Many components make up cells, the most obvious being a cell membrane, a nucleus, and cytoplasm. Additional observable structures in plant cells include chloroplasts and a cell wall. The purpose of this learning cycle is to acquaint the students with the use of the microscope and to familiarize them with cells, cell structure, and some of the general postulates that together constitute one of the basic theories of biology known as cell theory. These general postulates, which concern structure, formation, function, and growth, are as follows:

### Structure:

1. All organisms are composed of one or more cells and cell products.
2. A cell is a microscopic unit consisting of an outer cell membrane, cytoplasm, and nucleus in the cytoplasm.

### Formation:

3. Cells form by the division of pre-existing cells.
4. The nucleus divides prior to division of cytoplasm, so each new cell contains a nucleus, cytoplasm, and cell membrane.

### Function:

5. The activities of all organisms are due to the activities of their cells.
6. The major activities of cells can be included in one or more of these general activities: metabolism, absorption, secretion, movement, growth, and division.

### Growth:

7. Growth of multicellular organisms is due to the increase in the number and size of cells.
8. Substances absorbed from the cell's environment are essential to growth and cell division. This learning cycle introduces the first two postulates, while other postulates of cell theory are the topics of subsequent learning cycles.

## Advance Preparation

Obtain some pond water. Any source of permanent or semipermanent water should contain the necessary microorganisms. You may wish to prepare a hay infusion if pond water is not available. If so, do this a week in advance. Cultures also may be purchased from biological supply companies.

Make three collections of objects: living, once-living, and never-living.

## Teaching Tips

### Exploration

1. This may be your students' first introduction to the use of the microscope. If so, you will want to discuss the delicate nature of this instrument and its care, but students should be allowed to discover how it works through manipulation. You also may need to demonstrate how to make a wet-mount slide preparation.

2. The lab is designed to place students in the position of early scientists (Hooke, Schwann, Schleiden) looking at living and nonliving materials under a microscope, so do not introduce the term *cell* prior to the exploration.

### Term Introduction

3. Once the students have completed their drawings, have several students draw what they observed on the chalkboard, or you may use the chalkboard or an overhead projector to construct a "typical" cell as a class activity. The components of this model should come entirely from the students' data as they instruct you in how to proceed with the drawing. You may ask questions to elicit instructions from the students, but the final product must reflect the observations of the students. Emphasize that this constructed, typical cell is just that—an idealization, not an actual cell. At this point, the terms *cell, organism, nucleus, cell membrane, cell wall,* and *cytoplasm* should be introduced to label the observed structures. You also may wish to have students briefly speculate about possible functions of the identified structures and discuss how to test some of their ideas.

### Concept Application

4. Investigations 11, 12, and 13 allow for the application and extension of the ideas presented here.

5. Chapter 9 of the textbook should be assigned reading.

| Biological Terms | Thinking Skills |
|---|---|
| cell | accurately describe nature |
| organism | organize and analyze data |
| cell wall | draw and apply conclusions |
| cell membrane | |
| nucleus | |
| cytoplasm | |

## Sample Test Questions

*The following items refer to an experiment in which cells were cut into fragments. Some of the cell fragments contained a nucleus, and some did not. Fragments with nuclei were separated from fragments without nuclei. One hundred fragments from each group were placed into containers under uniform conditions. The table indicates the results.*

|  | Number of Nonnucleated Fragments | Number of Nucleated Fragments |
|---|---|---|
| Studied | 100 | 100 |
| Surviving 1 day | 80 | 79 |
| Surviving 2 days | 60 | 74 |
| Surviving 3 days | 30 | 72 |
| Surviving 4 days | 3 | 72 |

1. What was the hypothesis being tested?
   a. Any cell fragment will eventually die.
   b. Twice as many cells will grow if each is cut in half.
   c. The size of the cell fragment determines the amount of time it will live.
   d. A nucleus is necessary for the continued life of a cell.

2. Which of the following is the most important assumption in this experiment?
   a. The average size of the nucleated fragments was the same as the average size of the nonnucleated fragments.
   b. More nucleated fragments than nonnucleated fragments will be living at the end of three days.
   c. The same cytoplasmic materials were present in the nonnucleated fragments as in the nucleated fragments.
   d. All of the fragments were the same size.

   Use the following key to identify each statement (3–12).

### KEY

A. An accurate statement of the results

B. A misstatement of the results

C. A reasonable hypothesis consistent with the results

D. A reasonable prediction (expected result)

3. The rate of dying in the nonnucleated fragments was greater than in the nucleated fragments.

4. During the first day, the death rate was about the same for the two groups of fragments.

5. Nuclei of the nucleated fragments that died in the first 2 days had been injured.

6. The amount of cytoplasm of the nucleated fragments that died during the first 2 days was too small to support the life of the cell fragments.

7. Cells or cell fragments die as soon as the nucleus is removed.

8. By the sixth day, all of the nonnucleated fragments will die.

9. The percentage of nonnucleated fragments that died increased each day after the first day.

10. An increase occurred in the percentage of nucleated fragments that died each day after the first day.

11. If the nutrient medium in which the nucleated cells were living was adequate, the fragments probably would become complete cells, live, and divide normally.

12. The nucleus is normally necessary for the continued life of the cell.

## Answers

| | | | |
|---|---|---|---|
| 1. | D | 7. | B |
| 2. | C | 8. | D |
| 3. | A | 9. | A |
| 4. | A | 10. | B |
| 5. | C | 11. | D |
| 6. | C | 12. | C |

# Cell Diversity • Cell Structure and Function

## Investigation 10 *How Does Cell Structure Relate to Function?*

## Synopsis

Students view ten numbered but unnamed prepared slides of various plant and animal cells and tissues. They observe and draw structures and speculate about possible functions. This is an empirical-abductive learning cycle.

## Suggested Time

Two to three class periods

## Background Information for the Teacher

Cells in multicellular organisms exhibit structural differences that allow them to perform a variety of functions. Sometimes these functions can be inferred from examination of their structural characteristics. Slides of the following cells illustrate this point: Nerve cells are elongated to facilitate their function as conduits of electrical impulses. Red blood cells have a smooth oval shape to ease their passage through narrow vessels in the circulatory system. Sperm cells have a tail that serves as a means of locomotion. Epithelium cells, which comprise the outer layer of skin, are flat and scalelike and appear to be stacked much like shingles that protect a house from weather. The large, rounded form of fat cells allows the storage of excess materials.

A group of similar cells providing a common function is called a tissue. Sometimes the cells within specific tissues are arranged in ways that facilitate functioning as well. Slides of the following tissues illustrate this: The cells of arteries and veins are arranged to produce tubes to allow the passage of blood. The walls of the artery are thicker than veins, allowing them to withstand greater pressure. Tissue from the inner lining of the small intestine is highly convoluted, providing increased surface area to maximize absorption. A leaf cross section shows upper and lower epidermal cell layers that have thick cell walls and no chloroplasts and serve a protective function. Between these layers, the chlorenchyma cells contain chloroplasts, providing the capacity to produce food. Finally, the cross section of a stem reveals vascular cells that make up small tubes, allowing the transport of food and water.

This learning cycle is designed to familiarize students with the broad range of cell and tissue characteristics and to promote insight into the relationships between the characteristics and the functions they are designed to facilitate.

## Advance Preparation

Prepared, unlabeled slides may include the following:

| | |
|---|---|
| longitudinal section of neuron | artery cross section |
| blood | vein cross section |
| sperm | small intestine |
| stratified squamous epithelium | variety of leaf types (cross section) |
| adipose | both monocot and dicot stem cross sections |

## Teaching Tips

### Exploration

1. You may wish to introduce the investigation by discussing examples of structure-function relationships, such as those presented in the Introduction of the student manual and by asking students for additional examples (e.g., walking shoes vs. running shoes, football helmets vs. baseball caps). Students may be able to generate ideas of how various cell types may differ. For example, ask them to speculate how a nerve cell may look different from a blood cell or skin cell. Do not provide answers at this time. Instead, use the discussion merely to provoke interest and some initial thought.

### Term Introduction

2. Using either students' drawings on the chalkboard, a projection microscope, or 35-mm slides, present each slide image. Initiate a discussion by telling the students what the organism is and where in the organism the various cells came from, but do not tell them the "correct" functions. These "correct" functions are not important at this time, and introducing "correct" answers will only undermine future attempts at getting students involved in inquiry. The correct answers are the ones that make the most sense, based on the present evidence. For each cell type, ask students to present hypothesized functions and their reasons. You may wish to ask what additional evidence might be needed to support or refute their hypothesized functions. You may present some of this evidence yourself, provided you do not suggest that the issue of cell function is totally resolved. Introduce names of specific tissue types (e.g., epithelium and chlorenchyma) if you wish, but do not stress the names and do not ask students to memorize them.

### Concept Application

3. Investigations 12, 13, 19, and 27 provide further opportunities for students to examine cell diversity and structure-function relationships.

| Biological Terms | Thinking Skills |
|---|---|
| cell structure/function | accurately describe nature |
| cell diversity | state causal questions |
| tissues | create alternative hypotheses |
| | generate logical predictions |
| | organize and analyze data |
| | draw and apply conclusions |

## Sample Test Questions

*For items 1–5, use cell shape to match the animal cells labeled A–E with their likely functions.*

1. Cell travels around the body in tubes to transport molecules that enter and exit the cell through its cell membrane.

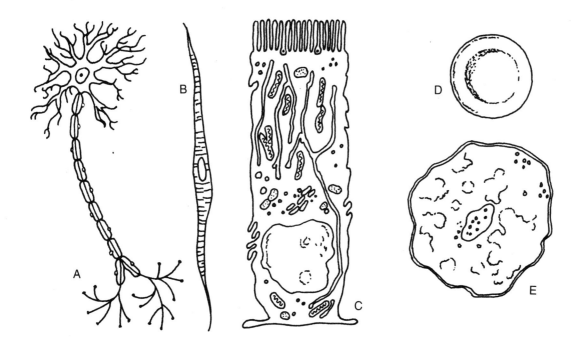

2. Cell picks up electrical signals from a number of other cells and transmits a common signal to another cell or cells.

3. Cell is capable of contracting lengthwise to move structures such as bones.

4. Cell is found in skin and can expand and contract to change skin color.

5. Cell is found on the inside of the intestinal wall and absorbs food molecules from the digestive tract.

*Items 6–10 refer to the diagram of a leaf cross section shown below. Use the cell's size, shape, and location to match it with its likely function.*

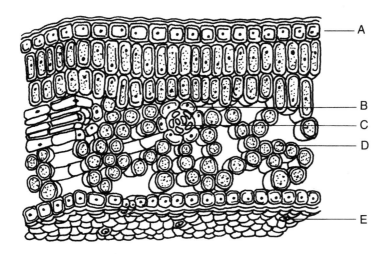

6. Cells expand and contract to increase or decrease the size of the opening between them, which regulates the passage of air into and out of the leaf.

7. Cells are covered on the top side with a waxy substance that does not allow water to pass through easily.

8. Cells function primarily to conduct molecules of food or water from one part of the plant to another.

9. Cells absorb light, air, and water to produce food.

10. Cells surround food-and-water-conducting cells and may serve to regulate movement of various types of molecules.

## Answers

| | |
|---|---|
| 1. D | 6. E |
| 2. A | 7. A |
| 3. B | 8. C |
| 4. E | 9. D |
| 5. C | 10. B |

# Organelle Structure and Function • Prokaryote • Eukaryote

## Investigation 11   *What Is Inside Cells?*

## Synopsis

Students observe electron micrographs of cells and cell organelles and compare prokaryotic with eukaryotic cells. From their observations, they generate a list of structures found in most eukaryotic cells and create alternative hypotheses about possible functions. They then read a list of discoveries about the organelles to allow testing and revision of their hypotheses. This is an empirical-abductive learning cycle.

## Suggested Time

Two to three class periods

## Background Information for the Teacher

Cells first were observed and described in the early 1600s and first named by Robert Hooke in 1665. But it was not until 1838 that Schleiden and Schwann proposed the first part of the cell theory, which proposes that all organisms are composed of one or more cells.

As light microscopes and staining techniques improved, biologists discovered the larger organelles (mitochondria, chloroplasts, and nuclei) and some evidence for others. It was not until the invention of the electron microscope in the 1930s, with its ability to magnify up to one million times, that cell organelles could be examined closely. Since then, cytologists have studied the functions of the organelles by using such techniques as biochemical analysis, microsurgery, and ultracentrifugation.

The basic cell organelles explored in this investigation are the nucleus, endoplasmic reticulum, ribosomes, Golgi bodies, lysosomes, mitochondria, chloroplasts, and cell walls. The following historical background about each organelle is to be provided to students during the investigation.

## Historical Background

A. Nucleus
  1. Recognized as present in all but bacterial and blue-green algae cells
  2. Contains chromosomes that were stained and observed in 1888
  3. Goes through a series of complex changes during cell division
  4. Surrounded by a double, porous membrane. If pierced, the cell will die.
  5. Cells that have their nuclei removed have shortened life spans and cannot reproduce.
  6. Most genetic material is found in the nucleus.

B. Endoplasmic Reticulum (ER)
  1. Found throughout the cytoplasm in plant and animal cells
  2. Appears as a channel system of double membranes that is connected to the outer nuclear membrane

3. "Rough" ER is associated with the manufacture of protein molecules and is abundant in cells that secrete molecules.
4. "Smooth" ER is connected to Golgi bodies.

C. Ribosomes
   1. Found in all plant and animal cells
   2. Are attached to the outer nuclear membrane and the rough ER
   3. Abundant in cells engaged in protein synthesis
   4. Amino acids labeled with radioactivity concentrate at ribosomes

D. Golgi Bodies
   1. First seen as a black network in silver-stained cells
   2. Not definitely identified until after the invention of the electron microscope
   3. Made of flattened membranes, tubes, and vacuoles filled by nearby smooth ER
   4. Abundant in active secretory cells

E. Lysosomes
   1. First discovered as particles centrifuged from liver cells
   2. High levels of enzyme activity were discovered when the single surrounding membrane was broken.
   3. Abundant in cells that secrete enzymes
   4. Twenty-four different digestive enzymes found inside

F. Mitochondria
   1. Found in plant and animal cells but not in bacterial cells
   2. Average number of mitochondria is 200 to 300 per cell. The number varies from 1 in some algae cells to 1,000 in muscle cells.
   3. Can move freely within a cell
   4. Discovered to be bounded by a double membrane. The outer membrane is smooth, while the inner membrane is folded.
   5. Contain 70 different enzymes
   6. Staining indicates energy-release processes
   7. Location of most oxygen uptake in the cell
   8. Location of carbohydrate breakdown in the cell

G. Chloroplasts
   1. Discovered in 1884 to be involved in oxygen production and light absorption
   2. Found to contain enzymes for joining carbon dioxide molecules together
   3. Found to be most abundant in plant cells with light exposure

H. Cell Wall
   1. The cell part described in print in 1665 by Robert Hooke
   2. Located outside the cell membrane in plants and bacteria
   3. Composed of cellulose, the world's most common organic molecule

## Advance Preparation

Photocopy the five electron micrographs for procedure steps 1 and 2 in the student manual.

Photocopy the remaining micrographs and the historical information (above) for procedure steps 4 and 5, and place them at separate stations in the classroom.

## Teaching Tips

### *Exploration*

1. Initiate exploration with a discussion of the introductory material in the student manual.

2. Have students work in teams of two or three as they make their initial observations of the first set of five electron micrographs.

### *Term Introduction*

3. When your students have completed procedure steps 1 and 2, bring them together for a class discussion. Discussion should bring out the similarities and differences between the cells with few observable organelles (blue-green algae and bacterial cells) and those with many (all others). Tell the students that all cells are of these two major types—those with organelles and those without. Tell them that those with no organelles are called *prokaryotes*, while those with organelles are called *eukaryotes*. Write these terms on the board. You may wish to ask the class which type of cell is probably the more primitive and why.

4. Next, post the cell drawings around the room, and compare them, looking for organelles that are common to most or all of them. Make a drawing of a "generalized cell," naming the organelles as you go. Note that cell walls and chloroplasts are found only in plant cells.

5. Now have students examine the second set of electron micrographs, including the lists of historical information about individual organelles.

6. Encourage students to create their initial hypotheses about organelle function before reading the historical information or textbooks. This will give them an idea of problems faced by early cytologists.

7. In a class discussion, ask students to defend their hypothesized functions for the cell structures. Point out that different groups may have different ideas even though they are using the same information. Argumentation should ensue and should be encouraged. You may choose to play the role of devil's advocate to facilitate an interesting and thought-provoking discussion.

### *Concept Application*

8. Have students compare cells of a multicellular organism to a single-celled protist. Students should consider how organelles fulfill the functions of organs.

9. Investigations 12 and 13 allow for the application and extension of the ideas presented here.

10. Chapter 9 of the textbook should be read if not previously assigned.

| **Biological Terms** | **Thinking Skills** |
|---|---|
| organelle | accurately describe nature |
| nucleus | state casual questions |
| endoplasmic reticulum | create alternative hypotheses |
| ribosomes | generate logical predictions |
| lysosomes | organize and analyze data |
| Golgi body | draw and apply conclusions |
| mitochondria | |
| chloroplasts | |
|    cell wall | |
|    vacuole | |
|    prokaryote | |
|    eukaryote | |

## Sample Test Questions

1. Some algae cells have only one mitochondrion. What can you infer about the energy needs of these cells?
   a. They are very low.
   b. They are very high.
   c. They fluctuate, depending on temperature.
   d. More information is needed.

2. If a cell spontaneously self-destructs, which organelle is probably responsible?
   a. ribosome
   b. Golgi body
   c. lysosome
   d. endoplasmic reticulum

3. Red blood cells lack nuclei at maturity. This may account for their
   a. ability to carry oxygen.
   b. red color.
   c. abundance in blood.
   d. short life span.

4. A bacterium is a single-celled organism with a cell wall, no membrane-bound nucleus, and a ring-shaped chromosome. Some bacteria are able to move. Until recently, they were included in the Plant Kingdom. Why?
   a. They are single-celled.
   b. They have a cell wall.
   c. They have the ability to move.
   d. They have a different chromosome.

5. Investigators have cultured cells in a medium containing radioactive molecules. Within 20 minutes, the molecules have been taken into the cell. Within 60 minutes, the molecules are found throughout the endoplasmic reticulum. This evidence supports the hypothesis that the endoplasmic reticulum
   a. deals only with radioactive materials.
   b. is a transport system within the cell.
   c. has an unknown function.
   d. is active in breaking down harmful materials.

*The next eight items are based on the following cell diagrams.*

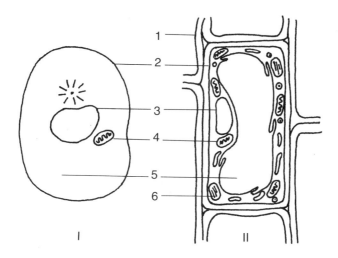

6. With Structure 3 removed, a cell could not
   a. reproduce.
   b. provide its own energy.
   c. exchange materials with the environment.
   d. secrete.

7. An organism whose cells possess Structure 1 is most likely to be
   a. dead.                          c. immobile.
   b. large.                         d. small.

8. If Structure 6 is green, the presence of many of these structures allows the organism to
   a. reproduce.                     c. secrete.
   b. exchange material with the environment.   d. make its own food

9. During cell division, some contents of Structure 3 would become
   a. Golgi bodies.                  c. chromosomes.
   b. plastids.                      d. mitochondria.

10. Early cell theory included the assumption that all cells have structures
    a. 2 and 3.                      c. 3 and 4.
    b. 2 and 4.                      d. 4 and 5.

11. In which structure is light energy "trapped" and changed into chemical energy?
    a. Cell I-1                      c. Cell II-1
    b. Cell I-5                      d. Cell II-6

12. Which part consists of cellulose?
    a. Cell I-2                      c. Cell II-1
    b. Cell I-3                      d. Cell II-6

13. Cell II probably would be
    a. an animal cell.               c. the cell of a protist.
    b. a plant cell.                 d. a cork cell.

*The next eight items are based on the following key. Use the key to classify the following series of items.*

**KEY**

Evidence to support each of the following statements probably has come from studies

A.   without the aid of a microscope.

B.   using at least a light microscope.

C.   requiring an electron microscope.

14.   The molecules of a gas or liquid are in motion.

15.   Diffusion through a nonliving membrane depends on the size of the diffusing particles and of the membrane pores.

16.   Vacuoles in plant cells grow, pushing the cytoplasm against the cell walls.

17.   "Cells arise only from preexisting cells."—Virchow

18.   The cross sections of a sperm's tail and that of some one-celled organisms appear to have the same substructure.

19.   Endoplasmic reticulum is present throughout the cytoplasm.

20.   Ribosomes contain RNA and protein molecules.

21.   The plasma membrane is composed of lipoprotein.

## Answers

| | | |
|---|---|---|
| 1. A | 8. D | 15. A |
| 2. C | 9. C | 16. B |
| 3. D | 10. A | 17. B |
| 4. B | 11. D | 18. C |
| 5. B | 12. C | 19. C |
| 6. A | 13. B | 20. A |
| 7. C | 14. A | 21. A |

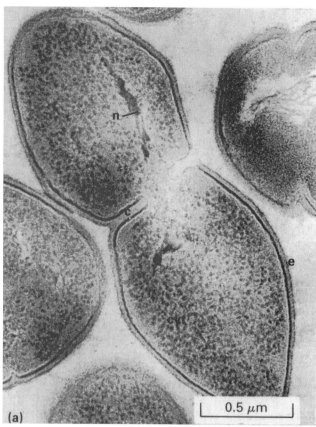

The bacterium *Streptococcus fecalis* undergoing division.

Yeast

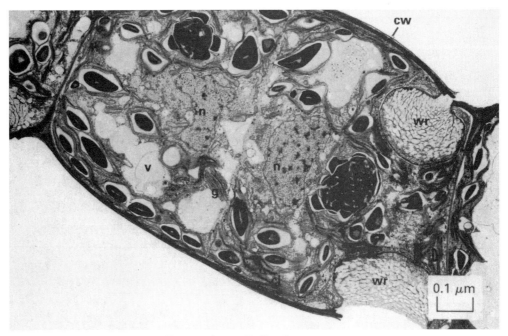

Green algae: *Bulbochaete.*

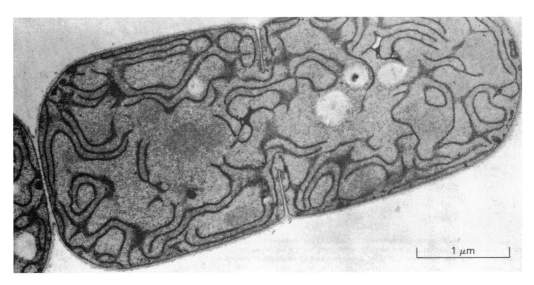

Section of the blue-green alga *Anabaena cylindrica*. This cell is dividing.

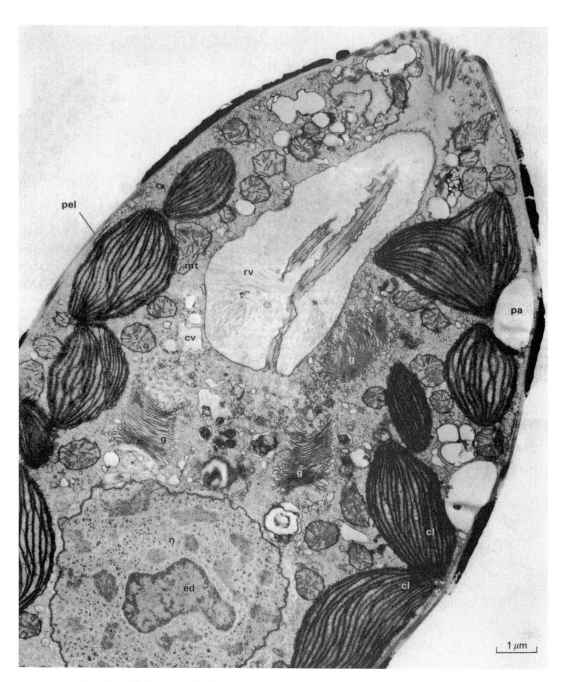

Euglenoid. Longitudinal section of the euglenoid *lepocinclis ovum*.

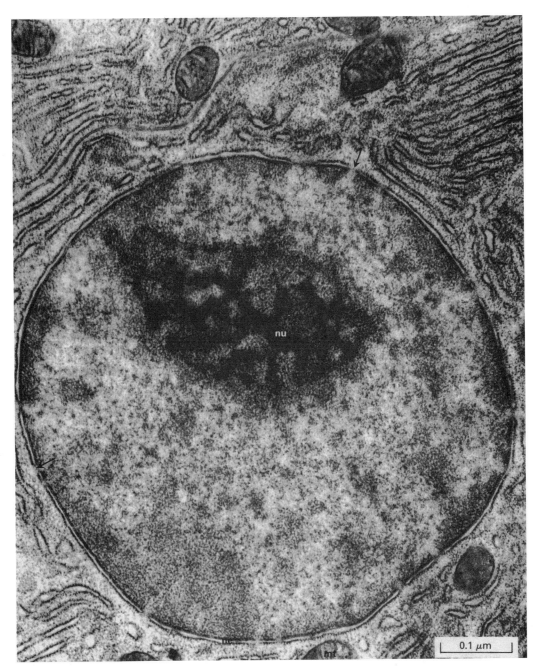

Nucleus.

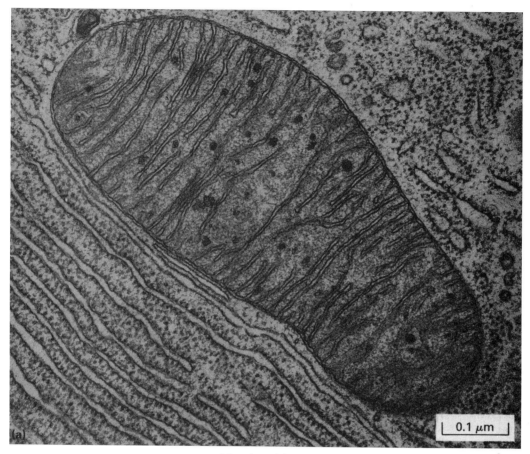

Mitochondria.

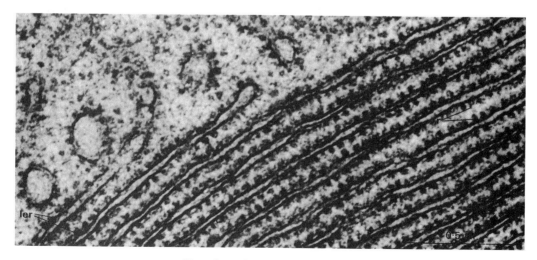

Rough endoplasmic reticulum.

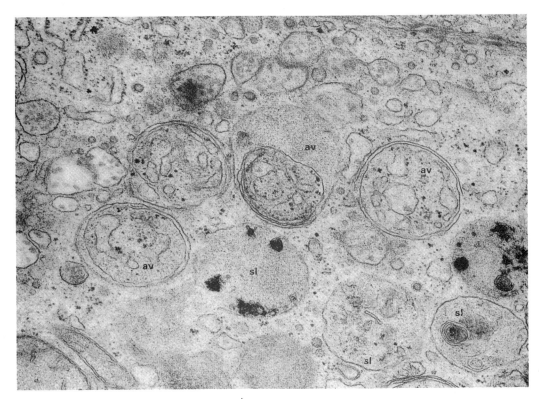

Lysosomes.

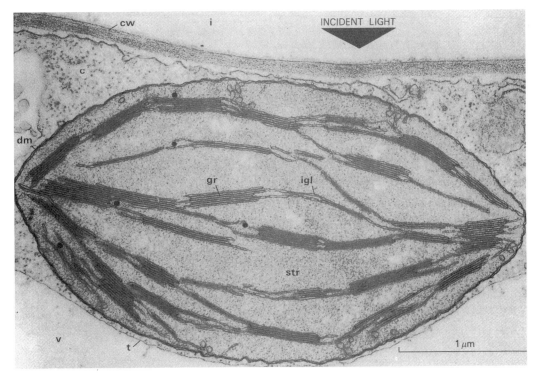

Chloroplast.

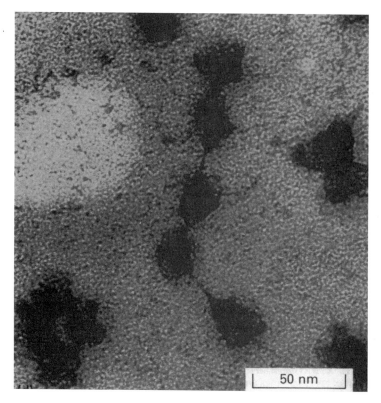

Six ribosomes.

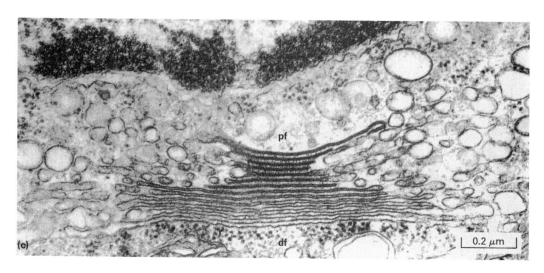

Golgi apparatus of the alga *Nitella sp.* Ribosomes are present.

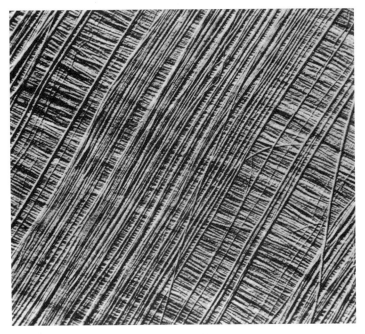

Plant cell wall.

# Budding • Cellular Respiration

## Investigation 12    *What Gas Do Growing Yeast Cells Produce?*

## Synopsis

Students design experiments to discover necessary conditions for yeast population growth and test two alternative hypotheses to determine the type of gas produced during growth. Analysis of experimental results indicates that sugar and a supply of fresh air (but not light) are necessary for growth and that carbon dioxide is the gas produced. The term *respiration* is then introduced to name this process. The term *cellular respiration* is also introduced because we can be reasonably certain that the respiration process is taking place inside the yeast cells. This is a hypothetical-deductive learning cycle.

## Suggested Time

Two to three class periods

## Background Information for the Teacher

Yeasts are unicellular members of a group of organisms called *Ascomycota* (sac fungi) that reproduce asexually by budding. Yeasts are used extensively in the manufacture of alcoholic products and to make bread dough rise. Ecologically speaking, yeasts, like other fungi, are decomposer organisms because they obtain food/energy by direct absorption through their cell wall. Likewise, waste products are eliminated directly through the cell wall.

Like nearly all organisms, yeasts rely on the same basic chemical pathway to derive energy from food molecules. In cellular respiration, food and oxygen are taken into the cell and combine to yield usable energy and release carbon dioxide and water. This process is called cellular respiration. The following equation summarizes the basic raw materials and products of cellular respiration:

$$C_6H_{12}O_6 \quad + \quad 6O_2 \quad \rightarrow \quad 6CO_2 \quad + \quad 6H_2O \quad + \quad 38\ \text{ATPs}$$

sugar          oxygen                    carbon          water          energy
                                                              dioxide

Precisely what happens inside the cell to convert food and oxygen to carbon dioxide and water and release usable energy has been the subject of considerable biochemical research. It suffices to say that the details of the process have yet to be worked out completely, and for the purpose of the present investigation they are immaterial. All that students will be able to discover is that a solution of sugar and yeasts and oxygen produce a gas that turns blue BTB indicator to green and then to yellow. From what they are told about the use of BTB as an indicator, students can conclude that the gas produced is $CO_2$, but they have no direct evidence that energy is obtained from the breakdown of sugar. (Indirectly, they can observe that the yeast population grows only when sugar is present; therefore, they may conclude that sugar is necessary.) Likewise, they have no evidence of how the process takes place. It should be clear, however, that the process does require a gas, sugar, and the yeast cells but does not require light.

## Advance Preparation

Prepare 5% table sugar (sucrose) solution by dissolving 5 g of table sugar per 95 mL of water.

Insert the S-shaped glass tubing into the 1-hole stoppers, or have the students do this. **CAUTION: In either case, coat the end of the tubing well with glycerin, wrap your hand in toweling, and gently twist the tube as you insert it into the stopper. Forcing the tube may cause it to break and severely lacerate the hand.**

## Teaching Tips

### Exploration

1. Start with a discussion of the introductory information and questions in the student manual. Have students list conditions they think might be necessary for yeast growth (e.g., light, sugar, air). Show them the apparatus for growing yeast, and describe how a BTB solution can be used to indicate the production of $CO_2$ gas (color changes from blue to green to yellow). Ask them to speculate on the gas produced by yeasts, and discuss ways of testing their ideas.

2. Leave freedom for variation in students' experimental designs, but you may need to stop the class after 10 to 20 minutes to discuss various designs. Students should set up experiments to test the effect of
   a. presence of light (shine light on one culture tube, and leave the other in the dark).
   b. presence of sugar (add sugar solution to one culture tube, water to the other).
   c. presence of air (leave air space above culture in one tube, no air space in the other).
   Three separate experiments can be conducted to test the effects of these three variables.

3. To determine the nature of the gas produced, experiments above should be replicated: One set of three should have blue BTB solution in them, and one set of three should have yellow BTB solution. The first set assumes $CO_2$ will be produced; the second set assumes $O_2$ will be produced.

4. You may not want all groups of students to conduct all of the experimental variations, as equipment may be limited and results will be pooled at the end anyway. Make certain, however, that some replication exists, as not all of the experiments can be expected to produce clear-cut results.

5. The experiments may need to run more than a day to produce good results. When color changes clearly have occurred, have the students record results and observe some of the growing yeasts under a microscope (procedure steps 5-7).

### Term Introduction

6. As the students observe the yeast slide, tell them to write descriptive statements and/or sketch their observations. Ask students to report their observations, and introduce the term *budding* as a form of asexual cellular reproduction.

7. Have groups report results of their experiments. Results should be recorded on the board for inspection and should include original conditions, original color, and final color.

8. Ask one or more students to summarize the general trend in the data. Then introduce the term *respiration* and the general formula: sugar + air → $CO_2$. It is reasonable to

conclude that the process (sugar + air → $CO_2$) is taking place inside the yeast cells; therefore, you should introduce the term *cellular respiration* at this time. Introduce the structural formula for sugar if you feel that it is appropriate to do so. You may wish to tell students that scientists have done a considerable amount of experimentation to understand better what is going on during cellular respiration. You may want to introduce the slightly more detailed and balanced equation,

$$C_6H_{12}O_6 + 6O_2 \rightarrow 6CO_2 + 6H_2O + 38 \text{ ATP}$$

Going into more detail than this, however, is probably not productive. Having students memorize biochemical details of cellular respiration is not necessary and generally only confuses students and dampens enthusiasm.

9. The fact that students' experiments will not produce the same results under presumably the same conditions will allow the class to discuss differences among experimental designs. Of course, each experiment should be "controlled"—only one independent variable should vary. Students, however, when left on their own, may confuse variables. Discussion of these uncontrolled experiments and their shortcomings allows you to introduce the term *controlled experiment* and to define it in the context of students' experiments.

**Concept Application**

10. Reasoning Module 4, Controlling Variables, should be completed following this investigation.

11. You may want to discuss the problem of cellular respiration in multicellular organisms: *How do $O_2$ and food get to the cells?* and *How is $CO_2$ transported away?* The need for a circulatory system should be apparent.

12. Chapter 10 of the textbook should be assigned reading.

| **Biological Terms** | **Thinking Skills** |
| --- | --- |
| cellular respiration | accurately describe nature |
| cell reproduction | state causal questions |
| budding | identify alternative hypotheses |
| | generate logical predictions |
| | plan and conduct experiments |
| | organize and analyze data |
| | draw and apply conclusions |

## Sample Test Questions

*Items 1–10 refer to the following experimental design:*

One gram of dry baker's yeast was added to six test tubes of equal size and mixed with 30 mL distilled water or 30 mL of 5% sucrose solution. The test tubes then were placed under different conditions of light and temperature, as shown in the table. BTB was added to each solution. The color of the solution at the start of the experiment is shown. Note that $CO_2$ was bubbled into test tubes 1 and 3 to produce a green BTB solution. BTB was added to each test tube at the end of the experiment, and the color of the solution was noted.

**Experimental Conditions**

| Test Tube Number | Solution Type | Amount of Light | Temperature (°C) | BTB Color at Start |
|---|---|---|---|---|
| 1 | distilled water | light | 10° | green |
| 2 | 5% sucrose | dark | 23° | blue |
| 3 | distilled water | dark | 10° | green |
| 4 | 5% sucrose | dark | 10° | blue |
| 5 | 5% sucrose | light | 10° | blue |
| 6 | distilled water | dark | 23° | blue |

1. Solution type, amount of light, temperature, and color of BTB solution at the start of the experiment are
   a. variables held constant.
   b. independent variables.
   c. dependent variables.
   d. values of the experiment.
   e. possible results.

2. The color of the BTB solution at the end of the experiment is a(n)
   a. variable held constant.
   b. independent variable.
   c. dependent variable.
   d. value of the experiment.
   e. possible cause.

3. Which test tubes can be compared to test the effect of amount of light?
   a. 2 and 4
   b. 2 and 6
   c. 1 and 3
   d. 4 and 5
   e. 1 and 6

4. Which test tubes can be compared to test the effect of the temperature?
   a. 2 and 4
   b. 2 and 6
   c. 1 and 3
   d. 4 and 5
   e. 1 and 6

5. Which test tubes can be compared to test the effect of solution type?
   a. 2 and 4
   b. 2 and 6
   c. 1 and 3
   d. 4 and 5
   e. 1 and 6

6. Which test tubes can be compared to see whether yeasts are plants and can produce $O_2$ using light as an energy/food source?
   a. 2 and 4
   b. 2 and 6
   c. 1 and 3
   d. 4 and 5
   e. 1 and 6

7. Assuming the hypothesis that yeasts are like animals and take in $O_2$ and expel $CO_2$ is true, what is the predicted (expected) color of the BTB solution at the end of the experiment in test tube 2?

   a. blue
   b. green
   c. blue or green
   d. dark blue
   e. green or yellow

8. Assuming the hypothesis that yeasts are actually plants and take in $CO_2$ and expel $O_2$ is true, what is the predicted color of the BTB solution at the end of the experiment in test tube 1?

   a. blue
   b. green
   c. blue or green
   d. yellow
   e. green or yellow

9. Based on the results of your class experiments, one would predict that cellular respiration would take place at the highest rate in which test tube?

   a. 1
   b. 2
   c. 3
   d. 4
   e. 5

10. At the end of the experiment, the test tube 5 solution turned greenish/yellow, while the solution in test tube 6 remained blue. What caused the solutions to differ in color?

   a. amount of light
   b. temperature
   c. the solution type
   d. There is no way to tell.
   e. the yeast

## Answers

1. B
2. C
3. D
4. A
5. B

6. C
7. E
8. A
9. B
10. D

# Controlled Experimentation

## Reasoning Module 4 *Controlling Variables*

## Synopsis

After being introduced to the term *controlled experiment* in a familiar context, students attempt to identify and control variables in a series of experiments involving a "Whirlybird."

## Suggested Time

Two class periods

## Background Information

The procedure of *controlled experimentation* (a comparison between two events in which only one independent variable differs to determine whether that variable alone produces an effect) unifies those attitudes and actions that permit one to critically judge experience, rather than be led by it. As an ideal, the controlled experiment (valid comparison, fair test) serves not only in the sciences but in all endeavors where alternative hypotheses and evidence are to be evaluated.

Numerous investigations using developmental criteria of students' and adults' reasoning skills have found that this procedure is lacking in about 50 percent of the adult population. This does not imply that students are completely ignorant of controlled experimentation. Rather, it appears that in simple and familiar contexts even first-graders can tell when a situation is "fair" or not. Thus, if asked whether it would be fair to run a race in which they wore boots and the opponents wore tennis shoes, they would object vehemently. Even very young students have an intuitive grasp of fairness, yet older students often fail to become consciously aware of this intuition to the extent that it becomes a reliable guide to thinking.

The purpose of this reasoning module is to provide hands-on experiences and to provoke students to reflect on those experiences in order to transform their limited intuitions about "fair tests" into a conscious verbal guide to controlled experimental design and data analysis.

## Advance Preparation

Whirlybirds® are available from Delta Education, P. O. Box 915, Hudson, NH 03051-0915, (800) 258-1302, FAX (603) 880-6520.

You will need to make copies of the Example Record Sheet (p. 61 of the student manual), one per student.

## Teaching Tips

### Exploration

1. Initiate the module either by discussing the introductory material and/or a recent classroom experiment in which variables were not controlled (e.g., *What conclusions can be drawn from an experiment in which mealworms went to the dark, damp, sandy end of the box?* or *What conclusions can be drawn from an experiment comparing the color change of a BTB solution in a test tube in the dark containing yeast, sugar, and water, with a test tube in the light containing yeast and water?*). Students should quickly recognize the difficulty of determining a specific cause.

### *Term Introduction*

2. After students have read the two essays and have performed the whirlybird experiments, review their results and introduce the terms *independent variable* and *dependent variable*. Define a controlled experiment as one in which only one independent variable is allowed to vary—while all others are held constant. Note that the term *controlled* is somewhat misleading. Remind students that what we really are concerned with is doing a fair test to determine a possible cause.

### *Concept Application*

3. Assign the Study Questions, and allow as much time as necessary to discuss them in class.

4. A number of subsequent investigations will allow students additional opportunities to design and conduct controlled experiments.

| **Biological Terms** | **Thinking Skills** |
|---|---|
| independent variables | identification of variables |
| dependent variables | control of variables |
| constants | controlled experimentation |
| controlled experiment | |

# Mitosis • Meiosis

## Investigation 13 *How Do Multicellular Organisms Grow?*

## Synopsis

Students generate alternative hypotheses to account for growth in multicellular organisms and observe prepared slides of growing tissues (e.g., onion root tip, whitefish blastula) to test their hypotheses. Support is obtained for the increase in cell size and cell division hypotheses. Students then attempt to generate a correct sequence of phases in the division process. A time-lapse film of a single living cell undergoing division is shown to help students decide which of the proposed sequences is correct. Appropriate terms are introduced by the teacher when needed. This is a hypothetical-deductive learning cycle.

## Suggested Time

Two to three class periods

## Background Information for the Teacher

In multicellular organisms, growth results primarily from the addition of new cells and from the increase in size of existing cells. In plants, growth takes place due to cell division and enlargement only in specific locations, such as the tips of roots, stems, or in a zone just under the bark. The growth of roots takes place due to rapid cell division in a zone just behind the tip. Farther up the root, cell division becomes much less frequent, and most growth is due to cell elongation.

Growth in plant stems is similar to that in the root because the tip of the stem consists of a zone of rapidly dividing cells. The cells just below that zone elongate and mature into the differentiated cells of the stem. Growth in both length and diameter of cells in the stem may last quite a bit longer than in the root.

At the onset of cell division in both plants and animals, the cell nucleus appears as a dark but rather nondescript object somewhere near the center of the cell. As division proceeds, structures in the cytoplasm, such as mitochondria and plastids (in plants), begin to duplicate themselves and to migrate to separate locations within the cell. Such structures have their own DNA and can duplicate without the aid of nuclear DNA.

The process of duplication of cell parts other than the nucleus is called *cytokinesis*. Although cytokinesis is important, the crucial aspect of cell division concerns the cell nucleus because the nucleus contains the major portion of the cell's DNA (located in the chromosomes). Thus, the essential task of cell division is to ensure that each new daughter cell receives a full set of chromosomes. To do this, the chromosomes must duplicate themselves and then divide and migrate to two separate locations. This process is called *mitosis*.

The first noticeable change around the nucleus prior to chromosome duplication is that the tiny centrosome that lies just outside of the nucleus divides into two parts that move to opposite sides of the nucleus. As they move, fibers begin to form and stretch between the centrosomes. The nuclear membrane begins to disintegrate and disappear. The nuclear DNA duplicates and begins to coil up like a spring.

The duplicated and coiled DNA molecules appear as two strands connected at one small point in the middle. The two-stranded, coiled DNA molecules are the chromosomes. Each strand of a chromosome is referred to as a *chromatid*. The point at which the chromatids are attached to one another is called the *centromere*. A number of these double-stranded chromosomes are present.

The chromosomes then arrange themselves on a plane across the center of the cell, right between the two centrosomes. Fibers from the centrosomes attach to the center of the chromosomes at the centromeres. After the fibers are attached, they appear to shorten and pull the chromatids in opposite directions, separating the chromatids. As they migrate to opposite sides of the cell, they bend at the center. Once the chromatids reach the opposite sides of the cell, they begin to uncoil. The fibers begin to disintegrate, and a nuclear membrane begins to form around each batch of chromatids. The centrosomes remain just outside the newly formed nucleus.

At this point, each new nucleus has exactly the same number and kind of chromatids (now called *chromosomes* once again); thus, the duplication of the nucleus is complete. Cell division is complete as soon as a furrow that begins to develop in the cell membrane deepens and gradually divides the cell in two. The result is two new cells with nuclei identical to that of the parent cell. The entire process of cell division, including cytokinesis and mitosis, can take as little as 30 minutes or as much as several hours.

The process of meiosis takes place in the sex cells of multicellular organisms and is slightly more complicated. First comes a duplication of chromosomes from, say, a *diploid* number of 8 to 16. Then the 16 chromosomes divide into two groups of 8 in each of two newly formed cells. The two cells with 8 chromosomes each divide to produce four cells with 4 chromosomes each (the haploid number). These cells with the haploid number of chromosomes are called *gametes* (usually egg and sperm cells).

When an egg and sperm fuse, the chromosomes from each cell pair up, and the original diploid number (8, in this case) is restored. The resulting fused cell with the full compliment of chromosomes is called a *zygote*.

The dividing cells viewed by the students in this investigation will not reveal all of these events of cell division, but they will reveal the major structures and the major changes they undergo. Viewing of the cells also will challenge the students' ability to make careful observations and to use what they see to support or refute the alternative hypotheses that have been proposed.

## Advance Preparation

Bean seeds from a grocery store will germinate well for Application Question 6. They should be soaked overnight prior to setting them up for germination. A small amount of bleach in the water will help retard mold growth, as the seeds must be kept moist in enclosed containers during the experiment.

Photocopies of the chromosomes for Study Question 7 will have to be made and distributed. (See student manual p. 68.)

The 35-mm slide sequence of meiosis mentioned in Study Question 5 is available from Carolina Biological Supply Company, Powell Laboratories Division, Gladstone, OR 97027, (800) 547-1733 or (800) 334-5551. The sequence is also available in video format.

An alternative film loop or 16-mm reel (*Mitosis in Plant Cells*) is available through Kalmia Co., Inc., 71 Dudley Street, Cambridge, MA 02140, (617) 864-5567.

## Teaching Tips

### Introduction

1.  Initiate the investigation with reference to the introductory paragraphs in the student manual. Write the question *How do multicellular organisms grow?* on the board, and encourage students to speculate about some possible mechanisms (e.g., *What might be occurring at the cellular level to account for increase in size?*). This part of the lab should resemble a brainstorming session in which any and all ideas are viewed as acceptable and are written on the board and labeled "alternative hypotheses." Stress that the class is only considering possibilities at this point. Evaluation of the alternative hypotheses will come later, when actual plant and animal tissues are observed.

### Exploration

2.  Students already should know the names of obvious cell structures (e.g., cell membrane, cell wall, cytoplasm, nucleus) from previous labs. If not, these terms should be introduced after initial observations have been made.

3.  Tell the students they are observing slides of a growing root tip (whitefish blastula, etc.), but do not mention the process of cell elongation or cell division at this time. They are to think about what their hypotheses lead them to expect to find and then observe carefully to see whether those expectations are confirmed. For example, if they have hypothesized that growth takes place due to the increase in amount of space between adjacent cells, then they should expect (predict) to see more space between the cells in older portions of the roots (those areas farther away from the tips). Likewise, if they have hypothesized that growth takes place due to an increase in cell size, then the prediction follows that cells farther away from the tips should be larger than those near the tips. On the other hand, if they think that growth occurs solely due to increase in the number of cells, then no obvious differences in cell size are predicted. It may be helpful to discuss these predictions prior to initial observation.

4.  If students have trouble locating relevant differences or deciding what to look for to test their ideas, stop the class and use a quick drawing on the board to help them locate the area of the slide for best viewing. You also may want to a) discuss specific hypotheses and predictions if you have not already done so, b) cue students to look for changes in the threadlike structures near the cell's center and to introduce the term *chromosome* to refer to those structures, and c) challenge students to figure out a way of determining whether the observed differences among the cells are due to differences in cell types or to differences within one type of cell that is undergoing some sort of change.

5.  After students have observed the drawings of other students, hold a class discussion to answer the following questions: *What hypotheses have been supported? Contradicted? What are the major differences among the observed cells?* Also discuss students' responses to the question posed in procedure step 5. If a student hypothesizes that he or she is observing a sequence of changes in a single cell type, ask how this idea might be tested. If no student advances this hypothesis, you will have to advance it yourself.

6. Before showing the film loop on cell division (*Mitosis: A Single Topic Inquiry Film,* Biological Sciences Curriculum Study, 1967), compare the various sequences that students have generated to discover similarities and differences.

7. Show the film loop as a source of evidence to discover which of the hypothesized sequences seems most correct.

### Term Introduction

8. The term *cell elongation* should be introduced after the students have discovered the elongated cells that appear on the root tip slides.

9. After deciding which sequence of cell changes seems most correct, introduce the term *mitosis* to refer to the replication of chromosomes during the cell division process.

10. Avoid showing students visual materials that emphasize stage names and discrete steps. Emphasize cell division and mitosis as dynamic processes.

### Concept Application

11. Have students work through the Application Questions. One of these provides an opportunity to view and discuss the process of meiosis as an extension of the cell division process in which the number of chromosomes is reduced to half of its original number in the resulting egg and sperm cells.

12. Chapters 11 and 12 of the textbook should be assigned reading.

---

## Biological Terms

cell division
cell elongation
mitosis
meiosis

## Thinking Skills

describe nature accurately
create alternative hypotheses
generate logical predictions
organize and analyze data
draw and apply conclusions

---

## Sample Test Questions

*Items 1 and 2 refer to the information and the illustration shown below.*

These cells were observed on an onion root tip slide. One student generated the hypothesis that the cells are really three different "types" of cells that perform different functions. Another student generated the alternative hypothesis that the cells are really one "type" of cell that is undergoing cell division. She thought the differences in appearance were due to the fact that we are seeing cells at different points of time in the division process.

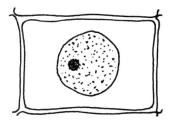 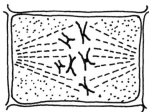 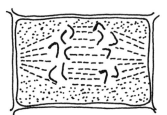

1. Which of the following predictions would follow logically from the first student's hypothesis?
   a. The three "types" of cells should be located next to each other.
   b. Time-lapse photography of the cells should show no change of one "type" of cell into another "type."
   c. The three "types" of cells should not be located next to each other.
   d. Time-lapse photography of the cells should show a change of one "type" of cell into another "type."
   e. The size of the cells should not vary over time.

2. Which of the predictions mentioned in question 1 would follow logically from the second student's hypothesis?
   a. The three "types" of cells should be located next to each other.
   b. Time-lapse photography of the cells should show no change of one "type" of cell into another "type."
   c. The three "types" of cells should not be located next to each other.
   d. Time-lapse photography of the cells should show a change of one "type" of cell into another "type."
   e. The size of the cells should not vary over time.

*Items 3–5 refer to the information and graph below.*

Chromosomes are made up of long complex molecules that loop and coil around and around. The graph shows changes in the amount of these long molecules present in the cell during cell division. In the following items, match the number on the graph to the events of mitosis described.

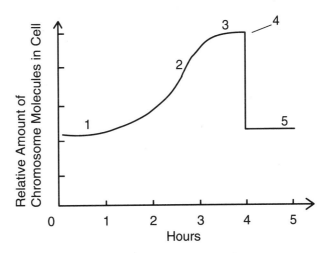

3. New chromosomes are being manufactured in the cell.
   a. 1      b. 2      c. 3      d. 4      e. 5

4. The nucleus has completed division, and now each new nucleus has a set of chromosomes identical to the original.
   a. 1      b. 2      c. 3      d. 4      e. 5

5. The chromosomes have separated, and the cell is starting the process of dividing.
   a. 1      b. 2      c. 3      d. 4      e. 5

*Items 6 and 7 are based on the following drawings.*

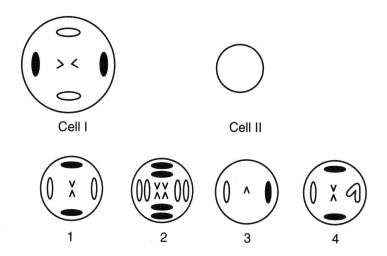

6. Cell II is a reproductive cell (gamete) produced from Cell I. The chromosome situation of Cell II would be best represented by drawing number
   **a.** 1.　　　**b.** 2.　　　**c.** 3.　　　**d.** 4.

7. Which of the four drawings would represent a cell that failed to divide following mitosis?
   **a.** 1　　　**b.** 2　　　**c.** 3　　　**d.** 4

## Answers

1. B　　　　5. D
2. D　　　　6. C
3. B　　　　7. B
4. E

# Hypothesis Creation and Test

## Reasoning Module 5  *Doing Science*

## Synopsis

The term *science* is introduced during class discussion of the activities of the first one-third of the semester. Students then try to classify 32 sentences into five to ten categories that reveal key steps in the process of creating and testing hypotheses. Students next read an essay and identify the general pattern of scientific reasoning in a simple and familiar situation, and they attempt to identify this pattern in the more complex situation of scientists discovering how homing pigeons find their way home.

## Suggested Time

About one class period or as homework. The reading can be done as a homework assignment. Expect to spend 30–50 minutes discussing Study Questions.

## Background Information

Science is basically a hypothetical-deductive enterprise. In other words, contrary to popular belief, science does not proceed by a closer and closer observation of nature. Our senses and common experiences often deceive us. It looks as if the sun travels around the earth, but not so. We water plants so that they will grow. Is water therefore an energy source for plants? We know better, but many students do not. The route to overcoming these naive misconceptions is not through closer and closer observation but through the creation of clever hypotheses and their tests.

The pattern of scientific investigation consists of the following five steps: 1) raising a causal question, 2) creating alternative hypotheses, 3) imagining experimental conditions and generating logical predictions (expected results assuming that the hypothesis under consideration is correct), 4) gathering and analyzing data, and 5) drawing conclusions. The words *If . . . and . . . then . . . therefore* are used to glue elements of this investigative process together to argue for or against a particular hypothesis.

Because many of your students are unfamiliar with this pattern of hypothetical-deductive reasoning, it will be difficult for them to comprehend and use quickly. Therefore, do not require anything close to mastery at this point. Rather, this Reasoning Module and the previous investigations should be used to help students become more aware of the process so that they will be able to use it in new contexts. The remainder of the learning cycles plus the five other Reasoning Modules all are needed to achieve this goal. Progress surely will be made, but students need repeated hands-on experiences and considerable opportunity for reflection prior to success.

## Advance Preparation

Make copies of the 32 sentences for distribution to groups of students.

## Teaching Tips

### Exploration

1. This Reasoning Module should be used about one-third of the way through the school

year, after students have had a number of opportunities to "do science." In other words, the first third of the school year constitutes the exploration phase of a learning cycle that allows you to introduce and define the term *science* and the hypothetical-deductive pattern of scientific reasoning.

2.  Initiate a review of prior activities by asking students to tell you the sorts of activities they have been doing in class. List those activities on the board. The list should include observing, creating hypotheses, experimenting, collecting data, analyzing data, drawing conclusions, raising questions, making predictions, graphing, discussing, and so on.

### Term Introduction

3.  When the list seems fairly complete, ask the students what they think the list should be titled. If no one suggests the title *Science*, you may suggest it and write *Science* at the head of the list. Define *science* as the activity of observing, creating hypotheses, experimenting, and so on. Because this is a rather lengthy definition, you may wish to redefine science as "people's attempts to describe and explain nature (using the previously listed activities)."

4.  Ask the students to decide which of the listed activities is done first, second, and so on. Number the activities in the suggested order. Although no one order is correct, the students should recognize that science progresses generally from raising questions, to creating alternative hypotheses, to designing experiments, to generating predictions, to data gathering, and to drawing conclusions.

5.  At this point, you may wish to draw Figure 1 from the student manual on the board and to label the boxes as shown, providing example questions, hypotheses, predictions, and so on from a previous learning cycle. You may want to point out the distinction between the processes of science (previously listed) and its products (the collection of previous conclusions).

### Concept Application

6.  Assign the activity described in procedure step 1 of the student manual, and assign the essay to be initiated in class and completed as homework.

7.  Take as much time as student interest will allow to discuss the Study Questions. Do not be too concerned if students remain confused by the distinction between hypotheses and predictions. This is an extremely important distinction, yet they will have many more opportunities to try to sort out the differences in subsequent learning cycles.

---

## Biological Terms

science
causal question
alternative hypotheses
experiments
predictions
results/evidence
conclusions

## Thinking Skills

hypothetical-deductive reasoning

---

### 32 Sentences

When the sunlight was blocked, the child slept much longer.

If the questioner did not know the answers, then his or her expressions could not cue Hans, and Hans's success rate should drop considerably.

Most of the birthday candles were pink.

Can Clever Hans tap his hoof up and down?

What time does the child usually wake up?

The water came in the cylinder to fill the empty space created when the flame consumed the oxygen.

The sunlight caused the child to wake up.

Hans is a large black horse.

Perhaps the sunlight is awakening him.

What caused the water to rise in the cylinder?

The child has gotten up too early for the past six mornings, so I expect that he will get up too early tomorrow.

Hans is able to monitor subtle changes in the questioner's facial expressions, posture, and breathing that occur when Hans arrives at the correct answer.

The last time I set up the experiment this way, the water rose 10 cm, so I can expect it to rise 10 cm this time.

The child was hungry, and his hunger had awakened him.

The child is 1 year old.

When the interrogator knew the answers, Hans succeeded on nine out of ten problems, but when the interrogator did not know the answers, Hans's score dropped to just one out of ten.

The water level rose higher with four candles than it did with one candle.

Under the circumstances, the child is expected to sleep less.

Hans is questioned by persons who know the answers and by persons who do not know the answers.

The child was given a bottle of milk before he went to bed, and he still woke up too early.

The flame heated the air and caused some of it to leave the cylinder, and when the flame went out, the air cooled and contracted and the water was forced in by the outside air pressure.

Why was the child waking up so early?

Hans has not answered a math question incorrectly for 2 weeks, so I am sure he will answer your question correctly.

The level of water rise in the cylinder is measured after burning one candle and after burning four candles.

Increasing the number of burning candles should cause the water level to rise higher in the cylinder.

If the sunlight is blocked with a heavy cover over the window, the child will awaken later.

Hans has learned how to read people's faces and their body language.

More candles will not burn up more oxygen, so the water should rise to the same level regardless of the number of candles used.

Feeding the child before he goes to bed should result in his sleeping longer.

How is Hans the horse able to answer the questions correctly?

What color were the birthday candles?

We should block the sunlight.

# Egg Structure and Function • Embryonic Development

## Investigation 14 — *What Happens During the Development of Chicken Eggs?*

## Synopsis

Students observe chicken eggs and propose hypotheses about the functions of identified structures. They then observe and record development in a series of fertilized eggs incubated to 48 and 72 hours and to 4, 5, and 10 days. Events and trends in development are discussed, and biological terms related to embryonic development are introduced. Students are encouraged to compare the observed development to that of other organisms. This is an empirical-abductive learning cycle.

## Suggested Time

Part of six class periods

## Background Information for the Teacher

Embryonic development of multicellular organisms begins immediately following fertilization of the female egg cell by a single male sperm cell. In birds, such as the chicken, the egg is relatively large and contains the entire food supply needed for embryonic development. You may want to consult reference material (see below) for more details of chick embryo development, but what follows is an overview that should orient you to the major developments through Day 10.

Unincubated Egg: The yolk is surrounded by a shell and a membrane connected to the albumen by a twisted opaque cord (chalaza) of heavy albumen (egg white). The membrane and shell provide protection and retain water. The yolk and albumen contain food and water. The yolk provides primarily fats, the albumen primarily proteins and water. The living portion of the egg, the blastoderm, is observable as a whitish dot on the upper surface of the yolk. When fertilized, it becomes the embryo.

Incubated 48-Hour Egg: The yolk-sac membrane is visible as a ring of blood vessels surrounding the embryo and yolk. The heart should be visible and beating. The beginnings of the head and spinal cord can be seen.

72-Hour Egg: The circulatory and nervous systems now are developing rapidly. The allantois has started to develop; it becomes the organ of respiration and excretion.

Day-4 Egg: The head cavities are clearly visible. It may be possible to see the beginning of the leg and wing buds. Body tissues are beginning to enclose the heart. The yolk sac and allantois have both increased in size.

Day-5 Egg: Rapid development is most evident in the head region. The amnion, the clear sac surrounding the embryo, is now discernible. The attachment of allantois to the gut of the embryo can be seen. The leg and wing buds are more clearly defined.

Day-10 Egg: Organs and structures are formed and are evident at this time. Feathers can be seen. The period of most rapid differentiation is complete. Growth rather than differentiation characterizes development during the final two-thirds of the total period of embryonic development.

This learning cycle provides you with an excellent opportunity to emphasize the importance and wonder of life; therefore, students should be impressed with the importance of this activity, and the examination of these embryos should be terminated before development proceeds so far that sacrificed embryos too closely resemble newly hatched chicks.

## Advance Preparation

Have students provide eggs from their refrigerators at home for the initial observation.

For fertile eggs, contact local chicken farmers, feed stores, and co-ops. Also inquire around the community. Individuals who raise chickens may donate eggs.

*A Sourcebook for the Biological Sciences*, 3rd ed., by E. Morholt and P. Brandwein, Harcourt Brace Jovanovich (1986), provides details on the maintenance of fertilized eggs in the classroom.

You may want to candle the eggs before giving them to students for observation. Disappointment and frustration may run high if too many undeveloped eggs are found.

## Teaching Tips

### Exploration

1. Students should work in groups of two to four.

2. It may be helpful and very interesting for the students if you also have some fertilized amphibian eggs available for observation. These could be kept in an aquarium in the classroom.

### Term Introduction

3. Conduct a class discussion at the end of each student observation session. Have students report on new structures and any developmental patterns they have observed. Use this opportunity to introduce and define terms and to label the observed structures and patterns.

### Concept Application

4. The following references will help provide necessary background information on development. The audiovisual materials may be used following the laboratory observations and discussions.

### References

*An Atlas for Staging Mammalian and Chick Embryos*, Harry Butler and B. H. Juurlink (CRC Press) 1987

*An Introduction to Embryology*, B. I. Balinsky (W. B. Saunders Co.) 1981, 5th edition

*Development of the Avian Embryo, A Behavioral and Physiological Study* (Wiley) 1974

*Laboratory Studies of Chick, Pig, and Frog Embryos*, Ray L. Watterson and Robert M. Sweeney (Burgess Publishing Co.)

*A Child Is Born*, Lennart Nilsson (Dell Publishing Co.) 1986

**Audiovisuals**

*Cleavage and the Formation of the Blastocyst* SB/J/4 (8-mm animated film loop), W. B. Saunders Co.

*The Fish Embryo: From Fertilization to Hatching* (sound, color, 12 min) Encyclopaedia Britannica Educational Corp.

*The Chick Embryo: From Primitive Streak to Hatching* (sound, color, 13 min), Encyclopaedia Britannica Educational Corp.

*Development and Differentiation* (sound, color, 20 min), McGraw-Hill Films

*Human Physiology: Embryology* (2 filmstrips, cassettes, or records), Schloat Productions

5.  Chapter 13 of the textbook should be assigned reading.

---

### Biological Terms

| | | |
|---|---|---|
| yolk | albumen | cell cleavage |
| yolk sac (cell membrane) | chalaza | morula |
| eggshell | embryo | blastula |
| shell membrane | amnion | gastrula |
| blastodisc | allantois | differentiation |

### Thinking Skills

describe nature accurately
state causal questions
create alternative hypotheses
generate logical predictions
draw and apply conclusions

---

## Sample Test Questions

1.  In organisms in which the embryo develops outside the mother's body, the eggs contain enough stored food to last until the
    a.  sperm fertilizes the egg.
    b.  zygote begins to divide.
    c.  embryo develops a circulatory system.
    d.  new organism can get food on its own.

2.  The significance of the greater amount of yolk in bird eggs as compared to the amount of yolk in mammalian eggs is that
    a.  birds need more energy for development.
    b.  mammals do not depend totally on the yolk for development.
    c.  birds develop slower and therefore need a greater supply of yolk.
    d.  the yolk of mammals is more concentrated.

3.  The fact that human embryos have gill slits lends support to the idea that
    a.  fish are our closest relatives.
    b.  the embryo breathes underwater.
    c.  all vertebrates are related.
    d.  fish are in the same genus as humans.

4. The fertilized egg is a single cell containing
   a. two nuclei.
   b. chromosomes of only the female parent.
   c. chromosomes of both the sperm and the egg.
   d. one nucleus and a monoploid set of chromosomes.

5. Differentiation of cells involves
   a. increase in size.
   b. production of more cells.
   c. modification of cells into different types.
   d. movement of cells into new regions of the body.

6. After differentiation, the cells of an embryo also must
   a. stop mitosis or else an abnormal embryo will result.
   b. organize into various structures.
   c. change into special types of cells.
   d. reduce their chromosome number by half.

*The diagram below shows a 72-hour chick embryo. For items 7–11, match the structures labeled A–E with the organ each will become in the adult.*

7. Structure A will become the
   a. heart.
   b. tail.
   c. brain.
   d. hair.
   e. stomach.

8. Structure B will become the
   a. ear.
   b. heart.
   c. nose.
   d. eye.
   e. brain.

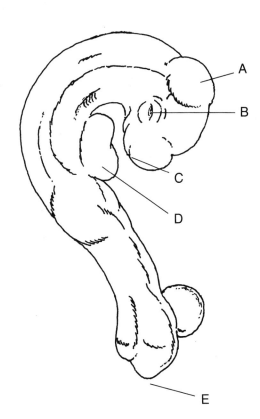

9. Structure C will become the
   a. ear.
   b. heart.
   c. nose.
   d. eye.
   e. brain.

10. Structure D will become the
    a. heart.
    b. stomach.
    c. lung.
    d. brain.
    e. eye.

11. Structure E will become the
    a. leg.
    b. tail.
    c. wing.
    d. heart.
    e. brain.

## Answers

| | |
|---|---|
| 1. D | 7. C |
| 2. B | 8. D |
| 3. C | 9. C |
| 4. C | 10. A |
| 5. C | 11. B |
| 6. B | |

# Chemical Indicators • Molecules (Proteins, Carbohydrates, Fats) • Chemical Reaction • pH

> ## Investigation 15    *What Are Foods and Beverages Made Of?*

## Synopsis

Students group common foods and beverages together based on what type of molecule(s) they think the items are made of (e.g., sugars, proteins, starches) and combine them with a number of indicators to test their ideas. Class data are analyzed, and the teacher introduces names for the molecules responsible for the observed reactions (e.g., testing starch molecules for the reaction of corn, rice, and potato chips with iodine). This is an empirical-abductive learning cycle.

## Suggested Time

Three class periods

## Background Information for the Teacher

The basic organic components of foods and beverages are sugars, starches, fats, and proteins. Sugars and starches are both carbohydrates and are composed of carbon, hydrogen, and oxygen. The main cell fuel for organisms is glucose, a simple sugar. Its molecular formula is $C_6H_{12}O_6$. Starches are chains of glucose units. Fats are lipids composed, like carbohydrates, of carbon, hydrogen, and oxygen; however, the ratio of hydrogen atoms to oxygen atoms is much greater than the 2:1 ratio in carbohydrates. Generally, a lipid molecule contains three fatty acids bonded to a molecule of glycerol. Proteins are highly complex chains of amino acids and exist in many forms. Amino acids are of 20 different kinds, all of this form:

$$H_2N - \overset{\overset{\textstyle R}{|}}{\underset{\underset{\textstyle H}{|}}{C}} - C \overset{\displaystyle \nearrow O}{\underset{\displaystyle \searrow OH}{}}$$

The *R* represents a side branch of one or more atoms that differ from one amino acid to another. The simplest amino acid, glycine, has a side branch of a single hydrogen atom. The amino acid alanine has a side branch of one carbon atom and three hydrogen atoms. Other amino acids have progressively more complex side branches.

When complex molecules are mixed with water, many break apart (dissociate) into smaller parts. If the dissociation of a molecule adds more hydrogen ions ($H^+$) than hydroxyl ions ($OH^-$) to the solution, the solution is said to be acidic. Solutions with an excess of hydroxyl ions are said to be basic. A quantitative measure of the degree of acidity or basicity of a solution is its pH, which stands for "potential for hydrogen," and is defined as the negative logarithm, to the base 10, of the solution's hydrogen ion concentration. The pH of solutions generally ranges from 0 (highly acidic) to 14 (highly basic). Pure water has an equal number of $H^+$ and $OH^-$ ions and therefore has a neutral pH of 7. The level of pH is important to living systems because levels that depart significantly from 7 disrupt the molecular reactions of cells. The pH values of some common substances are shown in the table.

| Approximate pH of some common substances* | | | | | |
|---|---|---|---|---|---|
| Apples | 2.9–3.3 | Human duodenal | | Pickles, dill | 3.2–3.5 |
| Apricots (dried) | 3.6–4.0 | contents | 4.8–8.2 | Pickles, sour | 3.0–3.5 |
| Asparagus | 5.4–5.7 | Human feces | 4.6–8.4 | Pimento | 4.7–5.2 |
| Beans | 5.0–6.0 | Human gastric | | Plums | 2.8–3.0 |
| Beer | 4.0–5.0 | contents | 1.0–3.0 | Pumpkins | 4.8–5.2 |
| Beets | 4.9–5.6 | Human milk | 6.6–7.6 | Raspberries | 3.2–3.7 |
| Blackberries | 3.2–3.6 | Human saliva | 6.0–7.6 | Rhubarb | 3.1–3.2 |
| Bread, white | 5.0–6.0 | Human spinal | | Salmon | 6.1–6.3 |
| Cabbage | 5.2–5.4 | fluid | 7.3–7.5 | Sauerkraut | 3.4–3.6 |
| Carrots | 4.9–5.2 | Human urine | 4.8–8.4 | Shrimp | 6.8–7.0 |
| Cherries | 3.2–4.1 | Jams, fruit | 3.5–4.0 | Spinach | 5.1–5.7 |
| Cider | 2.9–3.3 | Jellies, fruit | 3.0–3.5 | Squash | 5.0–5.3 |
| Corn | 6.0–6.5 | Lemons | 2.2–2.4 | Strawberries | 3.1–3.5 |
| Crackers | 7.0–8.5 | Limes | 1.8–2.0 | Sweet potatoes | 5.3–5.6 |
| Dates | 6.2–6.4 | Magnesia, | | Tomatoes | 4.1–4.4 |
| Flour, wheat | 6.0–6.5 | milk of | 10.5 | Tuna | 5.9–6.1 |
| Ginger ale | 2.0–4.0 | Milk, cow | 6.4–6.8 | Turnips | 5.2–5.5 |
| Gooseberries | 2.8–3.1 | Molasses | 5.0–5.4 | Vinegar | 2.4–3.4 |
| Grapefruit | 3.0–3.3 | Olives | 3.6–3.8 | Water, distilled (carbon | |
| Grapes | 3.5–4.5 | Oranges | 3.0–4.0 | dioxide free) | 7.0 |
| Hominy | 6.9–7.9 | Peaches | 3.4–3.6 | Water, mineral | 6.2–9.4 |
| Human blood | | Pears | 3.6–4.0 | Water, sea | 8.0–8.4 |
| plasma | 7.3–7.5 | Peas | 5.8–6.4 | Wines | 2.8–3.8 |

*Data from *Handbook of LaMotte Chemical Control Units for Science and Industry,* 13th ed., La Motte Chemical Products Co., Chestertown, MD. 1944.

In this investigation, students are given a variety of foods and beverages and initially speculate on what substances they consist of primarily. Students then combine the substances with a number of indicator molecules to see which foods and beverages react in similar ways. Groups of foods and beverages are then formed and named (e.g., proteins, sugars, fats). The following indicators are used:

### *For Starch*

Iodine Test: A few drops of dilute iodine solution added to solutions that contain starch will turn dark blue. Starch granules turn blue due to the formation of an adsorption complex of starch and iodine. **CAUTION: Iodine stains skin and clothing and is poisonous if ingested.**

### For Glucose Sugar

Benedict's Test: Benedict's solution may be purchased or prepared as follows:

Dissolve 173 g sodium citrate and 100 g sodium carbonate in 800 mL warm distilled water. Filter and add water up to 850 mL. Dissolve 17.3 g copper sulfate in 100 mL water; slowly add this to the sodium citrate-sodium carbonate solution, stirring constantly. Add distilled water to make 1 L. The reagent will not deteriorate upon standing.

Benedict's solution indicates the presence of such simple sugars as glucose. To test an unknown, pour 5 mL of Benedict's solution into a test tube and add 8 drops of the unknown solution. Shake well. Place the tube in a boiling water bath for 3 minutes. When the solution cools, a precipitate forms that ranges from green to yellow to red, depending on the amount of glucose present.

### For Fats/Lipids

Paper Test: A simple test for lipids is the formation of a translucent spot when a test substance is chopped or rubbed on a piece of unglazed paper (brown paper bag).

### For Proteins

Biuret Test: To test for the presence of proteins, mix 2 to 3 mL of the unknown solution with an equal volume of a 10% sodium hydroxide solution. Then add drop by drop a 0.5% copper sulfate solution. Swirl between the addition of drops. A pinkish or purplish violet color indicates the presence of proteins with at least two peptide linkages. Proteoses and peptones give a pink color, while gelatin turns blue. **CAUTION: The sodium hydroxide solution is caustic.**

### For Carbon Dioxide

Limewater Test: To 1 L distilled water add an excess of calcium hydroxide powder or calcium oxide powder. Cork the bottle, shake well, and let stand for 24 hours so that the excess solid can settle out. Then decant the clear supernatant fluid and keep tightly stoppered (filter if necessary). The limewater should remain clear. When $CO_2$ is added, a milky precipitate of calcium carbonate ($CaCO_3$) is formed. **CAUTION: Calcium hydroxide is caustic.**

$$CO_2 + H_2O \rightarrow H_2CO_3$$

$$Ca(OH)_2 + H_2CO_3 \rightarrow CaCO_3 + 2H_2O$$

### For pH

Bromthymol Blue (BTB) and Phenolphthalein Tests. Both are indicator dyes used to test the pH of a solution. As the number of hydrogen ions in a solution changes, a rearrangement of the dye molecules occurs and the solution changes color. Figure 1 lists the ranges of a variety of indicator dye molecules.

Bromthymol Blue (BTB): Dissolve 0.04 g of dibromthymolsulfonphthalein in 100 mL 95% ethyl alcohol. Indicator in pH range of 6.0 to 7.6.

Phenolphthalein: Dissolve 1 g of phenolphthalein in 100 mL 95% ethyl alcohol. Indicator in pH range of 8.2 to 10.0.

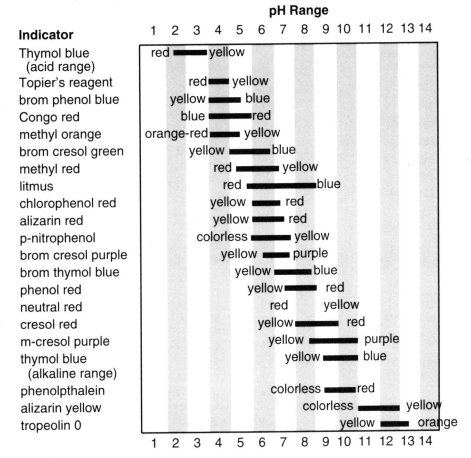

## Advance Preparation

Prepare indicator solutions as indicated in Background Information for the Teacher.

Below is a list of foods and beverages, 10 to 15 of which should be provided to the students. Have the group members split the items so that they can all be tested by all groups. Caution students not to taste or eat any of the test foods.

| Foods and Beverages | Positive Reactions Possible |
| --- | --- |
| carbonated water | BTB, limewater, phenolphthalein |
| glucose water | Benedict's |
| soft drink (clear) | BTB, limewater, phenolphthalein, Benedict's |
| rice water (soluble starch solution) | iodine |
| *pure lemon juice | BTB, phenolphthalein, Benedict's |
| milk | Biuret |
| salt water | none |
| Karo® syrup | Benedict's |

| | |
|---|---|
| cooking oils | paper |
| (three different types and colors | |
| of oils: corn, peanut, soybean) | |
| corn starch suspension | iodine |
| tap water | none |
| salt (crystals) | none |
| *table sugar | Benedict's |
| (granular or powdered sucrose) | |
| flour (dry) | iodine |
| apple juice | Benedict's, BTB |
| dry bread | iodine |
| bacon (raw or cooked chips) | paper, Biuret |
| butter or margarine | paper |
| apple slice (raw) | Benedict's |
| potato slice (raw) | iodine |
| potato chip (crushed) | iodine, paper |
| cracker (crushed) | iodine |
| *honey (dilute 1:10) solution | Benedict's |
| sugared cereal (crushed) | Benedict's, iodine |
| *fresh orange juice | Benedict's, BTB, phenolphthalein |
| onion | Benedict's |
| raw hamburger | Biuret |

*These tests using Benedict's solution indicate sugar, but the reaction is a color change to green instead of the usual yellow or orange.

## Teaching Tips

### Exploration

1. Initiate the investigation with reference to the introductory material in the student manual. Do not tell the students what each indicator tests for. Some students may not have clear ideas of what substances the unknown foods and beverages contain. This is not a problem. Simply have the students do the best job they can at grouping the unknowns. Go over the use of the indicators, and hold a brief discussion of students' ideas concerning possible groups. Point out that students can obtain support for their ideas if, for example, all of the substances they think contain sugar react to the indicators in the same way. Inconsistent reactions will not support their ideas.

2. After the students have tested and grouped their substances, have each team illustrate their grouping on butcher paper, poster board, or the chalkboard. Discuss the group results, and make up a class table of groups.

### Term Introduction

3. Once the unknowns have been grouped, tell the students that scientists believe unknowns react in a similar way with indicators because they contain similar building blocks. Reintroduce the term *molecule* to refer to these building blocks. Because unknowns react with indicators in different ways, they must be different types of molecules that can be given names (without knowing anything about their structure). Introduce the term *starch molecules* to name the building blocks that make up unknowns that react with iodine. Introduce the term *simple sugar (glucose) molecules* to name the

building blocks of substances that react with Benedict's solution. Introduce the terms *proteins*, *lipids*, and *pH*, as well. In other words, introduce operational definitions: A lipid is a substance that produces an oily spot on paper. A starch is a substance that turns dark blue when iodine is added to it. Simple sugar is a substance that in solution reacts positively in the Benedict's test.

4. Clearly, we have no evidence at this point to determine the actual molecular structures of the substances identified, nor do we have any indication of the actual chemical reactions taking place. Therefore, you may wish to tell students simply that scientists hypothesized from such data as ours that the molecules themselves were changing when mixed (hence the term chemical reaction) but that it took many years of additional experimentation to determine molecular structures and reactions. Whether you go further to introduce specific structures and reactions is up to you, but make clear to students that the class has not obtained evidence for their validity.

### Concept Application

5. A number of subsequent investigations involve chemical reactions and the indicators used in this investigation.

| **Biological Terms** | **Thinking Skills** |
|---|---|
| molecular structure | describe nature accurately |
| indicators | state casual questions |
| chemical reactions | generate alternative hypotheses |
| proteins | generate logical predictions |
| fats | plan and conduct experiments |
| carbohydrates | organize and analyze data |
| sugars | draw and apply conclusions |
| starches | |

## Sample Test Questions

*In the table below, a + indicates a positive reaction, a 0 indicates no reaction, and a blank indicates that no test was made.*

Indicators

| Unknown Substance | Iodine | Benedict's | Paper | Biuret | BTB | Phenol-phthalein |
|---|---|---|---|---|---|---|
| 1 | + | 0 | 0 | 0 | | |
| 2 | + | + | | 0 | | |
| 3 | + | | | | | red |
| 4 | + | | + | | yellow | |
| 5 | + | | | | yellow | |
| 6 | | 0 | + | 0 | blue | red |
| 7 | 0 | 0 | + | + | | |

*Use the data in the table and the following key to answer items 1–7.*

**KEY**

A. Statement is probably true

B. Statement is probably false

C. Insufficient data

1. Unknown 1 contains molecules made up of many carbon and oxygen atoms.

2. Unknown 2 contains starch molecules, some of which have been broken apart into smaller molecules.

3. If heated, Unknown 3 probably would react positively with Benedict's solution.

4. Unknown 4 has a pH less than 3.

5. Unknown 5 could be a soft drink.

6. Unknown 6 has a pH greater than 7 and contains starch and fat molecules.

7. Unknown 7 is most likely a potato.

8. The statement that a potato and a piece of red meat contain different types of molecules would be contradicted by which of the following conditions?
   a. The liquids extracted from ground-up potatoes and red meat react differently when mixed with another liquid.
   b. The liquids extracted from ground-up potatoes and red meat react the same way when mixed with another liquid.
   c. The potato and red meat taste different.
   d. The liquids extracted from ground-up potatoes and red meat are different colors.
   e. Potatoes and red meat taste better when cooked.

9. Knowing that oranges have a pH of about 3 and carbonated water has a pH of about 9, what would you predict the pH of an orange soda would be?
   a. less than 3               d. 9
   b. 3                         e. more than 9
   c. 6

10. A sample of corn seeds was ground up, and the liquid that was produced was collected in a test tube. The liquid was heated, and 5 drops of a clear unknown liquid were added. To this mixture a dilute solution of iodine was added, which did not cause a color change. A reasonable explanation for this is:
   a. The heat broke down the corn molecules.
   b. The clear unknown liquid broke down the corn molecules.
   c. Both a and b are reasonable possibilities.
   d. Corn contains starch molecules.
   e. If the corn liquid were not heated, then the mixture would have turned blue when iodine was added.

## Answers

| 1. A | 3. A | 5. A | 7. B | 9. C |
|------|------|------|------|------|
| 2. A | 4. C | 6. C | 8. B | 10. C |

# Chemical Breakdown

## Investigation 16 *What Is the Function of Saliva?*

## Synopsis

Students design and conduct experiments to test alternative hypotheses concerning the function of saliva (a powdered pancreatic amylase may be used as a substitute for salivary amylase). Students' experiments support the hypothesis that saliva helps convert starch to glucose, and the teacher introduces the term *chemical breakdown* to refer to this process. Other instances of chemical breakdown are discussed. This is a hypothetical-deductive learning cycle.

## Suggested Time

Two class periods

## Background Information for the Teacher

Starch is a large molecule composed of many linked glucose molecules. Enzymes found in saliva (e.g., salivary amylase) begin the chemical breakdown of the large starch molecules into glucose molecules, which are small enough to be transported into the bloodstream and into the body's cells.

## Advance Preparation

Have the hot-water bath ready in advance for the Benedict's test.

If you are going to ask the students to use their own saliva, be sure to tell them not to snack or chew gum before coming to class.

The following is probably the "least offensive" way to collect saliva. Place a clean plastic drinking straw into a test tube (or 10-mL graduated cylinder); generate saliva in the mouth; spit the saliva down through the straw and into the tube. Or, to make students less apprehensive about spitting into a test tube in front of others, you may wish to set up a corner of the room (e.g., behind a demonstration chart) for "private" collection of saliva. Also, pancreatic amylase can be purchased from a biological supply house and made available for students who do not wish to use their own saliva.

If you substitute the powdered pancreatic amylase for students' saliva, have a solution prepared in advance and label it "Substitute Saliva."

## Teaching Tips

### Exploration

1. Students should be familiar with the use of chemical indicators before conducting this lab. See Investigation 15, *What Are Foods and Beverages Made Of?*

2. Encourage a range of alternative hypotheses to answer the question, *What does saliva do?* For example: Saliva is involved in taste; a hormone in saliva is swallowed and affects the stomach; saliva helps filter air when you breathe through your mouth; and saliva breaks down some foods but not others.

3. Show students the materials they will have to work with, as these will limit the types of

hypotheses that can be tested. List the alternative hypotheses on the board, grouping similar hypotheses together, particularly those involving chemical breakdown.

4. Review the chemical tests for starch, simple sugar, protein, and fat. Emphasize that each sample food is used only for a single test and then is discarded. A new sample is to be used for each test. Also emphasize that boiling is only part of the Benedict's test. Test tubes must be used for this procedure, but spot plates work best for the other tests.

5. Emphasize that only a small amount of each food item is needed for each test. Direct students to formulate a plan of experimentation to test their hypotheses. Procedures should be discussed prior to their initiation. Question procedures that have no controls or that just test the sample with saliva but do not test the sample alone. Ask, *What can you conclude from such an experiment? How do you know the saliva did anything? What could you add to your design to produce more conclusive results?*

6. The following procedure will test the hypothesis that saliva contains a substance that converts one type of molecule (starch) to another type of molecule (glucose). This is the hypothesis that at least some of your students should be encouraged to test.

Remove a small portion from each food sample, and test with each indicator. Collect and add an equal amount of saliva to the sample solutions. Retest the sample solutions (plus saliva) with each indicator. Test saliva alone with each indicator. The following is a possible data table.

**Reaction To:**

| Food | Biuret | Iodine | Benedict's | Paper | Biuuret + Saliva | Iodine + Saliva | Benedict's + Saliva | Paper + Saliva |
|------|--------|--------|-----------|-------|-----------------|-----------------|--------------------|----------------|
| 1. potato | | | | | | | | |
| 2. cracker | | | | | | | | |
| 3. honey | | | | | | | | |
| 4. artificial sweetener | | | | | | | | |
| 5. lunch meat | | | | | | | | |
| 6. corn syrup | | | | | | | | |
| 7. saliva | | | | | | | | |

7. Be certain that students rinse out their mouths if they have just eaten or have been chewing gum, as these food substances will confound their results.

### *Term Introduction*

8.  Collect class results on the board in a table like that shown in step 6.

    The most striking result should be that the cracker and potato tested positive for sugar after being well mixed with saliva. If some basic biochemistry has been covered, then students may be able to conclude that the saliva is breaking the starch into sugar subunits. If this has not been covered, one simply may infer that some chemical change is occurring to produce sugar from starch. At this point, introduce the term *chemical breakdown* to refer to this process of molecule splitting. The starch molecule can be represented as follows, with the G's representing glucose molecules. The saliva (or something in it) is separating the individual units.

    $$\text{G-G-G-G-G-G-G-G-G-G-G-G-} \ldots + \text{saliva} \rightarrow \text{G,G,G} \ldots + \text{G-G-G-G} \ldots$$
    $$\quad\quad\text{(starch)} \quad\quad\quad\quad\quad\quad\quad\quad\quad\quad \text{(glucose)} \quad\quad \text{(starch)}$$

    Some starch also will remain, indicating that saliva's effect on starch begins in the mouth but the chemical reaction is not complete.

    Because group results will vary, question the class about the possible sources of variation. Some suggestions might be that the amount of saliva or degree of mixing varied or that the glassware was not clean or that students' judgments of color changes were not the same. Perhaps the potency of saliva may be involved. Regardless of the possibilities, methods to better control these factors should be discussed (e.g., regulate amount, mixture time).

    The other samples should have remained unaffected. The single exception to this could be the lunch meat, which may have had carbohydrate fillers.

### *Concept Application*

9.  You may wish to discuss other instances of chemical breakdown, as well as conducting Investigation 17, *What Happens to Molecules During Chemical Breakdown?*, which allows students to discover the role of enzymes in chemical breakdown. Investigation 18, *How Do Molecules Pass into and Out of Cells?*, implies the necessity of the breakdown of starch to glucose for the passage of molecules through the cell membrane.

---

**Biological Terms**

chemical breakdown
controlled experiment

**Thinking Skills**

describe nature accurately
state causal questions
create alternative hypotheses
generate logical predictions
plan and conduct experiments
organize and analyze data
draw and apply conclusions

---

## Sample Test Questions

*Items 1–8 refer to the following experiment.*

In testing the hypothesis that some type of molecule contained in saliva causes a chemical change in starch molecules by splitting them into smaller sugar molecules, you come up with the data contained in the following table.

| Food | Indicator | | | | | | | |
|---|---|---|---|---|---|---|---|---|
| | Biuret I | Iodine II | Benedict's III | Paper IV | Biuret V | Iodine VI | Benedict's VII | Paper VIII |
| Crackers | – | + | – | – | – | + | + | – |
| Syrup | – | – | + | – | – | – | + | – |
| Honey | – | – | + | – | – | – | + | – |
| Lunch meat | + | + | + | + | + | + | + | + |
| Potato | – | + | – | – | – | – | + | – |
| Saliva | – | – | – | – | – | – | – | – |

1. The major independent variable investigated in the eight tests using crackers is
   a. the type of food used.
   b. the type of indicator used.
   c. the amount of indicator used.
   d. the reactions of the various mixtures.
   e. the amount of saliva used.

2. The dependent variable in this experiment is
   a. the type of food used.
   b. the type of indicator used.
   c. the amount of indicator used.
   d. the reactions of the various mixtures.
   e. the amount of saliva used.

3. In comparing the reactions listed in column I with those in column V, what variable should not be held constant?
   a. the type of food used
   b. the amount of food used
   c. the amount of indicator used
   d. the amount of saliva used
   e. the order in which the solutions are mixed

4. The purpose of designing the experiment to test samples of food substances alone and then repeat the test with saliva and the food substance is to
   a. determine the effect, if any, of saliva on the food.
   b. get more practice in observing changes with indicators.
   c. provide more data from which to draw conclusions.
   d. make the best use of time in the lab by running more tests.
   e. make certain the test results are accurate.

5. The purpose of including saliva alone in the various indicators (as shown in the last row of the table) is to
   a. test for all possible combinations of variables.
   b. get more practice in observing changes with indicators.
   c. provide more data from which to draw conclusions.

    d. allow a comparison of saliva's reaction with those of the various foods listed.

    e. indicate that a positive reaction in columns V through VIII is caused by the food and not by the saliva.

6. Assuming that crackers contain starch, which of the following represents a predicted outcome that logically follows from the stated hypothesis and the experimental design?

    a. If saliva causes a chemical change, then starch molecules will be split into sugar molecules.

    b. The reaction of the crackers should be negative in column III and positive in column VII.

    c. The reactions of the crackers should be positive in columns I through IV and negative in columns V through VIII.

    d. Starch molecules should be split.

    e. Starch molecules are made up of many sugar molecules linked together.

7. Which of the following test results support the stated hypothesis?

    a. crackers in II, III, VI, and VII; lunch meat in II and IV; potato in II and VI

    b. crackers and potato in III and VIII

    c. crackers and potato in II, III, VI, and VII

    d. potato in all tests

    e. insufficient data to indicate the truth or falsity of the hypothesis

8. You are somewhat puzzled by a positive test for starch in lunch meat and compare your results with those of the results of the rest of the class. You find eight out of ten of the tests were positive for starch and simple sugar in lunch meat. You decide that

    a. the test is inaccurate and should be thrown out.

    b. this is a false-positive test, suggesting contamination.

    c. you need to gather more data with more classes before reaching any conclusion.

    d. some starch molecules probably are in the lunch meat.

    e. it would be better to find another test for starch.

9. Assume you have reached the tentative conclusion that some type of molecule contained in saliva causes a chemical change in starch molecules by splitting them into smaller molecules. You now wonder whether this chemical change also takes place at temperatures and pH levels other than the ones you have tested. Instead of varying food samples, you decide to work only with starches. The major independent variables are now

    a. temperature and pH range.      d. length of time and amount of mixing.

    b. indicators used.                e. food substances used.

    c. reactions of the mixtures.

10. Suppose you propose the hypothesis that high temperature causes complex molecules to split apart. To test this, you heat a cracker-and-water solution to boiling for 15 minutes. Which of the following represents a predicted outcome that logically follows?

    a. High temperatures should cause molecules to split apart.

    b. If high temperatures cause a breakdown of molecules, then the cracker molecules will be broken apart.

    c. A test with Benedict's and no saliva should be negative.

    d. A test with iodine should be positive.

    e. A test with Benedict's and no saliva should be positive.

*Items 11–21 refer to the data presented below.*

Some test tubes were set up, and each contained 1 g of starch. They were labeled 1, 2, 3, 4, and 5. Mark each item according to the test tube number called for. Various substances were dissolved in water before they were added to the starch. All test tubes were kept at 29.4°C (water boils at 100°C). For Tube 5, Substance A was boiled and then allowed to cool before it was added to the starch.

| Test Tube Number | Contents of Tubes | Amt. of Glucose Present After 24 Hrs. |
|---|---|---|
| 1 | Starch + Substance A | .1 gram |
| 2 | Starch + Substance A + Substance C | .5 gram |
| 3 | Starch + Water | .0 gram |
| 4 | Starch + Substance C | .0 gram |
| 5 | Starch + Substance A (boiled) | .0 gram |

11. Which test tube acts as a control (comparison) for the entire experiment?

12. Which tube gives evidence that starch does not break down spontaneously into glucose in 24 hours?

13. Which tube is used to show that a temperature of 29.4°C was not sufficient to cause starch to be broken down into glucose?

14. Which tube gives evidence that Substance A is the active substance in the breakdown of starch to glucose?

15. Which tube is the control (comparison) in item 14?

16. Which tube provides evidence that Substance C alone is ineffective in the breakdown of starch?

17. What is the control in item 16?

18. Which test tube gives evidence that Substance C accelerates the rate of activity of Substance A?

19. Which test tube is the control in item 18?

20. Which test tube gives evidence that Substance A is a substance whose properties can be destroyed?

21. Give the control for the test tube in item 20.

## Answers

| | | | | |
|---|---|---|---|---|
| 1. E | 6. B | 10. E | 14. 1 | 18. 2 |
| 2. D | 7. C | 11. 3 | 15. 3 | 19. 1 |
| 3. D | 8. D | 12. 3 | 16. 4 | 20. 5 |
| 4. A | 9. A | 13. 3 | 17. 3 | 21. 1 |
| 5. E | | | | |

# Catalyst Enzymes

## Investigation 17 *What Happens to Molecules During Chemical Breakdown?*

## Synopsis

Students design and conduct an experiment to test alternative hypotheses about what happens to liver and hydrogen peroxide molecules when combined. Following an analysis of results, the terms *catalyst, enzyme,* and *endothermic reaction,* and *exothermic reaction* are introduced. This is a hypothetical-deductive learning cycle.

## Suggested Time

Two class periods

## Background Information for the Teacher

A number of chemicals speed up reactions between other chemicals. A mixture of hydrogen and oxygen, for example, does not react; but if a spark (activation energy) is provided, the mixture will explode. The same explosion will occur if a small piece of platinum is added. After the reaction is over, the platinum will still be present and unchanged.

A substance such as platinum that speeds up a chemical reaction but is itself unchanged when the reaction is over (even though it may have been altered temporarily during the reaction) is known as a *catalyst*. A catalyst affects only the rate of reaction. It simply speeds up a reaction that is thermodynamically possible to begin with. Catalysts decrease the activation energy needed for a reaction to take place by increasing the number of reacting molecules energetic enough to react. The catalyst does this by orienting the reactants to each other in such a way that important internal bonds are weakened, thus making them easy to break (e.g., by being struck by other molecules) and allowing new bonds to form (e.g., by striking and sticking to other molecules).

An inorganic catalyst, such as platinum, is rather unselective about the reactions it speeds up. Living things contain a huge variety of large globular proteins that act as catalysts. These organic catalysts are called *enzymes*.

One such enzyme, investigated in this learning cycle, is produced by liver cells. The enzyme increases the rate of breakdown of hydrogen peroxide ($H_2O_2$) to water ($H_2O$) and oxygen ($O_2$). When students add liver to hydrogen peroxide, bubbles of a gas (oxygen) can be seen immediately in the liquid, and the solution heats up rapidly due to the increase in motion of the split molecules. Students do not know which molecules are reacting, nor do they know that the liver molecules are not altered during the reaction. Nevertheless, the introduction to the lab presents a number of alternative hypotheses for the students to test. They discover that old hydrogen peroxide and old liver *do not* react but that new hydrogen peroxide and old liver *do* react, suggesting that the liver, which is not altered, contains molecules that facilitate a change in the hydrogen peroxide. This conclusion allows you to introduce the term *enzyme* to refer to a type of organic catalyst that speeds up a reaction but remains unchanged at the reaction's completion. The observation that the reaction produces heat allows you to introduce the term *exothermic reaction* (a chemical reaction that increases the temperature of the reactants, as opposed to an *endothermic reaction,* which decreases the temperature) as you discuss reasons for the rise in temperature.

## Teaching Tips

### *Exploration*

1.  When the introductory reaction takes place, have students note the increase in temperature. Introduce the term *exothermic reaction* for any reactions that give off heat. Challenge students to think of reasons for the temperature increase (molecules of $O_2$ are given off, then hit the inner surface of the test tube, causing the glass molecules to move and strike your fingers, which in turn causes the molecules of your skin to move more rapidly—perceived as an increase in temperature).

2.  A procedure to test two of the hypotheses presented is as follows:

    Use two test tubes and a small piece of liver. With a glass rod, push the liver to the bottom of one of the tubes. Put the tube in a rack and add 2 mL hydrogen peroxide. (You may have to keep pushing the liver down with the glass rod.) Allow the reaction to continue until all bubbling stops. Stir gently with a glass rod until the bubbles disappear. Pour this reaction liquid into the other test tube. Put another piece of liver (of the same size) into this liquid. Observe. Pour 2 mL hydrogen peroxide on the liver in the first tube.

    The liquid remaining from the original reaction and the "new" piece of liver should show no reaction. The liquid is water and not hydrogen peroxide. The "old" liver will still react with fresh hydrogen peroxide because the enzymes have not changed. Only the hydrogen peroxide has changed. If the peroxide had not changed, a reaction between the liver and the liquid remaining from the original reaction should have taken place. Do not tell this to your students, as you want them to think of ways of testing the hypotheses. You may, however, need to provide some helpful hints.

3.  After students have performed their experiments, collect the results on the board. These might be listed as follows:

    a.  new liver + new $H_2O_2$ → +, +, +, etc.
    b.  old liver + new $H_2O_2$ → +, +, +, etc.
    c.  old liver + old $H_2O_2$ → −, −, −, etc.
    d.  new liver + old $H_2O_2$ → −, −, −, etc.

    The + indicates the production of bubbles, and the − indicates no bubbles.

4.  Select a student to summarize the results, and initiate a discussion of which hypothesis or hypotheses are supported. Challenge students to propose an explanation at the molecular level for the observations.

### *Term Introduction*

5.  To introduce the terms *catalyst* and *enzyme*, summarize the results as follows: Whenever molecules interact in such a way that one type of molecule is changed (the $H_2O_2$) but the other is not changed (some sort of molecule or molecules in the liver), the unchanged molecule is called a *catalyst*. When the catalyst happens to be a molecule produced by a living thing (an organic molecule), it is called an enzyme and the reaction is called an *enzymatic reaction*. Catalysts and enzymes function to speed up chemical changes, in this case, the change of $H_2O_2$ to $H_2O$ and $O_2$.

6.  Some students may protest that the appearance of the liver does indeed change during

the reaction with $H_2O_2$. Do not ignore this observation; it is a valid one. Challenge students to explain the change. You may wish to suggest that the liver probably contains many types of molecules, some that do not change (the enzyme), and some that do. You may have to acknowledge the possibility that the enzymes actually may change somewhat during the reaction but certainly not at the rate of the other molecules.

### Concept Application

7. Students should be encouraged to think of other examples of catalysts and enzymes. Relevant textbook readings (Chapter 14) should be assigned at this time.

8. When students investigate the role of chlorophyll in Investigation 28, they should compare and contrast its role to that of enzymes.

---

**Biological Terms**

catalyst
enzyme
exothermic reaction
endothermic reaction

**Thinking Skills**

describe nature accurately
state causal questions
create alternative hypotheses
generate logical predictions
plan and conduct experiments
organize and analyze data
draw and apply conclusions

---

## Sample Test Questions

*The next three items refer to the following experiment.*

One gram of freshly ground liver was placed into a test tube with 1 mL of hydrogen peroxide ($H_2O_2$). A gas formed in the tube. It was tested with a glowing splint. The splint burst into flames, identifying the gas as oxygen ($O_2$).

The 1 g of ground liver was then boiled. When fresh hydrogen peroxide was added to the boiled liver, no gas formed. Ground liver treated with strong acid or base produced results similar to those obtained by boiling.

1. A prediction about enzyme activity in liver is being tested. The prediction is that this activity should be destroyed by
   a. acids, bases, boiling, and hydrogen peroxide.
   b. acids, bases, and hydrogen peroxide.
   c. acids, bases, and boiling.
   d. grinding the liver.

2. One of the test tubes was the control for this experiment. It was the test tube containing the
   a. heated liver and hydrogen peroxide.
   b. freshly ground liver and hydrogen peroxide.
   c. liver treated with base.
   d. liver treated with acid.

3. If the substance that broke down the hydrogen peroxide was an enzyme, it could
   a. not be recovered because it had been destroyed.
   b. not be recovered because it was used up.
   c. be recovered from the acid solution.
   d. be recovered from the liver after gas had formed.

*For the next four items, refer to the graphs of the activity of an enzyme.*

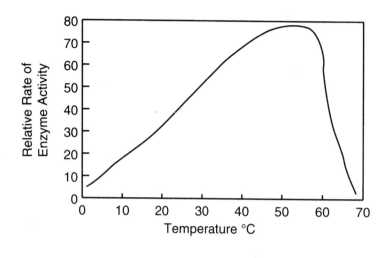

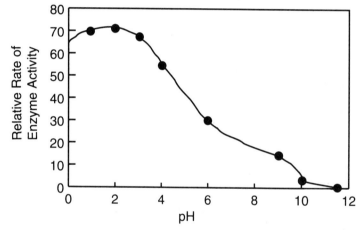

4. Enzyme X will work best in
   a. an acidic medium.
   b. a basic medium.
   c. a neutral medium.
   d. a carbohydrate medium.

5. The optimum pH for this enzyme is about
   a. 2.   b. 4.   c. 7.   d. 12.

6. Enzyme X will work best at a temperature of
   a. 10° to 20°C.   b. 20° to 30°C.   c. 30° to 40°C.   d. 40° to 50°C.

7. Enzyme X would be destroyed at a temperature of
   a. 0°C.   b. 50°C.   c. 75°C.   d. An enzyme cannot be destroyed.

*The next four questions refer to the following experimental results.*

Four experiments were conducted in four separate test tubes. Bubbles were seen in some of the test tubes as indicated in the table.

| Test Tube Number | Contents of Test Tube | Results |
|---|---|---|
| 1 | new liver + new hydrogen peroxide | bubbles |
| 2 | old liver + new hydrogen peroxide | bubbles |
| 3 | old liver + old hydrogen peroxide | no bubbles |
| 4 | new liver + old hydrogen peroxide | no bubbles |

8. Suppose the hypothesis is advanced that molecules in the liver change and that those in hydrogen peroxide do not change when the two substances are mixed. What predicted outcome results from this hypothesis and experiment? The mixture in
    a. Tube 3 should produce bubbles.
    b. Tube 1 should not produce bubbles.
    c. Tube 4 should produce bubbles.
    d. Tube 4 should not produce bubbles.
    e. Tube 2 should produce bubbles.

9. Because bubbles were produced only in Tubes 1 and 2, the hypothesis in item 8 has
    a. been supported.      b. been contradicted.      c. not been tested.

10. Suppose an alternative hypothesis is advanced that molecules in the liver do not change and that those in hydrogen peroxide do change when the two substances are mixed. What predicted outcome results from this hypothesis and experiment? The mixture in
    a. Tube 1 should not produce bubbles.
    b. Tube 2 should produce bubbles.
    c. Tube 2 should not produce bubbles.
    d. Tube 3 should produce bubbles.
    e. Tube 4 should produce bubbles.

11. Because bubbles were produced only in Tubes 1 and 2, the hypothesis in item 10 has
    a. been supported.      b. been contradicted.      c. not been tested.

## Answers

| | | | | |
|---|---|---|---|---|
| 1. C | 3. D | 5. A | 7. C | 9. B | 11. A |
| 2. B | 4. A | 6. D | 8. C | 10. B |

# Diffusion • Osmosis

## Investigation 18 *How Do Molecules Pass Into and Out of Cells?*

## Synopsis

Students discover that elodea cells and red blood cells expand when emersed in distilled water and contract when emersed in a 5% salt solution. Students attempt to explain their observations and to test their explanations using model cells made of dialysis tubing placed into starch, glucose, and water solutions. Experimental results are analyzed, and the processes of osmosis and diffusion are introduced to aid in the explanation of results. This is a hypothetical-deductive learning cycle.

## Suggested Time

Two to three class periods

## Background Information for the Teacher

Imagine a small box containing 25 marbles clustered together at one end. When the box is shaken, the marbles disperse over the entire bottom. Clearly, of all the directions a single marble may take, more lead away from the center of the cluster than toward it; therefore, random movement of the marbles due to shaking of the box will tend to disrupt the cluster rather than maintain it.

At the molecular level, such movement of particles from an area of high concentration to an area of low concentration due to their random collisions with other molecules is called *diffusion*. This is what happens, for instance, when a lump of sugar dissolves in a cup of coffee. The warmer the liquid, the faster the diffusion as the rate of collisions increases. The rate of diffusion also depends on the size of the molecules. Large molecules diffuse more slowly than small ones because it takes more energy to get them to move.

The process of diffusion is exceedingly important to life. The high concentration of organic molecules within cells is very unlikely. Without the cell membrane, these organic molecules would diffuse outward and rapidly become unavailable for the cell's activities; thus, the membrane holds them in—yet the membrane must not act as an impermeable membrane to all molecules, because important new molecules (e.g., food) must enter the cell, and a variety of cell products (e.g., waste) must be able to exit. Cell membranes are said to be differentially permeable because they allow some molecules to pass through but not others.

Suppose a cell that contains water plus a number of large organic molecules is placed in distilled water. Suppose further that the cell has a selectively permeable membrane that allows the smaller water molecules to pass through but not the larger organic molecules. What will happen to the cell? Because the concentration of water molecules on the inside of the cell is lower than that on the outside, water will tend to diffuse into the cell (a movement of a solvent, usually water, through a selectively permeable membrane is called *osmosis*). Because the larger molecules cannot diffuse out, the net concentration of molecules inside the cell will increase, and the cell will swell and may burst. When a cell is placed into a solution in which the water concentration is greater inside the cell, water will diffuse out, and the cell will shrink.

As described above, most cell membranes are relatively permeable to water and certain simple sugars, amino acids, and lipid-soluble substances, but are relatively impermeable to starches, proteins, and other large molecules. In short, cell membranes let the small building blocks of complex organic molecules pass through but not the complex molecules themselves.

Shown below is a generally accepted "fluid mosaic" model of a cell membrane that can account for these observations. A double layer of lipids forms the main part of the membrane. Proteins are embedded in the lipid layers. Membrane pores occur as channels through one or a group of protein molecules. The pores are too small to allow passage of large molecules.

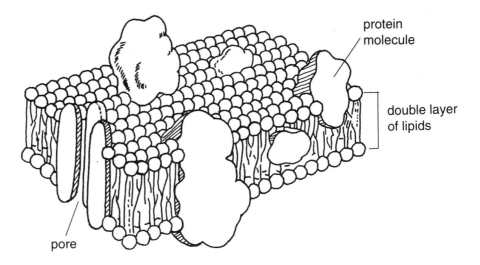

The fluid-mosaic model of the cell membrane.

## Advance Preparation

Make up the solutions and suspensions in advance. To make a 5% solution or suspension, add 5 g of the solid (glucose or starch) per 95 mL warm water. To make 1% solution or suspension, add 1 g of the solid (glucose or corn starch) per 99 mL warm water.

You will have to check your local area for a source of cow's blood. Before the blood is transported, add to each liter of blood a mixture of 2 g sodium oxalate and 60 mL water as an anticoagulant. Be careful not to shake the blood during transport. To dilute the blood for classroom use, mix 10 to 20 mL blood drawn from the middle layer with about 90 mL of an isotonic salt solution (9 g of salt per liter of distilled water).

## Teaching Tips

### Exploration

1. Have students report results of their elodea and red blood cell observations by drawing cells on the board. Challenge them to propose one or more explanations for what they saw. Accept all ideas at this point. Begin Part II by pointing out the available solutions and suspensions and the differences among the water, glucose, and starch molecules.

2. Ask students to speculate on the possible effects of molecular size and concentration on movement through cell membranes, and challenge them to design an experiment or experiments to test their ideas. They will need to be shown how to construct model cells

with the dialysis tubing and how to use bag weight and/or the iodine indicator as evidence of molecular movement. The iodine will turn dark blue when it comes in contact with starch molecules and thus can be placed on the opposite side of a membrane, allowing a color change to indicate starch flow through the membrane. In actuality, the starch molecules are too large to pass through; nevertheless, the absence of a color change provides useful information. Students should not be told which molecules will pass through the membrane, as discovering this is part of the exploration. Students may find it helpful to discuss ways of graphing data, along with possible results and their implications.

4.  Experimental designs and results will vary. Some dialysis tubing will allow only water to diffuse across, while other tubing may allow glucose to pass through as well.

### Term Introduction

5.  Following student experimentation, have one member of each group plot the group's graph(s) on the board. A typical graph might look like this when a "cell" filled with a starch suspension is placed into a distilled water/iodine indicator solution.

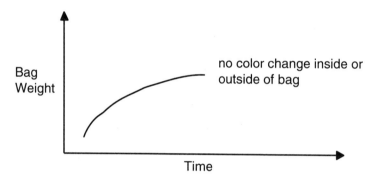

Be prepared for a wide range of graphs. Discuss the results of each group, and select one or more students to try to find and state a pattern or trend in the results.

6.  Challenge students to propose a molecular-level explanation for the results, and use the results to introduce the terms *diffusion, osmosis,* and *selectively permeable membrane.* The graph above, for example, suggests that "something" is entering the cell. That something must be water molecules because those were the only "things" outside the cell except for the iodine indicator, which must not have passed into the bag because the solution in the bag did not turn blue. Likewise, the starch molecules must not have passed out because the water/iodine solution did not turn blue. Therefore, the membrane is "selectively permeable," allowing water to move (diffuse) from an area of high concentration to an area of low concentration. Tell students that such a movement of water across a selectively permeable membrane is called *osmosis.*

7.  Attempt to explain all student results using these ideas. Results that cannot be interpreted should not be considered incorrect; however, you may wish to discuss procedures that were used to arrive at such anomalous results. Students may be able to suggest helpful modifications of those procedures.

8.  Now it is time to refer back to the explanations that the students proposed to account for the elodea and red blood cell observations. These explanations should be discussed once again, and any new explanation should be proposed and evaluated in light of the results

of the model cell experiments. Students now should be in a position to explain what happened to the elodea and red blood cells in terms of osmosis.

### Concept Application

9.  Investigation 20, *Where Will Brine Shrimp Eggs Hatch?*, provides an application to a new context of the concepts introduced here. Investigations 29 and 31 also provide opportunities to apply these ideas.

10.  Chapter 15 of the textbook should be assigned reading.

| Biological Terms | Thinking Skills |
| --- | --- |
| diffusion<br>osmosis<br>selectively permeable<br>dynamic equilibrium<br>fluid mosaic model of<br>    the cell membrane | describe nature accurately<br>state causal questions<br>create alternative hypotheses<br>generate logical predictions<br>plan and conduct experiments<br>organize and analyze data<br>draw and apply conclusions |

## Sample Test Questions

1.  A biologist dilutes blood cells with water on a glass slide and observes them through a microscope. The cells seem to burst. This is probably because
    a.  distilled water was used.
    b.  very salty water was used.
    c.  the water was added too rapidly.
    d.  dead cells were used.

*For the next four items, use the following diagram.*

2.  The cell in the above diagram probably would
    a.  expand and burst open.
    b.  shrivel up.
    c.  retain its normal shape.
    d.  lose its salt content.

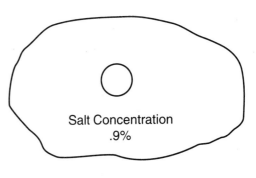

Salt Concentration
.9%

10% Salt Solution

3.  The concentration of water is
    a.  greater inside the cell than outside.
    b.  greater in the immediate environment than in the cell.
    c.  equal inside and outside the cell.
    d.  not important to the size of the cell.

4.  Which cell structure is responsible for this activity?
    a.  nucleus
    b.  cytoplast
    c.  cell membrane
    d.  cell wall

*The next five items refer to the following graph, which shows the data obtained when six potato cores of equal weight were placed into six different concentrations of salt water.*

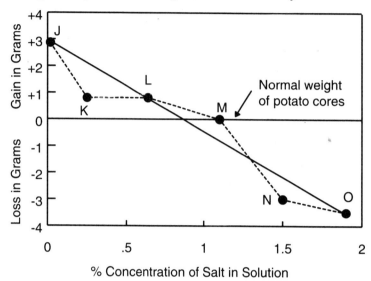

5. The dependent variable in this experiment is the
   a. concentration of salt in solution.
   b. size of potato cores.
   c. weight of potato cores at the start of the experiment.
   d. weight of potato cores at the end of the experiment.

6. The dots J, K, L, M, N, and O represent
   a. variables.
   b. assumptions.
   c. hypotheses.
   d. data.

7. If no change occurred in the weight of a potato core after immersion into a salt solution, it would indicate that
   a. water could not enter the core.
   b. water could leave the core.
   c. salt concentration inside the core was equal to the concentration outside.
   d. the potato cell membranes are not permeable to salt.

8. The best reason for drawing a straight line between but NOT connecting each dot is that
   a. it assumes the correct answer.
   b. averaging experimental results allow one to see relationships more clearly.
   c. the individual results are often wrong.
   d. the dotted line is a fact, while each dot is an assumption.

9. Cores J, K, and L are above the normal weight because
   a. water flowed from each core.
   b. salt entered the cores.
   c. water entered the cores and increased their weight.
   d. all these cores weighed more than 3 g.

10. To test the hypothesis that small molecules such as water can enter cells while large molecules such as starch cannot (because the cell membrane contains holes larger than water molecules but smaller than starch molecules), a student filled a dialysis bag with a 5% starch suspension. The bag then was tied so that nothing could enter or exit except through the bag wall. Then the bag was placed into a beaker of distilled water. If after 10 minutes the distilled water tested positive for starch, the student's hypothesis would have
    a. been supported.
    b. been contradicted.
    c. not been tested properly because no controls were used.

*Use the following information to answer the next five items.*

The surface area of a cube is equal to its length × width × number of surfaces. The volume of a cube is equal to its length × width × height. Therefore, the surface area of a cube 1 cm on a side would be 1 × 1 × 6 sides = 6 sq cm. Its volume would be 1 × 1 × 1 = 1 cu cm.

11. What is the surface area of a cube 2 cm on a side?
    a. 6 sq cm
    b. 2 cu cm
    c. 8 sq cm
    d. 24 sq cm
    e. 24 cu cm

12. What is the volume of a cube 2 cm on a side?
    a. 2 cu cm
    b. 8 cu cm
    c. 6 sq cm
    d. 24 sq cm
    e. 24 cu cm

13. As a cell increases in size, which increases faster?
    a. volume          b. surface area          c. neither

14. Assuming that diffusion of molecules takes place through cell membranes, which of the following cell sizes would be most efficient at allowing molecules in and out?
    a. 1 cm on a side
    b. 2 cm on a side
    c. 3 cm on a side
    d. 4 cm on a side
    e. 5 cm on a side

15. Which of the following factors is the most important limit on the size that individual cells can become?
    a. density
    b. surface area
    c. volume
    d. weight
    e. surface area/volume

## Answers

| | | |
|---|---|---|
| 1. A | 6. D | 11. D |
| 2. B | 7. C | 12. B |
| 3. A | 8. B | 13. A |
| 4. C | 9. C | 14. A |
| 5. D | 10. B | 15. E |

# DNA Structure and Function

## Investigation 19    *What Is the Structure of the Genetic Material?*

## Synopsis

Students use three sets of historical clues and cut-out models of nucleotides to construct a model of the genetic material deoxyribonucleic acid (DNA). This is a hypothetical-deductive learning cycle.

## Suggested Time

Two to three class periods

## Background Information for the Teacher

In 1962, James Watson, Francis Crick, and Maurice Wilkens were awarded the Nobel Prize for their work on the elucidation of the molecular structure of DNA, the molecule responsible for transmitting genetic information from parent to offspring. The crucial paper, entitled "Molecular Structure of Nucleic Acids: A Structure for Deoxyribose Nucleic Acid," that detailed the model was written by Watson and Crick and had appeared nine years earlier, in 1953, in the British journal *Nature*.

The story of the discovery of DNA structure and function covers roughly the years 1868 to 1953. The story is one of the most intriguing in the history of biology because it tells us a great deal about how science progresses and about the nature of the people who do science. The central purpose of this learning cycle is to help students better understand how theory and data interact to generate new knowledge.

The basic postulates of Watson and Crick's theory of DNA structure and function that emerged in 1953 are as follows:

1.  DNA consists of a two-stranded spiral helix, with the two strands made up of alternate molecules of deoxyribose and phosphoric acid.

2.  Pairs of bases form links between the two opposite deoxyribose molecules in the two strands. The base pairs are adenine-thymine (-A-T-) and cytosine-guanine (-C-G-).

3.  The base pairs may be in any sequence along the two-stranded spiral helix and may be positioned as follows: -A-T-, -T-A-, -C-G-, or -G-C-.

4.  When DNA replicates, the two bases in each pair separate, permitting the two strands to separate.

5.  As the strands separate, complementary nucleotides (deoxyribose + phosphoric acid + base) pair up sequentially with the organic bases in each strand.

6.  As the pairing occurs, the deoxyribose attaches to the phosphoric acid of the preceding nucleotide, thus forming the strand of the new spiral.

Students collectively will be able to arrive at these postulates through careful consideration of the three sets of "clues" presented at the end of this section.

## Advance Preparation

You will need to make copies of the molecular model cutouts and the three sets of clues.

To save class time, you may want to have students cut out and color code the molecules as a homework assignment prior to the start of the activity. Colored paper also can be used to produce color-coded molecules.

## Teaching Tips

### *Exploration*

1. Set the stage for the activity by discussing the information in the introduction of the student manual. Be sure to make the questions and their importance clear to the students. Chromosomes hold all of the genetic information for all of life's activities and carry this information from generation to generation. Thus, the molecule(s) that make up chromosomes are very special, and the questions *What is their molecular nature?* and *How do they function?* are of central importance in unlocking a major secret of life.

2. Hand out the first set of clues (1860–1952), and be sure to discuss the molecular models (both stick models, if some are available, and the more schematic geometric ones) so that the students understand their task.

3. The first set of clues should lead students to conclude that it is the DNA of chromosomes rather than the protein molecules that carries the genetic information. This idea should emerge in a class discussion following students' work with the first set of clues. This discussion should focus on each clue and its implications.

4. The second set of clues (1952) should be handed out, and the students should begin modifying their models in light of this new information. Essentially, these clues tell that DNA consists of a double helix with two strands of phosphate groups and sugar molecules. They do not, however, suggest how the strands and the bases are arranged. Should the bases be pointed inward, outward, or in some other fashion?

5. After students have attempted to incorporate these clues into their models, hold another class discussion to discuss their ideas. If some students have "hit" on the Watson and Crick model, simply accept this as one of a few possibilities, and challenge them to imagine what sets of data would be needed to confirm it.

6. Hand out the third set of clues (1952–1953), and have students refine their models in light of this evidence. The Chargaff results essentially show a 1:1 ratio for A-T and for G-C; therefore, the number of A and T bases should be equal in the model. The number of G and C bases also should be equal; that is, these bases should pair with one another. This, along with the hydrogen bonding information, supports the idea that the bases are on the inside of the molecule. Do not be concerned if students do not comprehend this immediately; neither did Watson and Crick.

### *Term Introduction*

7. A final discussion should be held in which the "correct" model is invented. Be sure to point out how such a model leads quite naturally to a fundamental model of gene replication. In fact, the term *gene replication* should be introduced at this time, and students can be left with the further intriguing questions about how genes function and precisely how long a strand of nucleotides is needed to "code" for specific characteristics.

### Concept Application

8. No further activities are included; however, text readings (Chapter 16) and the Study Questions may be used to reinforce and expand on some of the ideas introduced. You may wish to pursue the question of how genes control the synthesis of such important molecules as proteins (Chapter 17). Techniques exist for actually extracting DNA from bacterial cells. Most biological sourcebooks list required techniques.

---

**Biological Terms**

adenine, thymine, guanine, cytosine
X-ray diffraction
phosphate group
nucleotide
deoxyribonucleic acid (DNA)
gene replication

**Thinking Skills**

create alternative hypotheses
generate logical predictions
organize and analyze data
draw and apply conclusions

---

## Sample Test Questions

*The next five items are based on the following information and key.*

A virus that attacks bacterial cells is grown with radioactive phosphorous (P*) attached to its DNA and radioactive sulfur (S*) attached to its outer protein coat. The virus then is placed into a bacterial culture. Possible results of this experiment are listed below.

**KEY**

I.  P* is found inside bacterial cells.

II. S* is found inside bacterial cells.

III. P* is found outside bacterial cells.

IV. S* is found outside bacterial cells.

1. Which result would indicate that DNA from the virus enters the bacterial cell?
   a. I     b. II     c. III     d. IV

2. From Result III, one could tentatively conclude that
   a. the virus protein had mutated.
   b. virus protein had not entered the bacteria.
   c. virus DNA had not entered the bacteria.
   d. the virus does not contain DNA.

3. Which result would indicate that material from the outer core of the virus had entered the bacterial cell?
   a. I     b. II     c. III     d. IV

4. Which results would indicate that none of the virus had entered the bacterial cell?
   a. I and II     b. II and III     c. II and IV     d. III and IV

5. Why were the two elements (P and S) chosen for this experiment? They
   a. are cheap and easily obtained.
   b. are found in all living material.
   c. each combine with a different major part of a virus.
   d. are easily absorbed by bacteria.

*The next eight items are based on the following data table and key. Use the key to classify the statements.*

## KEY

A. The data provide evidence for this statement.

B. The data provide evidence against this statement.

C. The data provide no evidence either for or against this statement.

### Quantity of Nucleotides in DNA

| Source | Adenine | Thymine | Guanine | Cytosine |
|---|---|---|---|---|
| Calf | 1.13 | 1.11 | 0.86 | 0.85 |
| Rat | 1.15 | 1.14 | 0.86 | 0.82 |
| Moth | 0.84 | 0.80 | 1.22 | 1.33 |
| Virus | 1.17 | 1.12 | 0.90 | 0.81 |
| Sperm (of Rat) | 1.15 | 1.09 | 0.89 | 0.83 |

6. The DNA molecule is composed of nucleic acids, deoxyribose, and phosphoric acid.

7. Specific pairing of the nucleotide bases occurs in the DNA molecule.

8. Diameter constancy of the DNA molecule comes about by purine-pyrimidine pairings.

9. Adenine and guanine pair.

10. Thymine and cytosine are pyrimidines.

11. The ratio of adenine to guanine is fairly constant for all species.

12. The ratio of adenine to thymine is approximately the same in the sperm cells of a rat as it is in the body cells.

13. The amount of adenine and thymine in a cell is always greater than the amount of guanine and cytosine.

## Answers

| | |
|---|---|
| 1. A | 8. C |
| 2. C | 9. B |
| 3. B | 10. C |
| 4. D | 11. B |
| 5. C | 12. A |
| 6. C | 13. B |
| 7. A | |

## Clues Set 1

### *(1868–1952)*

1. In 1868, a young Swiss biochemist, Friedrich Miescher, found that when pepsin (a chemical known to break apart protein molecules) was added to chromosomes, atoms of oxygen, carbon, hydrogen, and nitrogen were detected. These were the atoms known to be present in proteins. He also detected phosphorous atoms. Because phosphorous atoms had never before been found in protein molecules, he suspected that another type of molecule, in addition to protein, must be present in chromosomes. He named the new molecule *nuclein.*

2. During the 1880s, a German biologist named Walter Flemming conducted the first detailed studies of the behavior of chromosomes during cellular reproduction. His work made it increasingly clear that chromosomes carry the genetic material—as he showed that new individuals begin with the union of sperm and egg cells, which always contain chromosomes and often little else.

3. During the early 1900s, Robert Feulger, a German chemist, discovered that all body cells of any particular organism contain precisely the same amount of nuclein but that the amount of protein varies from cell to cell. He also found that egg and sperm cells contain exactly one-half the amount of nuclein present in body cells. This was not necessarily the case for the amount of protein.

4. Later biochemists determined that nuclein is composed of combinations of just three different kinds of chemical substances: 1) a five-carbon sugar called deoxyribose, 2) an atom of phosphorous surrounded by four atoms of oxygen and two of hydrogen, called a phosphate group, and 3) ringlike molecules that contain two nitrogen atoms in each ring, called nitrogenous bases. Four different kinds of nitrogenous bases were found: adenine, guanine, cytosine, and thymine. Moreover, it was determined that each base always occurs in combination with one phosphate group and one deoxyribose sugar molecule. This combination was given the name *nucleotide.* Thus DNA consists of four different kinds of nucleotides—one with each of the four nitrogenous bases. Two representations of a nucleotide containing cytosine are shown below.

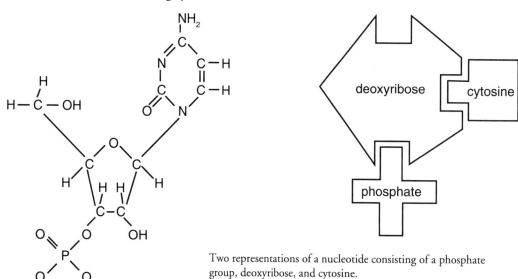

Two representations of a nucleotide consisting of a phosphate group, deoxyribose, and cytosine.

5. During the late 1940s, English biophysicists discovered that DNA crystalized when water is removed. This fact suggested that the atoms in DNA must be arranged in a very orderly fashion, perhaps with many repetitions of a fairly simple pattern.

6. In 1952, Americans Martha Chase and Alfred Hershey knew that viruses can attack bacterial cells and inject them with virus genetic information. They grew viruses with radioactive phosphorous in the DNA molecules and radioactive sulphur in the protein molecules. After these viruses attacked the bacteria and injected their genetic information, only radioactive phosphorus was found inside the bacteria.

## Clues Set 2

### *(1952)*

1. X-ray diffraction* photographs made by Rosalind Franklin and Maurice Wilkens of Kings College, London, indicated that the DNA molecule is shaped like a spiral helix.

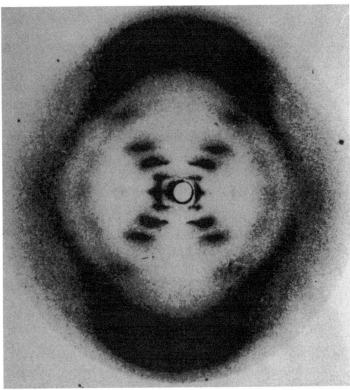

An X-ray photograph of DNA in the B form, taken by Rosalind Franklin late in 1952. (From *J. D. Watson, the Double Helix,* Atheneum, New York. 1968) Reprinted with permission.

2. Evidence indicates that the helix contains strands of phosphate groups and sugar molecules linked by relatively strong chemical bonds.

3. Watson and Crick calculated that a single chain of nucleotides would have a density only half as great as the known density of DNA.

* X-ray diffraction involves the passing of X rays through crystallized DNA and recording the ways the X rays are deflected. The procedure is somewhat like trying to figure out the shape of an object by looking at its shadow, but considerably more complex.

## Clues Set 3

### *(1952–1953)*

1. During the 1940s, Austrian biochemist Erwin Chargaff experimentally obtained the information shown in the table below. The implications of these data slowly were becoming clear to Watson and Crick in the summer of 1952.

### Adenine to Thymine and Guanine to Cytosine Ratios Found in DNA Molecules From Various Sources

| Tissue and Organism | Adenine | Thymine | Guanine | Cytosine |
|---|---|---|---|---|
| Thymus cells | | | | |
|    Human | 30.9 | 29.4 | 19.9 | 19.8 |
|    Sheep | 29.3 | 28.3 | 21.4 | 21.0 |
|    Pig | 30.9 | 29.4 | 19.9 | 19.8 |
| Spleen cells | | | | |
|    Human | 29.2 | 29.4 | 21.0 | 20.4 |
|    Sheep | 28.0 | 28.6 | 22.3 | 21.1 |
|    Pig | 29.6 | 29.7 | 20.4 | 20.8 |
| Liver cells | | | | |
|    Human | 30.3 | 30.3 | 19.5 | 19.9 |
|    Sheep | 29.3 | 29.2 | 20.7 | 20.8 |
|    Pig | 29.4 | 29.7 | 20.5 | 20.5 |
| Sperm cells | | | | |
|    Human | 30.7 | 31.2 | 19.3 | 18.8 |
|    Sheep | 28.8 | 27.2 | 22.0 | 21.0 |
| Colon bacterium | 26.0 | 23.9 | 24.9 | 25.2 |
| Yeast | 31.3 | 32.9 | 18.7 | 17.1 |

2. In the spring of 1953, Watson arrived at the lab early one day, cut out cardboard models of adenine, thymine, guanine, and cytosine molecules, and began arranging them in various combinations and patterns on his desk. He discovered that an adenine-cytosine pair presumably held together by two relatively weak hydrogen bonds is identical in shape to a guanine-cytosine pair also held together by at least two hydrogen bonds.

3. Later that same day, Watson showed Crick his result, and when they went to lunch at the Eagle Cafe in London, Crick told everyone within hearing distance that they had found the secret of life.

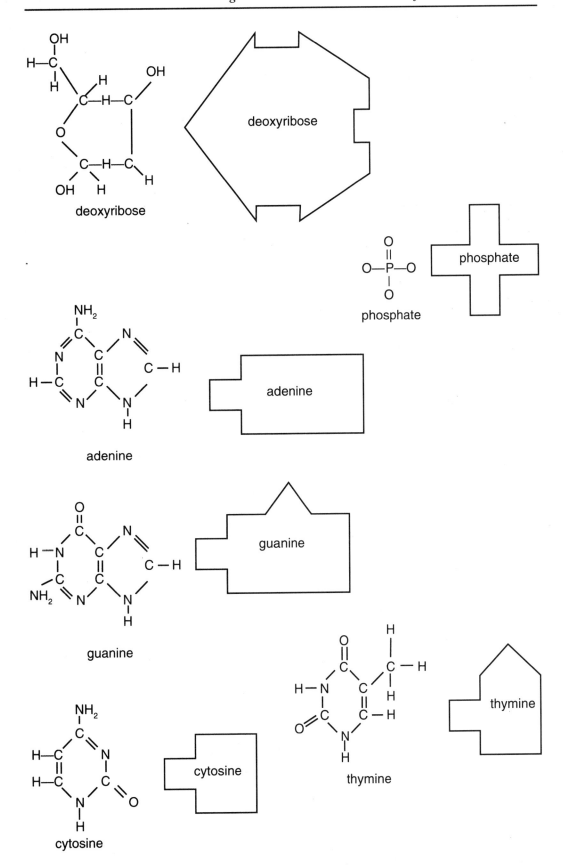

deoxyribose

deoxyribose

phosphate

phosphate

adenine

adenine

guanine

guanine

cytosine

cytosine

thymine

thymine

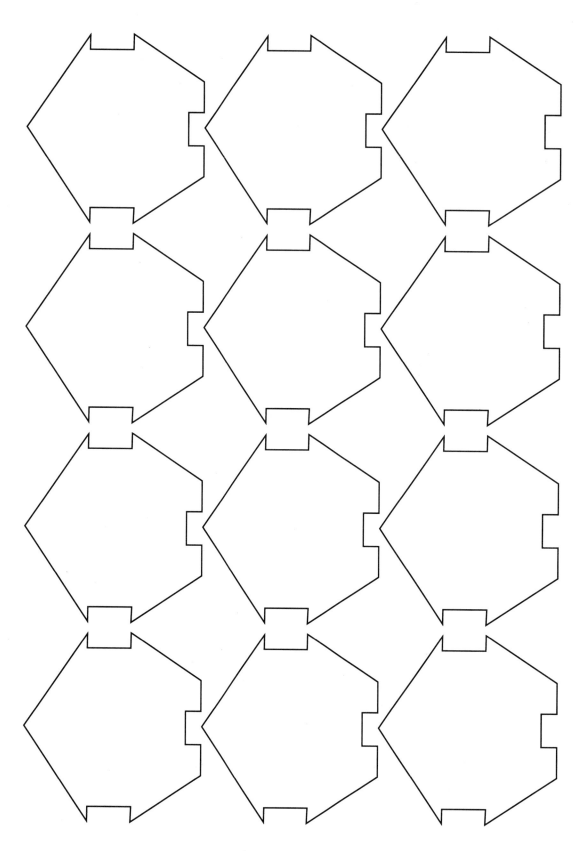

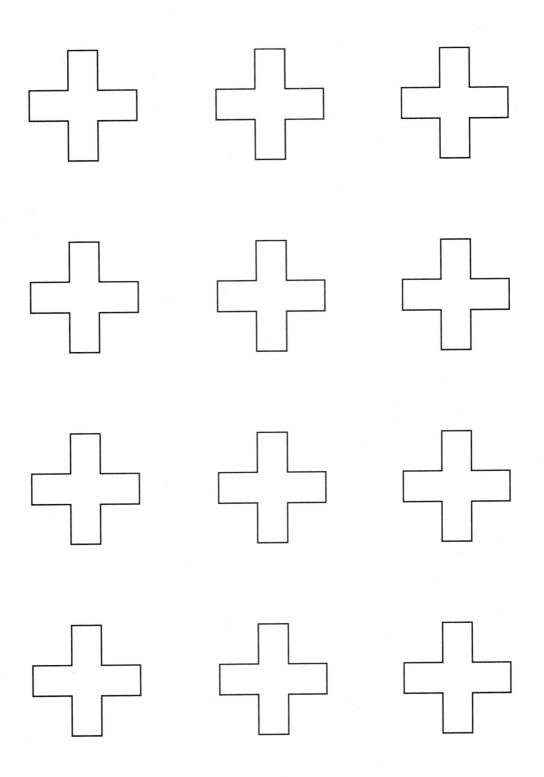

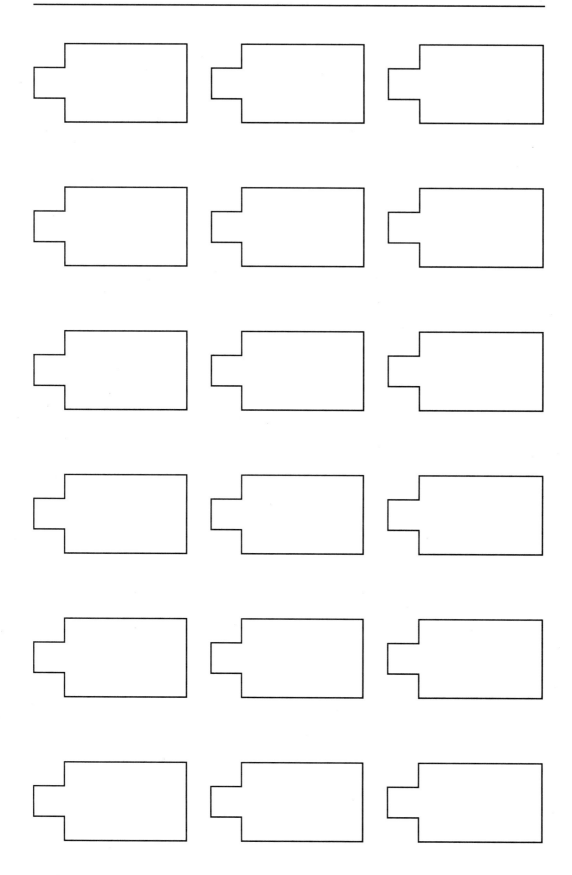

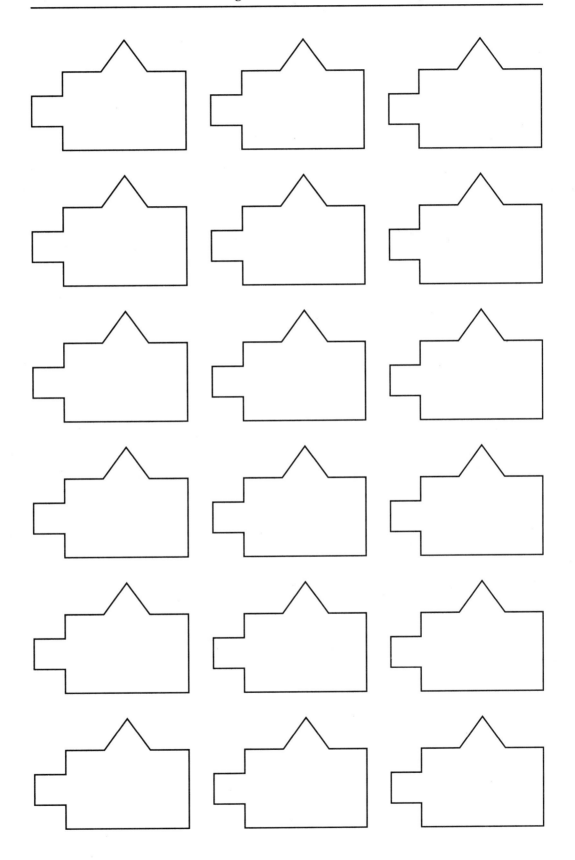

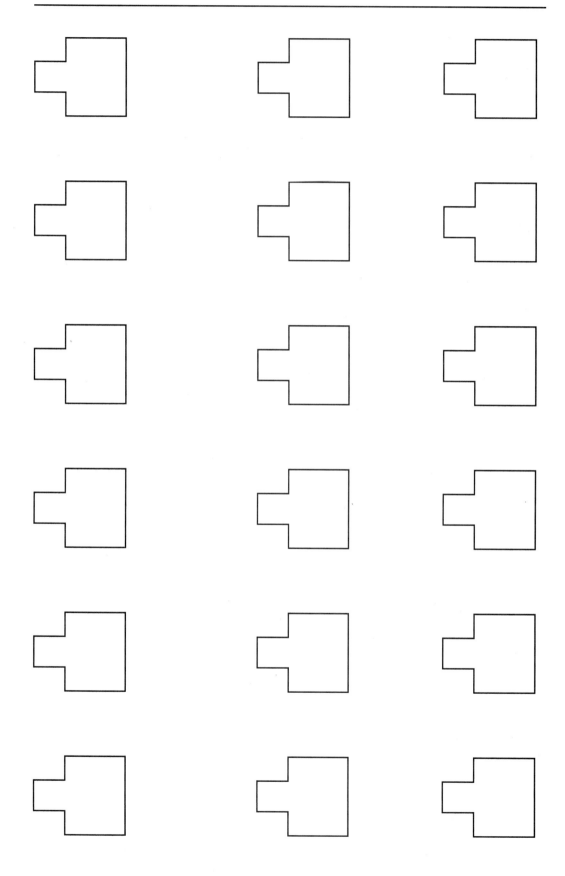

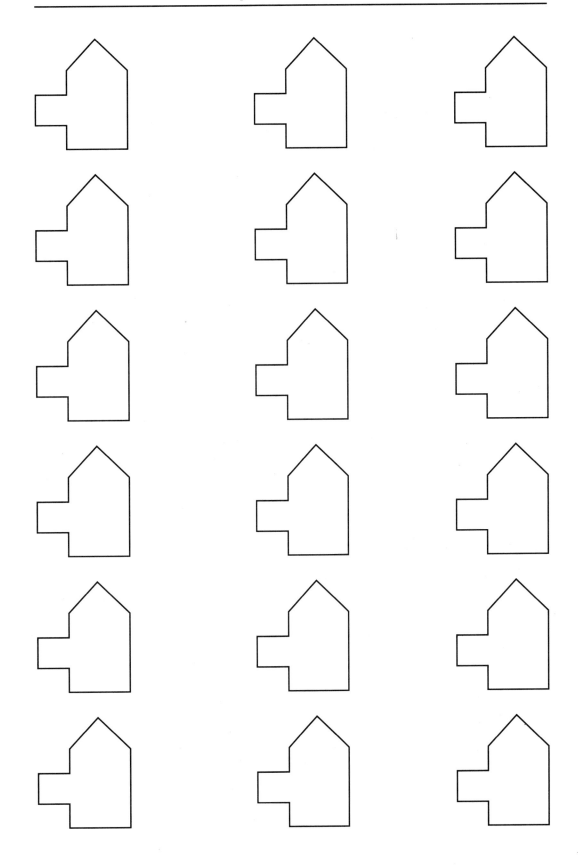

# Limiting Factors • Optimum Range

## Investigation 20 _Where Will Brine Shrimp Eggs Hatch?_

## Synopsis

Students prepare solutions with varying concentrations of salt and then design and conduct an experiment to determine the effect of salinity on the hatching of brine shrimp eggs. The terms _limiting factors_ and _optimum range_ are introduced, and the cause of poor hatching is sought. This is an empirical-abductive learning cycle.

## Suggested Time

One class period for setup, and one period for data analysis and term introduction

## Background Information for the Teacher

All organisms are affected by environmental factors that limit their abundance and distribution. Such environmental factors are called _limiting factors_. In the case of brine shrimp, one of these factors is the amount of salt in the water in which they live. These small crustaceans are found commonly in coastal regions and estuaries and can tolerate a considerable range of salt concentration, but their eggs hatch best in a concentration of salt water approximately equal to that of normal sea water (35 g of salt per liter of solution). In this learning cycle, students design an experiment to determine the range of salt concentration most conducive to hatching. This range is referred to as the _optimum range_. Above and below this range, osmosis will result in too much water either entering or leaving the egg, thus preventing hatching.

Because this learning cycle requires the solution of several problems involving proportions, it provides an excellent opportunity to promote the development of proportional reasoning.

## Advance Preparation

Prepare approximately 5 L of a salt solution three times (3X) the concentration of normal seawater (1X) by adding 105 g of table salt to each 1000 mL or 1 liter of water.

Brine shrimp eggs are available at local pet and aquarium shops.

## Teaching Tips

### Exploration

1. Introduce the lesson by discussing problems faced by seeds of plants that happen to land in environments unfavorable to growth. Note that these problems also are faced by eggs of such invertebrates as brine shrimp. Refer students to the map on page 98, pointing out how the salt concentration of the various regions of water will vary. You may wish to have students imagine that the map represents a portion of the Oregon or California coastline. Salt concentration will vary from fresh water (0X) at point A in the freshwater river; to one-third that of normal sea water (⅓ X) at point B, where some sea water penetrates the river at high tide; to ⅔ X at point C, near the mouth of the river; to 1X at point D, in the open ocean; and to 2X and 3X at point E, in the saltwater pond at various times during the evaporation of fresh water from its surface.

2. Ask students to speculate about how these varying concentrations may influence egg hatching. If some students apply the concept of osmosis to predict that some eggs will shrink and others will expand and burst (hence not hatch), accept this as a possibility that could be tested, but do not let on that this is "correct" at this time.

3. Refer to the questions in procedure step 3 of the student manual, and challenge students to prepare salt solutions of ⅓ X, ⅔ X, 1X, and 2X from the stock solution of 3X salt water to discover the answers. Aged tap water or distilled water may be used to simulate fresh-water conditions (point A). Students will need to be shown the vials and the eggs and be forewarned of the difficulties in preparing the solutions. Let them struggle with the problems for 20 to 30 minutes before you discuss approaches with the class as a whole. Preparing the solutions requires proportional reasoning, a reasoning pattern not well developed in many of your students. Their difficulties will make it clear to them that they need help and will put them into a receptive frame of mind.

4. The following steps have been found to be helpful, and you may wish to present them during a class discussion or to individual groups of students.

   a. Let the following diagram represent normal sea water (1X).

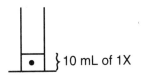

   The dot represents 1 unit of salt, and the line represents 10 mL of fresh water.

   Thus, the following represents a 3X solution, as it contains three times the amount of salt as the 1X solution contained in the same amount of fresh water (10 mL).

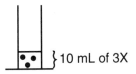

   b. Ask: *Given 10 mL of a 3X solution, how much fresh water must be added to produce a 1X solution?*

   Answer: Three times as much water is needed because the desired solution is 1/3 the original 3X solution (⅓ of 3X = 1X). Therefore, 3 × 10 mL or 30 mL is needed. Because we are given 10 mL and 30 mL – 10 mL = 20 mL, 20 mL must be added.

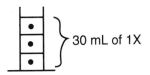

c. Ask: *Given 10 mL of a 3X solution, how much fresh water must be added to produce a 2X solution?*

Answer: Raising the level to 30 mL produced a 1X solution; therefore, raising the level to half that amount will produce a solution twice as concentrated (2X). Because half of 30 mL = 15 mL, the level should be raised to 15 mL or 15 mL – 10 mL = 5 mL so 5 mL must be added.

15 mL of 2X

d. A similar approach can be taken to produce the ⅓ X and ½ X solutions. To produce a ⅓X solution, raise the water level three times as far as you did to produce the 1X solution. You added up to 30 mL to produce the 1X solution; so add up to 3 × 30 mL = 90 mL. You almost have 10 mL so add 80 mL. To produce a ½X solution raise the water level two times as far as you did to produce the 1X solution. You added up to 30 mL to produce the 1X solution; so add up to 2 × 30 mL = 60 mL. You already have 10 mL so add 50 mL.

Students may offer other strategies, which should be accepted provided they produce correct results.

5. After the solutions are prepared, have students add the eggs and place the vials in an out-of-the-way place.

6. The eggs will hatch in 2 to 4 days, at which time students should observe the vials and attempt to determine which solutions produced the greatest amount of hatching. Hand lenses may be necessary to see the tiny brine shrimp. A black background also helps. Because counting individual shrimp is difficult, have students simply estimate which of the solutions produced the most hatching, down to those in which no hatching occurred. Assign numbers—5 for best, down to 0 for worst—and have groups plot their data on graphs. Sample data are shown below.

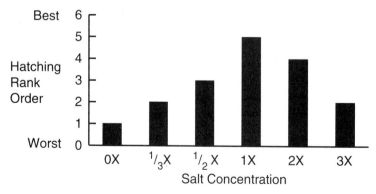

### Term Introduction

7. Have one member of each group reproduce the group graph on the board, and hold a class discussion in which the graphs are analyzed for trends/patterns.

8. A number of patterns may emerge (for example, see Sample Test Question 2). The terms *direct correlation, optimum range, inverse correlation,* and *bimodal distribution* may be introduced to name the appropriate patterns. If no clear consensus emerges, a discussion of possible reasons for the differences should be held (e.g., different numbers of eggs used, amount of water, location in room). Have the students decide how to control these variables and redo their experiments with the variables held constant.

9. After terms have been introduced, ask students to propose an explanation for their results (Why did the freshwater and 3X solutions cause little or no hatching?). Osmosis may be suggested. If other explanations are offered, a discussion of how to test the alternatives should be pursued.

### Concept Application

10. Reasoning Module 6, *Proportional Relationships*, should be used to help students acquire a better understanding of the quantitative relationships involved in this investigation.

| Biological Terms | Thinking Skills |
| --- | --- |
| optimum range | describe nature accurately |
| osmosis | state causal questions |
| limiting factors | plan and conduct experiments |
| | organize and analyze data |
| | draw and apply conclusions |
| | proportional reasoning |

## Sample Test Questions

1. The environmental factor investigated in brine shrimp egg hatching was
   a. the interaction between predators and consumers.
   b. brine shrimp caught by fishermen.
   c. saltwater concentration.
   d. the environment of seeds.
   e. the location of the eggs.

*Items 2–5 refer to the following graphs.*

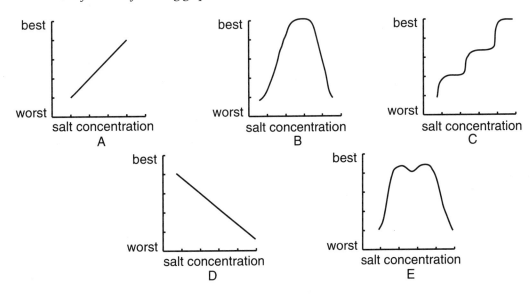

133

2. Which of the graphs best shows an optimum range for brine shrimp egg hatching with varying saltwater concentrations?

3. A biologist proposes the hypothesis that two different species of brine shrimp cohabit a coastal region but that the two species have different salinity tolerances. To test this hypothesis, the biologist attempts to hatch samples of eggs (presumably of both species mixed together) in solutions of varying salt concentration. Which of the possible results shown in the graphs would support this hypothesis?

4. A second biologist proposes the hypothesis that brine shrimp are able to use salt in the water as a food source and that more food promotes more hatching. Which of the results graphed supports this hypothesis?

5. A third biologist proposes the hypothesis that salt poisons eggs. Which of the graphs supports this hypothesis?

6. The dependent variable in the brine shrimp experiment is the
   a. size of hatching containers.
   b. saltwater concentration.
   c. optimum range.
   d. temperature range.
   e. relative number of eggs hatching.

7. Suppose the hypothesis is proposed that osmosis will affect the movement of water into and out of brine shrimp eggs. Suppose it is determined that normal eggs have an internal salt concentration nearly identical to that of sea water. What prediction follows?
   a. Eggs will fail to hatch in solutions that vary widely from normal sea water.
   b. Molecules will move from an area of high concentration to an area of low concentration.
   c. The experimental results will support the hypothesis.
   d. The hypothesis cannot be tested adequately because the water molecules are too small to see.
   e. One needs to control all variables except salinity.

*Use the following information to answer items 8–10.*

Suppose you are given a sample of sea water five times as concentrated as normal sea water. Normal sea water contains about 35 g of salt per 1000 mL of water.

8. How much fresh water should be added to 10 mL of this 5X solution to produce a sample of normal sea water?
   a. 10 mL
   b. 20 mL
   c. 30 mL
   d. 40 mL
   e. 50 mL

9. How much fresh water should be added to 10 ml of this 5X solution produce a sample of water two times the concentration of normal sea water?
   a. 5 mL
   b. 10 mL
   c. 15 mL
   d. 20 mL
   e. 25 mL

10. How much fresh water should be added to 10 mL of this 5X solution to produce a sample of water that has half the salt concentration of normal sea water?
    a. 10 mL
    b. 20 mL
    c. 50 mL
    d. 90 mL
    e. 100 mL

## Answers

1. C
2. B
3. E
4. A
5. D

6. E
7. A
8. D
9. C
10. D

# Proportional Reasoning

## Reasoning Module 6 · *Proportional Relationships*

## Synopsis

Students assemble Cuisenaire® rod "walls" that represent observable proportional relationships. They then use coupled gears to generate more abstract proportions and try to solve balance-beam problems involving inverse proportional relationships. Finally, a series of pencil-and-paper problems requiring proportional or additive reasoning is worked through.

## Suggested Time

Two class periods

## Background Information

Proportions are the most ubiquitous mathematical tools of any introductory science course. Indeed, many physics and chemistry concepts, such as density, acceleration, and gravitational force, are, in effect, names given to proportional relationships. To a lesser extent, biology courses also involve such proportions as those underlying much of the energetics and the genetics of living systems. Students' ability to comprehend and to use effectively the "scheme" of proportions therefore is a major concern to science teachers.

Not only is students' understanding of proportionality a concern of the science teacher, it is a primary concern of the developmental psychologist. Jean Piaget, for example, regards the proportionality scheme as a primary acquisition at the stage of formal operations. Unfortunately, much evidence suggests that as much as 50 percent of some samples of secondary-school and college-age students have failed to acquire a working understanding of the proportionality scheme (defined as the ability to confront a "real world" problem situation and determine whether and how quantitative proportions can be used in its solution).

Consider, for example, the following: Students are shown two transparent, hollow cylinders of differing diameters but equally spaced graduations. A quantity of water occupying 4 units in the wide cylinder is poured into the narrow cylinder, which it fills up to 6 units. The task is to consider a quantity of water filling the wide container up to 6 units and to predict how high it will rise in the narrow cylinder. Students' responses on the task vary, but the following four categories are common:

Category I (Intuitive): No explanation, illogical computation, guess; for example, "8 units, because the smaller cylinder won't hold as much water as the wide cylinder, so it has a tendency to rise."

Category A (Additive): Procedure focusing on the difference of water levels; for example, "8; in the narrow cylinder the water seems to rise two marks higher than the wide cylinder, so I added 2."

Category T (Transitional): Additive procedure focusing on correspondence of amounts of water, for example, "9, if the water rose 2 when the marking in the wide cylinder was 4, so for each two marks the water goes up 1. So from 6 it will go up 3 to 9."

Category R (Ratio): Using constant-ratio or converting units from wide to narrow cylinder; for example, "9, for every mark in the large one it goes 1½ times into the small one, because 4 went up to 6."

Only students who respond with Category R responses are able to generalize their use of proportions to more complex problems. Regrettably, many high-school students (80 to 90% in some samples) respond in Categories I and A, indicating poorly developed or nonexistent proportional reasoning skills. Because proportional reasoning is seen as fundamental to understanding science and to intellectual development in general and is lacking in a large percentage of adolescents, this Reasoning Module has been designed to help students acquire and successfully deploy proportional reasoning patterns.

## Advance Preparation

Balance beams (math balances) are available from Invicta Plastics Ltd., 200 Fifth Avenue, New York, NY 10010. Balance beams, coupled gears, and Cuisenaire® rods are available from Delta Education, P.O. Box 915, Hudson, NH  03051-0915, (800) 258-1302, FAX (603) 880-6520.

## Teaching Tips

1. Use Investigation 20, *Where Will Brine Shrimp Eggs Hatch?*, to introduce proportional relationships to your students. This Reasoning Module then provides an opportunity to extend their understanding of proportions.

2. Keep in mind that many students can cross multiply to find $x$ in a problem such as $\% = \%_x$ but will not use proportional reasoning to solve such tasks as the cylinders task. Proportional reasoning involves not just the math but also an understanding of real phenomena and a hypothetical-deductive mode of matching possible strategies (e.g., proportions) to real problems. This module will help students become more aware of this.

3. Have students work in groups of two or three to complete the tasks in Essays 2 through 4.

4. Assign the Study Questions as homework.

5. Allow a complete class period to discuss the problems if necessary.

| **Biological Terms** | **Thinking Skills** |
|---|---|
| proportional relationships (direct and inverse) | proportional reasoning |

# Flower Structure and Function

## Investigation 21  *What Is the Structure and Function of Flowers?*

## Synopsis

Students explore a variety of individual flowers and attempt to construct a model of a typical flower. Names for identified structures are introduced. Students then create alternative hypotheses for the functions of these structures. These alternative hypotheses can be the subject for optional experimentation. In this option, students design and conduct controlled experiments to test their hypotheses. This is either an empirical-abductive or a hypothetical-deductive learning cycle, depending on usage.

## Suggested Time

One-and-one-half to three class periods, depending on optional work; out-of-class time for optional follow-up experiments

## Background Information for the Teacher

The following parts can be observed in many types of flowering plants:

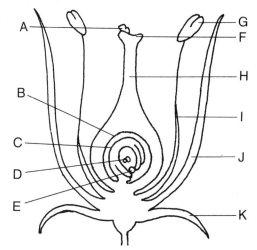

A. Pollen Grain
B. Ovary
C. Ovule
D. Egg (not observable)
E. Micropyle (not observable)
F. Stigma
G. Anther
H. Style
I. Filament
J. Petals
K. Sepals

The parts vary in number and exact structure, depending on the species.

Stamen—"male" organ of a flower, subdivided into the filament and the anther

Filament—stalklike portion of stamen; elevates anther for pollen distribution

Anther—pollen-producing portion of stamen

Pistil—"female" organ of a flower, subdivided into stigma, style, and ovary

Stigma—sticky top portion of pistil; adheres to pollen

Style—elongated, stalklike portion of pistil; provides passage for fertilization of ovules

Ovary—swollen lower portion of pistil; contains ovule(s); sometimes develops to form fruit

Ovule—structure within ovary; develops to form seed

Petals—often large, colorful portion of the floral envelope; usually function to attract pollinators

Sepals—often green bracts underlying petals; usually function to enclose flower in bud stage

## Advance Preparation

For free or inexpensive flowers, contact local growers, wholesale nurseries, mortuaries, and cemeteries. They often are happy to provide flowers for educational purposes. Many flowers can be collected near the school or brought by students from home. Often the best flowers are the ones that can be collected in the wild. Be sure to inform students of any protected flowers in your area.

## Teaching Tips

### Exploration

1. Have students work in teams of two or three to dissect and draw their flowers. If possible, have each group dissect two to three different flowers, look for similarities and differences, and try to identify common structures.

### Term Introduction

2. Have the students post their drawings on the wall or the chalkboard. Use these to construct a model of the typical flower. It is very important to rely strictly on observations made by class members. A single composite can be made by observing the drawings, listening to student descriptions, and making a corresponding sketch on the board. After stating something like, "Because most people saw these parts, we should have some names to label them," introduce names for the observed parts and write them on the board.

### Concept Application

3. Question students about possible reasons for the variations of flower structure they observed.

4. If you prefer to have students use the hypothesized functions of flower parts as the topic of experimentation, direct them to follow the optional procedure section of the student manual. If not, you should hold a discussion in which students generate possible functions of the major parts that have been identified. You may wish to discuss briefly how some of their ideas could be tested.

5. If you decide to have students test some of their ideas, they may grow plants in the classroom or school greenhouse or adopt plants growing on the campus.

6. Plant possibilities:
   a. If students adopt plants on campus, make sure that those plants go through an easily studied flower-to-fruit cycle in a reasonable amount of time.
   b. Students also may plant seeds, bulbs, or bedding plants that complete flowering and fruit formation in a reasonable amount of time.
   c. If you need more information on available plants suitable for this activity, consult your local plant nursery, extension agent, or local garden books.
   d. Some suggested plants:

| **Perennials** | **Annuals or Bulbs** |
|---|---|
| flowering shrubs | peas |
| flowering trees | tulips |
| stone fruit trees | lilies |
| citrus | amaryllis |
| olive | cabbage |
| pyracantha | lettuce |

7. Students should reread Chapter 12 and identify how and where meiosis and fertilization take place in flowering plants.

| **Biological Terms** | **Thinking Skills** |
|---|---|
| pistil | describe nature accurately |
| stamen | state causal questions |
| anther | create alternative hypotheses |
| petal | generate logical predictions |
| sepal | plan and conduct experiments |
| pollen | organize and analyze data |
| ovary | draw and apply conclusions |
| ovule | |
| stigma | |
| style | |
| seed | |

## Sample Test Questions

1. Reproduction in the broadest sense is least necessary for the survival of
   a. the individual.
   b. the species.
   c. continuation of life.
   d. formation of new species.

2. From the point of view of evolution, what is the greatest advantage of sexual reproduction?
   a. a great variety of organisms
   b. a consistency of traits generation after generation
   c. continuation of the species
   d. fewer eggs fertilized

3. The major result of internal fertilization is
   a. a shorter life cycle.
   b. a greater number of offspring.
   c. protection and nourishment for the developing organism.
   d. sexual reproduction.

4. Ovaries are to ova as testes are to
   a. embryos.
   b. zygotes.
   c. gametes.
   d. sperm.

5.  Corn plant cells have 20 chromosomes each. The number of chromosomes in a pollen
    grain sperm cell of corn is
    a.  10.                                  c.  40.
    b.  20.                                  d.  5.

6.  In a flower, pollination is accomplished when
    a.  the sperm unites with the egg.
    b.  double fertilization is accomplished.
    c.  the pollen is formed in the anther.
    d.  pollen is moved from the anther to the stigma.

7.  In which of the following ways are the reproductive patterns of flowering plants and
    land mammals alike?
    a.  Fertilization is internal.
    b.  The monoploid generation is prominent.
    c.  Ova contain a large amount of stored food.
    d.  Individual organisms possess the reproductive organs of one sex only.

8.  Given that sexual reproduction is an evolutionary advantage for plants because it
    increases variability, how can the presence in some flowers of both male (pollen) and
    female (ova) gametes best be explained?
    a.  Such plants have not evolved.
    b.  The pollen and ova do not mature during the same time of year.
    c.  Self-pollination results in more genetic diversity than would cross-pollination in
        such plants.
    d.  Genetic diversity increases due to environmental influences.
    e.  Evolution favors such flowers in rapidly changing environments.

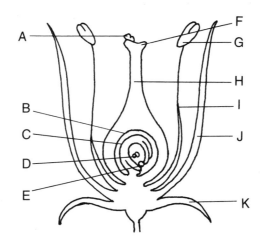

*For the next five items, match the letter in the above diagram to the stated functions.*

 9.  produces pollen

10.  smallest structure that contains ova

11.  holds pollen-producing structures aloft

12. collects pollen

13. protects reproductive organs and/or attracts insects

14. To test the hypothesis that ova must be fertilized to begin development, the styles of 40 flowers growing in a field were covered with a waxy coating before pollination could take place. Which of the following experimental results would contradict this hypothesis?

    **a.** Further development of the ova in 38 of the 40 flowers did not occur.

    **b.** Further development of the ova in 30 of the 40 flowers did occur.

    **c.** Neither a. nor b. would contradict the hypothesis because control flowers were not used.

    **d.** Both a. and b. would contradict the hypothesis because in both cases some development took place.

## Answers

| | |
|---|---|
| 1. A | 8. B |
| 2. A | 9. G |
| 3. C | 10. D |
| 4. D | 11. I |
| 5. A | 12. F |
| 6. D | 13. J |
| 7. A | 14. B |

# Fruit Structure and Function

## Investigation 22 · *What Is the Function of Fruits?*

### Synopsis

Students observe external and internal structures of a variety of fruits, attempt to identify common structures, and speculate about functions. The terms *ovary* as fruit and *ovule* as seed are introduced. Seed protection, dispersal, and biotic potential are discussed. From their own observations and from data they are given, students calculate the biotic potential of a given plant. This is an empirical-abductive or hypothetical-deductive learning cycle, depending upon whether the optional experiments are conducted.

### Suggested Time

Two-and-one-half to three class periods

### Background Information for the Teacher

A fruit develops from the ovary of a flower. The ovules within the ovary develop to form the seeds within the fruit. Therefore, the number and arrangement of ovules within the ovary determines the number and arrangement of seeds within the fruit. The seeds usually mature at the same time as the fruit ripens.

---

**A Dichotomous Key to Identify Simple Fruits**

1. Fruit dry at maturity ....................................................................... 2
   2. Fruit splits open (is dehiscent) .............................................. 3
      3. Fruit contains one chamber or compartment............................. 4
         4. Fruit splits open along one side .......................................... Follicle—example: milkweed
         4. Fruit splits open along two sides......................................... Legume—example: pea, bean
      3. Fruit contains two or more chambers and
          splits along more than two sides     .............................................. Capsule—example: lily
   2. Fruit does not split open (is indehiscent) ............................... 5
      5. Ovary wall very hard ........................................................... Nut—examples: oak, hickory
      5. Ovary wall easily cracked or opened .................................... 6
         6. Ovary wall with winglike growth................................ Samara—examples: ash, maple, elm
         6. Ovary wall without winglike growth .......................... 7
            7. Seed attached only at one place
               to inside of ovary wall........................ Achene—example: sunflower
            7. Seed completely attached to
               ovary wall so that the two
               cannot be separated ......................... Grain—example: wheat, rice, corn
1. Fruit fleshy at maturity.......................................................... 8
        8. Fruit contains several seeds....................... 9
         9. Fruit has firm leathery
           or hard rind..................................... 10
             10. Fruit has hard rind
               and no sections...................... Pepo—examples: cucumber, squash
             10. Fruit has leathery rind
               and many sections .................. Hesperidium—examples: citrus fruit
         9. Fruit has a peeling that is
           not leathery and may be eaten .......... 11
             11 Fruit has a core............... Pome—examples: pear, apple
             11. Fruit more or less
               fleshy throughout;
               seeds may be eaten.......... Berry—examples: grape, pepper, tomato

---

Fruits are classified as simple, aggregate, or multiple. The simple fruits are further classified as dry or fleshy. The table shows a dichotomous key to identify simple fruits. You may wish to have students develop their own key for the fruits used in this investigation and compare their key with this one.

Aggregate fruits consist of a number of enlarged ovaries of a single flower, massed or scattered over the surface of a single receptacle. The separate ovaries are called *fruitlets*. Examples include raspberry, blackberry, strawberry.

Multiple fruits consist of the enlarged ovaries of several flowers more or less coalesced into one mass. Examples include mulberry, fig, pineapple.

Simple fruits arise from the compound or simple pistil of a single flower. Simple fruits are divided into several categories based on their consistency, structure, and manner of opening. The two major groups include fleshy fruits and dry fruits.

a. Fleshy fruits: As an ovary develops into a fruit, the ovary wall, the pericarp, often thickens and becomes differentiated into three distinct layers. Proceeding from the outside to the inside of the fruit, these layers are called the *exocarp*, the *mesocarp*, and the *endocarp*. The development and consistency of these layers differ among types of fruits. Fleshy fruits are of several types, including berries (e.g., grape, tomato), drupes (e.g., cherry, peach), and pomes (e.g., pear, apple).

b. Dry fruits: Dry fruits are simple fruits usually classified according to whether they split open when ripe (e.g., pea, bean) or do not split open when ripe (e.g., sunflower, wheat).

Biotic potential is a function of the number of seeds per fruit and the number of flowers on the plant. This is considering only simple plants, in which a single flower contains only a single ovary with its array of ovules.

Development of the "body" of a fruit determines the mode of seed dispersal. Edible fruits will be carried away by animals. Often the fleshy fruit walls are eaten and the tough seeds are spit out, left behind in a "core," or may even pass through the animal to be deposited ultimately with a ready supply of fertilizer. Inedible seeds may be adapted to catch the wind or to snag onto the bodies of passersby.

## Teaching Tips

### *Exploration*

1. The following is a list of suggested fruits. Do not limit fruits to only the edible and familiar. Encourage students to bring in examples as well. Have them look around their own yards and neighborhoods.

| | | |
|---|---|---|
| acorns | filaree (heron's bill) | pyracantha |
| apples | lantana | rose pods |
| ash | mangoes | seed pods |
| bell peppers | maple | squash |
| cantaloupes | milkweed pods | sunflower seeds |
| citrus fruits | oleander | (must have shell) |
| cockleburs | peaches | tomatoes |
| coconuts (husk on) | peanuts (with shell) | walnuts |
| cucumbers | plums | (with shell) |
| dates | pomegranates | watermelons |
| desert legumes | pumpkins | wild oats |

2. Some students may want to dissect their fruits without paying too much attention to detail. Encourage care as they are doing the exploration. They should look for similarities and differences among the fruit types observed.

3. Solicit volunteers to place drawings of their "typical" fruit structures on the chalkboard, or develop a composite yourself by taking oral descriptions from class discussion.

### Term Introduction

4. Introduce terms to label the identified fruit parts. Discuss possible functions and developmental relationships between flower parts and the observed parts of fruits as described in Background Information for the Teacher.

5. Discuss classification schemes developed by the class. These will be based on seed number and arrangement, whether edible or inedible, and so on.

6. Discuss pericarp development.

### Concept Application

7. Discuss the hypothesized fruit part functions and the experiments that are proposed to test some of the students' alternative hypotheses. Discussion of the process of seed dispersal through these plant structures is appropriate at this point.

8. The extent to which you allow students to perform their experiments is up to you. Experiments could be done in or out of class. You may wish to have students work out of class and use a fruit-bearing plant near their home or school for experimentation.

9. After students have completed Study Questions 1–8, introduce the term *biotic potential* and discuss factors that influence the biotic potential of other organisms. This should include obviously contrasting animals such as mice and humans. Inquire into what factors make such contrasts. Possibilities include time to reach reproductivity, number of eggs produced at a time, or fertility frequency.

| **Biological Terms** | **Thinking Skills** |
|---|---|
| ovary | describe nature accurately |
| ovule | state causal questions |
| seed protection | create alternative hypotheses |
| seed dispersal | |
| biotic potential | |
| plant life cycle | |

## Sample Test Questions

1. Suppose an apple tree produces apples with an average of six seeds per apple. Suppose that the tree produces an average of 500 apples per year. Assuming that each seed grows into a new tree, about how many new trees would this apple tree be able to produce in 3 years?
   a. 516
   b. 3,000
   c. 9,000
   d. 90,000
   e. 30,000,000

2. Which of the following would not be a reason why some of the seeds mentioned in item 1 would not develop into trees?
   a. Some may be destroyed by bacteria.
   b. Some are eaten by animals.
   c. Some are not fertilized.
   d. Some fall within the shade of the parent plant.
   e. Some fail to develop due to genetic defects.

3. In general, fruits develop from what part of the plant?
   a. flowers                     d. cones
   b. leaves                      e. petals
   c. stems

4. To test the hypothesis that flower petals produce a chemical necessary for fruit development, a botanist removed all the petals from the flowers on one plant. The petals were left intact on a similar plant. What prediction logically follows from the hypothesis and experimental design?
   a. Fruits will develop regardless of whether the petals have been removed.
   b. If petals produce a chemical, then the chemical is necessary for fruit development.
   c. What causes fruits to develop?
   d. Fruits should develop only from the flowers with petals.
   e. A fruit develops from the flower's ovary, not from its petals.

5. Suppose (in item 4 above) the botanist found that on the plant with petals removed, 6 of its 20 flowers developed into fruits, while on the plant with petals intact, 10 of its 30 flowers developed into fruits. What conclusion can reasonably be drawn?
   a. The hypothesis has been supported because four more flowers were produced on the plant with petals intact.
   b. Less than half of the flowers developed into fruits in both experimental conditions.
   c. The experiment should be repeated with better controls before a conclusion is reached.
   d. Petals produce a chemical necessary for fruit development.
   e. The petal hypothesis has not been supported because approximately the same percentage of fruits developed in both conditions.

## Answers

   1. C        2. C        3. A        4. D        5. E

# Energy Transfer •
# Seed Structure and Function

## Investigation 23    *Where Do Seeds Get Energy?*

### Synopsis

Students dissect seeds to discover the parts and then set up experiments to test hypotheses about the functions. The teacher introduces names for the observed seed parts, following the dissection, and introduces the idea of energy transfer, following the analysis of experimental results. This is a hypothetical-deductive learning cycle.

### Suggested Time

One class period to set up; 10 minutes per period for eight to ten periods for follow-up measurements; one class period to analyze results

### Background Information for the Teacher

The seeds to be examined in this learning cycle possess distinctly different structures. A single-bodied seed, such as corn, is called *monocotyledonous*, or a *monocot*. A double-bodied seed, such as a lima bean or peanut, is called *dicotyledonous*, or a *dicot*.

Seeds and stages in the germination of some common dicotyledons:

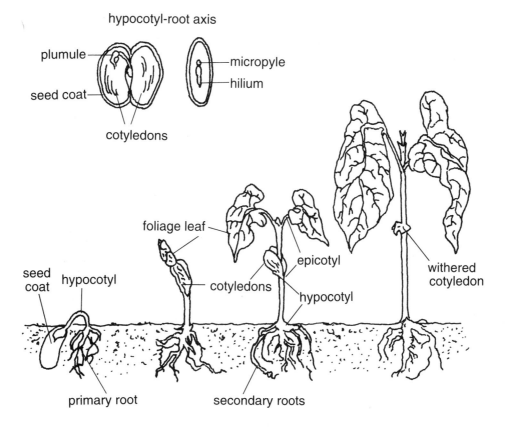

Garden bean (*Phaseolus vulgaris*); seed shown open and from external edge.

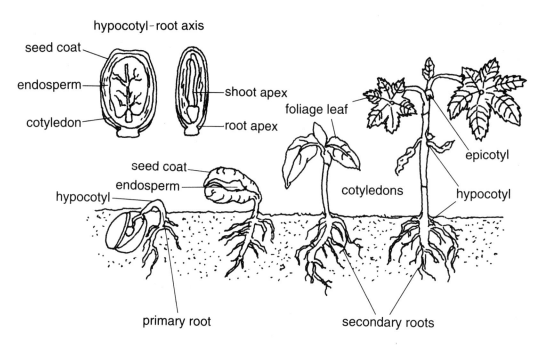

Castor bean (*Ricinus communis*); seed open, showing both flat and edge views of embryo.

The endosperm of the monocot seed is the food energy reserve, formed following the plant's fertilization. This is absorbed by the embryo during germination, through the cotyledon. As is true of many dicots, the endosperm of the bean is completely exhausted during the embryo development process. The cotyledons, produced by the embryo during seed formation, replace the endosperm as the energy source during germination. The principle

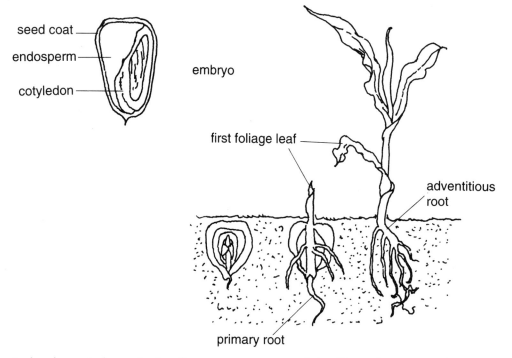

Seeds and stages in the germination of corn, a common monocotyledon (*Zea mays*).

food materials stored in seeds are carbohydrates, proteins, and lipids. These nutrients make the seed a food energy source for animals as well.

## Advance Preparation

Soak a variety of seeds in fresh water 24 hours before you start the exploration. It is extremely important that the seeds be kept as clean as possible to prevent mold and bacterial growth during the germination phase of this learning cycle. A small amount of chlorine bleach in the water will retard mold and bacterial growth but will not adversely affect the seeds. **CAUTION: Dissecting instruments and germination containers should be soaked in chlorine bleach solution, and students should wash their hands thoroughly before the dissection.**

Use at least six different types of common seeds (e.g., lima bean, corn, watermelon, pea, pinto bean). Most seeds can be purchased from a local grocery store less expensively than from seed companies or biological supply houses.

## Teaching Tips

### Exploration

1. The endosperm and cotyledons both will stain dark blue with the iodine solution in a positive reaction to the starch present. This makes observation of the various parts easy.

2. Provide about 30 minutes for the initial dissections.

### Initial Term Introduction

3. During a class discussion, have students report their observations. These should be drawn on the board. Obvious structures should be identified and named (e.g., *cotyledon, endosperm, embryo, seed coat*). You may wish to point out that some seeds have two cotyledons but others have only one and introduce the terms *monocot* and *dicot* as major types of seed plants.

4. Ask students to generate hypotheses concerning the functions of the seed parts—specifically, what is the energy source? Ideas should be listed on the board. Show students the sprouting containers (or petri dishes), and describe how they can be used. If petri dishes are used, direct students to moisten some paper toweling slightly and to fold it into the petri dish. The danger here is overwetting the towel. Challenge students in groups to design experiments to test their hypotheses. Let them discuss their ideas for 10 to 20 minutes, but if they have trouble getting started, resume the class discussion to compare ideas.

### Experimental Exploration

5. The experimental design should involve growing seed parts in all possible combinations (e.g., compare embryo grown alone to one attached to a single cotyledon to test the hypothesis that the embryo or cotyledon is the energy source: compare seeds grown with and without seed coat to test the hypothesis that the protective seed coat is necessary for growth). Remind students to measure the seed parts on Day 1 so that they will know which ones have grown on Day 2.

6. For best results, the sprouting containers must be cleaned with chlorine bleach before being used or else mold will grow. Also make sure the seed parts are moist but not immersed, as this also promotes mold growth. Lima beans work poorly because they are attacked easily by mold. Do not place containers in constant light.

### Second Term Introduction

7. Have one member of each group display the group's graph on the board. Review the original hypotheses and predictions, and discuss the data in order to draw conclusions. Some embryos (unattached) will show some growth. This contradicts the expected result but should be taken seriously. Students may offer alternative explanations, but the possibility of alternative energy sources should remain open.

8. Analysis of the class data should be in general agreement with the hypothesis that energy and food transfer from cotyledon to embryo takes place. As the embryo grows, food nutrients are transferred from the endosperm or cotyledons to the embryo for energy transfer (conversion from stored chemical energy to energy for growth). Reintroduce the term *energy transfer* at this time.

### Concept Application

9. Discuss the use of seeds as food for humans. This should develop into a discussion that ties the nutritional value of the endosperm and cotyledon(s) for the embryo to the nutritional value to humans.

---

| **Biological Terms** | **Thinking Skills** |
|---|---|
| seed structure/function | describe nature accurately |
| cotyledon | state causal questions |
| embryo | create alternative hypotheses |
| seed coat | generate logical predictions |
| germination | plan and conduct experiments |
| chemical energy transfer | organize and analyze data |
| food transfer | draw and apply conclusions |

---

## Sample Test Questions

*The next seven items refer to an experiment in which whole seeds and seed parts in various combinations were placed on moist paper in petri dishes in the dark. The following results were obtained.*

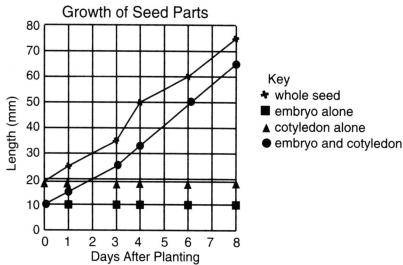

1. According to the graph, which seed parts grew best? (The whole seed grew the best; the embryo and cotyledon when connected to each other also grew well.)

2. Which seed parts showed little or no growth? (the embryo alone and cotyledon alone)

3. Do the data indicate what the food source for the developing plant was? If not, what additional information is necessary? Explain. (no; The data tells us that the food source was either the embryo *or* the cotyledon but the data do not indicate which, because we only have total length of both. We would need to know which of these got larger and which got smaller.)

4. The dependent variable in this experiment was:
   a. 0 to 8 days.
   b. length of the seed parts.
   c. days after planting.
   d. seed part.
   e. connections among seed parts.

5. The independent variable tested was:
   a. 0 to 8 days.
   b. length of the seed parts.
   c. days after planting.
   d. seed part.
   e. connections among seed parts.

6. What hypothesis cannot be tested with this design?
   a. The cotyledon is an energy source for the embryo.
   b. The amount of light affects growth of seed plants.
   c. The seed must be intact for growth.
   d. The embryo is an energy source for the cotyledon.
   e. The embryo can use water as an energy source.

7. What prediction logically follows from the design and from the hypothesis that the cotyledon is an energy source for the embryo?
   a. The embryo alone will grow, provided enough water is available.
   b. The seed coat must be present for growth.
   c. The cotyledon will increase in size if attached to the embryo.
   d. The embryo will not grow if detached from the cotyledon.
   e. The seed will germinate only when both cotyledons are present.

*The next six items refer to an experiment designed to test the idea that freezing kills seeds.*

Twenty corn seeds were planted on moist filter paper in each of two petri dishes. The dishes were covered with black paper to exclude light. Dish 1 was kept at 0°C, Dish 2 at 25°C. After 20 days, no seeds in Dish 1 had germinated; 18 seeds in Dish 2 had germinated after 5 days.

8. What is the independent variable in the experiment?
   a. light
   b. number of seeds germinating
   c. temperature
   d. number of days

*For the next items, use the above information plus the key to evaluate the following statements that were suggested as conclusions.*

**KEY**

A. The conclusion is tentatively acceptable.

B. The statement is contrary to the data.

C. The statement goes beyond the data.

D. The statement is probably correct but is unrelated to the idea being tested.

9. Corn seeds will not germinate in darkness.

10. Corn seeds do not germinate at freezing temperatures.

11. No growth occurs in mature corn plants at 0°C.

12. Moisture is necessary for the germination of corn seeds.

13. The corn seeds would have germinated more rapidly at 30°C than they did at 25°C.

## Answers

| | |
|---|---|
| 4. B | 9. B |
| 5. E | 10. A |
| 6. B | 11. D |
| 7. D | 12. D |
| 8. C | 13. C |

# Photosynthesis • Chlorophyll

## Investigation 24  *What Variables Affect Plant Growth?*

## Synopsis

Students design and conduct experiments to determine the effects of a variety of variables (including amount of light) on the growth of seeds. The term *photosynthesis* is introduced, following an analysis of results in which students discover that light but not soil, water, or air allows for sustained growth. This is a hypothetical-deductive learning cycle.

## Suggested Time

One class period for setup; 5 to 10 minutes every third day for 3 to 5 weeks to collect data; one class period at the end to analyze data and introduce terms

## Background Information for the Teacher

Many plants produce seeds as the primary mechanism for reproduction and dispersal. Seeds may be dispersed over relatively large distances by wind or water or animals. Some seeds are encased in burrs that adhere to the fur of animals and thus are transported long distances from the parent plant. Many plants produce their seeds within a fleshy fruit so that when the fruit is eaten by an animal, the seeds are transported within the animal and eventually are deposited during defecation.

The initial growth of seeds is influenced considerably by the environment into which they have been dispersed. Certainly the amount of water, the type and amount of soil, the amount of organic nutrients, and the presence of specific chemicals such as salt will affect growth. A light source, however, is not necessary at the outset because seeds carry a food source in their endosperm or cotyledons. Once this food source is depleted by the germinating seed, however, the plant will die unless a new source of food can be found. That new "source" is a process called *photosynthesis*, which occurs within the plant itself. Plants use the energy of light to produce their own food. In order for this food-producing process to occur, however, plants must have some raw materials, primarily water and air.

This lab allows students to investigate the influence of a variety of variables on seed growth; more important, it allows them to recognize the crucial role played by light as an energy source. Students' results should show that only plants grown in light become green and have sustained growth. Plants grown in the dark with ample soil, water, and air are yellow and eventually die, indicating that light is the crucial missing factor for the production of the green color and for sustained growth.

## Teaching Tips

### Exploration

1. Start by having students suggest possible energy sources for plant growth. They usually will suggest such items as nutrients, light, water, soil, air, heat, and the cotyledons. These should be listed on the board as alternative hypotheses to be tested.

2. After groups of students have had an opportunity to discuss experimental designs to test these hypotheses (procedure step 2), have students point out strengths and possible

weaknesses of the designs, but do not arrive at a single design that all must follow. Allow for some differences of opinion. Students should be encouraged to conduct at least three separate controlled experiments. Each experiment will investigate the effect of one of the variables suggested by the materials list.

3.  Each group of students does not need to test all variables. Group data will be compared at the end. All groups should be encouraged, however, to test the effect of the amount of light (plant same plants in the dark and others in direct light). A cupboard will serve nicely as a dark area, provided the doors close tightly. Other variables that may be tested are type of soil or amount of nutrients (gravel, sand, potting soil), amount of water (e.g., 50 mL, 100 mL, 150 mL per 48 hrs), amount of fresh air (plant in plastic bag, plant not in plastic bag), temperature (plant at room temperature, plant in refrigerator). You or your students may be able to think of other variables (e.g., amount of $O_2$ or $CO_2$, color of light) that could be tested. For the sake of simplicity, however, you may wish to restrict the experiment to only a few obvious variables.

4.  Students will need to record and graph data over 3 to 5 weeks; therefore, measurements need be taken only every few days. When students note that the plants placed in the dark are growing well but are not green, suggest that some of these plants be switched with plants growing in the light.

5.  Only after several plants have died (the ones in the dark) is it time to have students put their graphs on the board. Have students attempt to discover patterns displayed by the data. Review the hypotheses proposed and the predictions generated, and discuss any conclusions that can be drawn. Using a comparison of plants that continued to grow in light versus plants that eventually died in the dark, one can conclude that light is necessary for continued growth. It is the only factor that allowed for sustained growth after the food supply of the cotyledons was depleted. Thus, light can be suggested as an energy source, and the term *photosynthesis* can be introduced and defined as a process whereby plants take in light energy to combine substances such as air and water to produce food molecules that sustain the growth and development. The results also allow one to argue that soil, water, and air are not energy sources because although these were present in the dark conditions, the plants did not continue to grow. The green color of the plants grown in the light should be noted. The term *chlorophyll* can be introduced and defined as the pigment that produced the green color in the presence of light.

6.  Note that a number of questions remain. For example, *Why did the plants in the dark initially grow more rapidly than those in the light?* Students should be allowed to speculate about possible reasons. *Why does decreased temperature slow plant growth?* No attempt should be made to come to conclusions on all these issues.

| **Biological Terms** | **Thinking Skills** |
|---|---|
| photosynthesis | describe nature accurately |
| chlorophyll | state causal questions |
| | create alternative hypotheses |
| | generate logical predictions |
| | plan and conduct experiments |
| | organize and analyze data |
| | draw and apply conclusions |

## Sample Test Questions

1. A botany teacher raises bean plants in a greenhouse. Sometimes the beans grow very tall in 1 month, and sometimes they do not grow tall until 4 months. When you inspect the greenhouse, you notice two types of fertilizer (high-phosphate and low-phosphate). You also notice some bean plants planted very close together and others 30 cm apart. You notice that some beans receive direct sunlight, while others receive only artificial light.
   a. What variables might affect the growth of bean plants? (type of fertilizer: high, low phosphate; how far plants are apart: close, 30 cm; type of light: sunlight, artificial light)
   b. How could you experiment to find out the best way to raise large beans in only 1 month? (I would design an experiment in which large numbers of seeds [e.g., 25 seeds] were planted in all possible combinations of the six conditions above. This would give me a total of eight conditions, e.g., high phosphates, close together under sunlight; high phosphates, close together, under artificial light; etc. All other factors would be held constant; e.g., amount of water, temperature.)

*The next four items refer to your experiment comparing plant growth in the light with that in the dark. In that experiment, you were able to conclude that light—but not soil, water, or air—is a probable energy source.*

2. What evidence and reasoning did you use to draw that conclusion? (Plants in the light grew and continue to grow but those in the dark grew only for a period of time and died. Both sets of plants had soil, water, and air. Had either soil, water, or air been used as an energy source, then the plants in the dark should have been able to sustain growth. They did not; therefore we have evidence that soil, water, and air are not energy sources.)

3. In this experiment, which of the following is not a dependent variable?
   a. length of plants
   b. color of plants
   c. thickness of plants
   d. length of life
   e. amount of soil

4. Which of the following results would support the hypothesis that soil is an energy source for growing plants?
   a. Plants without soil die after their cotyledons are gone.
   b. Plants are able to grow with or without soil.
   c. Plants grow fastest without soil.
   d. Plants are greener if grown in rich soil.
   e. Plants die in the dark.

5. The plants grown in the dark (in soil, with water) died after the energy stored in their cotyledons was gone, while those grown in light (in soil, with water) continued to grow. What conclusion can reasonably be drawn?
   a. Soil is an energy source for initial growth.
   b. Water is an energy source for plant growth.
   c. Soil and water must not be energy sources.
   d. No conclusions can be drawn because no control group of plants was used.
   e. Soil and water are energy sources for plant growth.

*The next three items refer to an experiment conducted and reported by Jean-Baptist van Helmont (1577 – 1644).*

"That all vegetable [matter] immediately and materially arises from the element of water alone I learned from this experiment. I took an earthenware pot, placed in it 200 pounds of earth dried in an oven, soaked this with water, and planted in it a willow shoot weighing 5 pounds. After five years had passed, the tree grown therefrom weighed 169 pounds and about 3 ounces. But the earthenware pot was constantly wet only with rain or (when necessary) distilled water; and it was ample (in size) and embedded in the ground; to prevent dust flying around from mixing with the earth, the rim of the pot was kept covered with an iron plate coated with tin and pierced with many holes. I did not compute the weight of the deciduous leaves of the four autumns. Finally I again dried the earth of the pot, and it was found to be the same 200 pounds minus about 2 ounces. Therefore, 164 pounds of wood, bark, and root had arisen from the water alone."

6. What alternative hypotheses was van Helmont testing?
   a. Trees can grow with distilled water or rainwater.
   b. New plant matter (molecules) comes from the soil or from water.
   c. If a tree is placed into a pot of soil, it will grow larger and heavier in 5 years.
   d. The soil should weigh less or the same after 5 years.
   e. An iron plate over the pot will or will not kill the tree.

7. Why did van Helmont dry the soil at the start and at the end of his experiment?
   a. to find out how much the soil weighed
   b. to make sure that the soil weighed less at the end
   c. to kill the molds and bacteria in the soil
   d. to control the amount of water in the soil
   e. to see whether the tree used water for growth

8. Van Helmont thought that the plant matter came either from the soil or from water. Because he discovered that soil did not contribute to plant matter, he concluded that the plant matter must come from the water. What is wrong with this conclusion?
   a. Nothing. It is perfectly logical.
   b. He omitted consideration of the 2 ounces of soil missing at the end of the 5 years.
   c. He did not consider enough alternative hypotheses at the onset.
   d. He did not repeat his experiment enough times to be sure.
   e. His experiment lacked essential controls.

*Use this key to classify the suggested changes in van Helmont's experiment listed below.*

**KEY**

A.   This change is unimportant in the revision of this experiment.

B.   This change would improve the experiment because it would provide a test of an alternative hypothesis.

C.   This change would improve the experiment because it would permit broader conclusions to be drawn.

D.   This change would improve the experiment because it would permit expression of results in quantitative terms.

9.   Other plants besides willow should have been used.

10.  Only distilled water should have been used.

11.  The plant should have been grown in a greenhouse.

12.  The temperature should have been held constant.

13.  A second willow plant of similar size should have been grown in an atmosphere devoid of carbon dioxide.

*For the next four items, read the experiment and use the following key to evaluate each conclusion.*

**KEY**

A.   The conclusion is tentatively justified.

B.   The conclusion is unjustified because it does not answer the question.

C.   The conclusion is unjustified because the experiment lacks a control comparison.

D.   The conclusion is unjustified because the data are faulty or inadequate, though a control was included.

E.   The conclusion is unjustified because it is contradicted by the data.

   To determine some of the requirements for the sprouting of seeds, two groups of plants were planted in flowerpots. Conditions of both were the same except one group was put into a greenhouse at 4.4°C; the other group was put into a greenhouse at 21.1°C. Those in the cold room did not sprout; those in the warm room sprouted. Many kinds of seeds were used in each group.

14.  A temperature of 21.1°C is required for seeds to sprout.

15.  Moisture is one of the requirements for the sprouting of seeds.

16.  For anything to grow, energy is needed.

17.  Temperature affects the rate of sprouting.

## Answers

| | | |
|---|---|---|
| 3. E | 8. C | 13. B |
| 4. A | 9. C | 14. D |
| 5. C | 10. B | 15. C |
| 6. B | 11. A | 16. C |
| 7. D | 12. A | 17. A |

# Photosynthesis and Respiration Cycle •
# Light-Dependent and -Independent Reactions

## Investigation 25  *What in the Air Do Plants Need to Grow?*

## Synopsis

Students design and conduct experiments to test a theory of gas exchange between plants and animals. The theory is found partially correct and partially incorrect, allowing the introduction of the terms *light-dependent reactions* and *light-independent reactions* of photosynthesis. This is a hypothetical-deductive learning cycle.

## Suggested Time

One class period to set up experiments; one class period to discuss results and introduce terms

## Background Information for the Teacher

Most high-school students believe that green plants take in carbon dioxide and give off oxygen and that animals do the reverse. This belief, however, is seldom based on firsthand evidence or experimentation and in fact is an oversimplification.

Although plants do take in carbon dioxide and give off oxygen during photosynthesis, they use oxygen and give off carbon dioxide during their own respiration just as animals do. Plant respiration is easy to document experimentally in the dark when the masking effect of photosynthesis is not present.

This investigation uses the color change of a bromthymol blue (BTB) carbon dioxide indicator and a glowing splint oxygen indicator to test the students' theory about plant-animal gas exchange in the light and in the dark. Because the experimental results are clearly contradictory to part of their theory, students are placed in the position of having to modify their beliefs. A willingness to accept data when they contradict one's beliefs and to change those beliefs because of the data is basic to the scientific process. Many students will find this difficult to do, but the experiences gained in this investigation should help them become more sensitive to this issue.

Bromthymol blue (BTB) is a chemical indicator that changes color when it interacts with such acids as vinegar and citric acid. A BTB-and-tap-water solution is usually blue; if this solution is made increasingly acidic, the color will change through shades of green to yellow. In this investigation, BTB is used as an indicator for the presence of carbon dioxide—the only gas normally found in our atmosphere that will interact with BTB.

Human breath contains a small quantity of carbon dioxide. As breath is bubbled through water, some of this gas remains, making an acidic solution. The more carbon dioxide in the solution, the more acidic it becomes. The concentration of acid in a BTB solution determines the degree of color change. The amount of BTB present affects only the intensity of the color. Have your students demonstrate this to themselves by blowing through a straw into a blue BTB solution.

The success of the BTB test depends on the acidity of your tap water. Test your tap water by adding about 12 drops of BTB to about 125 mL of water. On stirring, the water will turn blue, green, or yellow. If the water becomes blue, blow into it through a straw. If the color then changes to green and to yellow within a minute or so, the water is satisfactory and needs no adjustment. Students can make their own BTB solutions for the experiments.

If the water does not change color after you have blown into it, it is too alkaline. In that case, fill a container to within 1 cm of the top with tap water. Add about 30 drops of BTB and stir. Slowly add drops of vinegar to the blue solution, stirring after each drop. When the color changes to green, stop adding vinegar.

Now slowly add ammonia solution, stirring after each drop. Stop when the solution turns blue. To test some of this blue solution, pour a little into a cup and blow through it with a straw. It should turn yellow in less than a minute. This blue solution can be used for the experiments.

If the tap water turns green or yellow after BTB is added to it, the water is too acidic. Fill a container to within 1 cm of the top with tap water. Add about 30 drops of BTB and stir. Slowly add ammonia solution, stirring after each drop. Stop when the solution turns blue.

To test some of this blue solution, pour a little into a cup and blow through it with a straw. It should turn yellow in less than a minute. This blue solution can be used for the experiment.

In conclusion, major general postulates of photosynthesis theory are listed below. Some but not all will be dealt with in this and subsequent learning cycles.

1. Photosynthesis consists of two sets of reactions—one set requires light, the light-dependent reactions; the other does not require light, the light-independent reactions.

2. The light-dependent reactions occur in the thylakoids of the chloroplasts when photons interact with electrons of chlorophyll molecules and cause them to move rapidly.

3. The light-dependent reactions break apart $H_2O$ molecules to produce $O_2$ molecules and $H^+$ ions and in the process convert ADP to ATP and NADP to NADPH.

4. The light-independent reactions occur in the chloroplasts outside the thylakoids.

5. The light-independent reactions (including the Calvin cycle) combine several $CO_2$ molecules and several $H^+$ ions to produce large molecules, such as glucose ($C_6H_{12}O_6$) and in the process reconvert ATP to ADP and NADPH to NADP.

6. Most of the $CO_2$ used in the light-independent reactions comes from the air, but some comes from cellular respiration inside the plant cell.

7. Most of the $O_2$ produced in the light-dependent reactions goes to the air, but some is used inside the plant cell in cellular respiration.

## Teaching Tips

### Exploration

1. Begin with a discussion of Priestley's results. Have students attempt to explain his results in terms of the gases produced by plants and animals. Expect students to propose that plants use $CO_2$ and expel $O_2$, while animals do the opposite. Diagram these relationships on the board as follows:

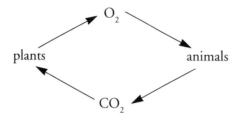

2. Explain to the students that the objective of this investigation is to test this theory. Elodea will serve as the experimental plant; pond snails will serve as the experimental animal. Have the students blow through a straw into a blue BTB solution and note the color change from blue to green to yellow. State that scientists have discovered that this color change is due to $CO_2$ in the breath; therefore, a similar color change in a blue vial containing a plant or animal would indicate that the organism was producing $CO_2$. Explain how students can use the glowing splint technique to test for $O_2$. To do this, a sample of the gas produced by the experimental organism will have to be collected in a test tube. This can be done by inverting a test tube containing the organism into a beaker of water. The gas produced by the organism will collect at the top of the test tube. To test for $O_2$, remove the test tube and immediately turn it upright and insert a glowing (not flaming) splint into the tube, avoiding the water. If $O_2$ is present, the splint will flame.

3. Tell students to design their experiments using the materials provided and the BTB and glowing splint indicators. They are to test their ideas in the presence and absence of light. Ask them to think how light might affect their results.

4. A typical experimental design should include the following:

| | Organism | Initial Color | Amount of Light | Predictions BTB Color | Flame |
|---|---|---|---|---|---|
| a. | elodea | yellow BTB | dark | blue | yes |
| b. | elodea | yellow BTB | light | blue | yes |
| c. | elodea | blue BTB | dark | blue | yes |
| d. | elodea | blue BTB | light | blue | yes |
| e. | snail | yellow BTB | dark | yellow | no |
| f. | snail | yellow BTB | light | yellow | no |
| g. | snail | blue BTB | dark | yellow | no |
| h. | snail | blue BTB | light | yellow | no |

5. Have students predict, when possible, the color the BTB will change to and whether a flame will be observed. For example, their theory proposed under procedure step 1 would lead to the predictions shown in the table above.

6. Students should work in teams of two or three to carry out their experiments. It will take a few days to obtain results. Note that in order to keep the snails in their inverted test tubes, the bottoms of the tubes will have to be taped. Holes should be punched in the tape.

7. Results of the groups' experiments should be tabulated and put on the board. Predicted results should be compared with actual results. Although variations are to be expected, a pattern should emerge that suggests the proposed theory is correct only in the presence of light. The results should indicate that in the dark the plants behave like animals, taking in $O_2$ and producing $CO_2$. A modified theory should be constructed as follows:

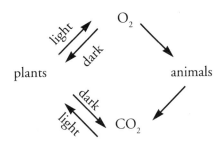

### Term Introduction

8. The terms *light-dependent reaction* and *light-independent reaction* in photosynthesis, as well as plant and animal respiration, should be introduced at this point.

### Concept Application

9. Subsequent investigations (26, 27, 28) deal with additional aspects of photosynthesis.

| **Biological Terms** | **Thinking Skills** |
| --- | --- |
| light-dependent and -independent reactions | describe nature accurately |
| plant respiration | state casual questions |
| animal respiration | create alternative hypotheses |
| $O_2$-$CO_2$ cycle | generate logical predictions |
| | plan and conduct experiments |
| | organize and analyze data |
| | draw and apply conclusions |

## Sample Test Questions

Fifty pieces of various plant parts were placed into each of five sealed jars of equal size under different conditions of color of light and temperature. At the start of the experiment, each jar contained 250 units of carbon dioxide. The amount of carbon dioxide in each jar at the end of the experiment is shown in the table.

| Jar | Plant Type | Plant Part | Color of Light | Temperature (°C) | $CO_2$* |
|-----|-----------|-----------|---------------|-----------------|--------|
| 1 | willow | leaf | blue | 10 | 200 |
| 2 | maple | leaf | purple | 23 | 50 |
| 3 | willow | root | red | 18 | 300 |
| 4 | maple | stem | red | 23 | 400 |
| 5 | willow | leaf | blue | 23 | 150 |

*This column indicates units of $CO_2$ in the jars at the end of the experiment.

1. Which jars would you select to make a fair comparison to find out whether temperature makes a difference in the amount of $CO_2$ used?
   a. 2 and 4
   b. 1, 3, and 5
   c. 1 and 3
   d. 1 and 5
   e. none of the above

2. What is the major independent variable in the experiment?
   a. plant type
   b. plant part
   c. color of light
   d. temperature
   e. $CO_2$ used

3. What is the major dependent variable in the experiment?
   a. plant type
   b. plant part
   c. color of light
   d. temperature
   e. $CO_2$ used

4. Which variables were not held constant in the experiment?
   a. size of jar
   b. $CO_2$ used
   c. $CO_2$ at the start
   d. temperature
   e. none of the above

5. An unknown organism was placed into a blue BTB solution that became yellow in the dark and changed back to blue in the light. Is this organism a plant or an animal? Explain. (It is reasonable, although not certain, to think that the organism is a plant because in the dark it released carbon dioxide, probably as a result of respiration. In the light, the carbon dioxide was consumed, presumably used in the process of photosynthesis. However, it is possible that this is an organism [such as a euglenoid] that has the characteristics of both plants and animals and is classified as a protist and not a plant. Also, it is possible that the organism has an unknown biochemical ability to increase the acidity of a solution in the dark and make it more alkaline in the presence of light.)

6. Photosynthesis has at least two major processes—a reaction controlled by light, and a reaction controlled by enzymes. Evidence for this would be:
   a. at maximum light intensity, an increase in temperature will increase photosynthesis.
   b. photosynthesis will not occur in the dark.
   c. photosynthesis must occur within a certain temperature range.
   d. photosynthesis will not occur in the absence of at least a certain amount of $CO_2$.

7. Is carbon dioxide used by plants?
    a. No, carbon dioxide is solely a waste product of respiration.
    b. Yes, it is used 24 hours a day during the process of photosynthesis.
    c. Yes, it is used all the time during the breakdown of food molecules.
    d. Yes, it is used only in the daytime during the process of photosynthesis.

8. Is oxygen used by plants?
    a. No, oxygen is only produced; it is not used by the plant.
    b. Yes, it used 24 hours a day during the process of photosynthesis.
    c. Yes, it is used all the time in the breakdown of food previously made by the plant.
    d. Yes, but it is used only at night, after the process of photosynthesis had ended.

9. Is oxygen used by fish?
    a. Yes, it is used 24 hours a day in the breakdown of food molecules.
    b. Yes, but it is used only at night, after the process of photosynthesis has ended.
    c. Yes, but it is used only in the daytime, when the sun is shining.
    d. No, the animal lives by carrying on fermentation.

10. The direct source of energy for fish is from
    a. sunlight absorbed through its body.
    b. breakdown of food molecules.
    c. stored fat among the body tissue.
    d. consumption of plants or smaller animals.

11. Is carbon dioxide produced by plants?
    a. Yes, but it is produced only at night, when the plants can no longer carry on photosynthesis.
    b. Yes, it is produced all the time as a result of the breakdown of food molecules.
    c. No, it is a waste product of animals only.
    d. No, plants take in only the waste products exhaled by animals.

Several kinds of aquatic plants, algae, bacteria, one-celled protists, snails, and fish were placed into an aquarium. The aquarium was sealed. Each week it was observed and carefully weighed.

12. The weight of the aquarium plus it contents probably would
    a. increase for a few week and then decrease.
    b. decrease for a few weeks and then increase.
    c. continually increase.
    d. continually decrease.
    e. not change.

13. If a small fish were placed into a beaker of water containing bromthymol blue, within 1 hour the water would become yellow. The change to yellow would occur because the water would show
    a. a decrease of $CO_2$.
    b. a decrease of $O_2$.
    c. an increase of $CO_2$.
    d. an increase of $O_2$.

14. If a fish were placed into a beaker of water containing bromthymol blue and some elodea, no change of color would occur in the water because the photosynthetic activity of elodea counteracts the

    a. decrease of $CO_2$.

    b. decrease of $O_2$.

    c. increase of $O_2$.

    d. increase of $CO_2$.

*For the next three items, read the experiment and use the following key to evaluate each conclusion.*

**KEY**

A. The conclusion in tentatively justified.

B. The conclusion is unjustified because it does not answer the question.

C. The conclusion is unjustified because the experiment lacks a control comparison.

D. The conclusion is unjustified because the data are faulty or inadequate, though a control was included.

E. The conclusion is unjustified because it is contradicted by the data.

An investigator wishing to determine whether oxygen is used during sleep analyzed the expired air of a large number of sleeping persons. It was found that the expired air contained oxygen.

15. The investigator concluded that oxygen is not used during sleep.

16. Another investigator concluded that oxygen is needed for life.

17. Yet another claimed that people breathe while they are sleeping.

## Answers

| | |
|---|---|
| 1. D | 10. B |
| 2. D | 11. B |
| 3. E | 12. E |
| 4. D | 13. C |
| 6. A | 14. D |
| 7. D | 15. C |
| 8. C | 16. C |
| 9. A | 17. A |

# Leaf Structure and Function

## Investigation 26    *How Do Different Parts of Leaves Function?*

## Synopsis

Students explore the external and internal structures of leaves and design a model of the typical leaf. They then generate alternative hypotheses about the functions of different leaf tissues and design and conduct experiments to test their hypotheses. This is a hypothetical-deductive learning cycle.

## Suggested Time

One class period to do Part 1; one class period to set up experiments for Parts II, III, and IV; some experiments will require observations over an extended period of time; one class period to discuss experimental results

## Background Information for the Teacher

Figure 1(a) shows major structural features of a leaf adapted to a temperate climate. Note the palisade mesophyll cells with numerous dark green spots. These spots represent chloroplasts—the organelles in which photosynthesis takes place. Chloroplasts are not found in bundle sheath cells. Figure 1(b) shows structural features of a leaf adapted to a hot, dry climate. The palisade mesophyll is arranged around the bundle sheath, and the sheath cells contain numerous chloroplasts.

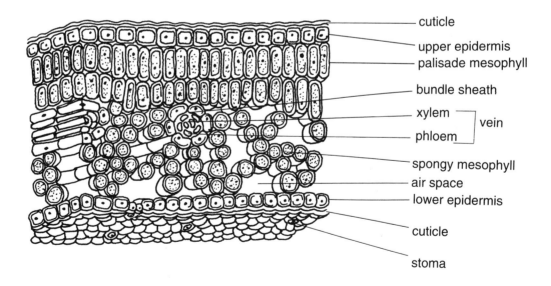

Figure 1(a). Drawing of a leaf from a plant that is adapted to temperate climate. In the leaf the palisade layer occurs typically in the upper part of the leaf. The bundle sheath cells lack chloroplasts.

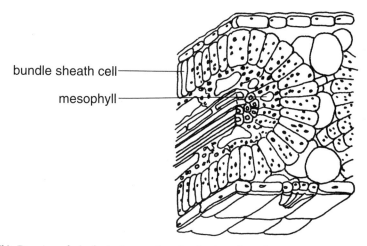

bundle sheath cell ——
mesophyll ——

Figure 1(b). Drawing of a leaf vein from a plant that is adapted to a hot, dry climate. In this type of leaf the palisade layer is arranged around the bundle sheath, and the bundle sheath cells have chloroplasts.

The cross sections in Figures 1(a) and 1(b) reveal an outer epidermis one cell thick. The exposed surface of both the upper and lower epidermis is covered by a waxy substance called the *cuticle*. The chief function of the epidermis and cuticle is to protect the internal cells from excessive water loss, from invasion by fungi, and from mechanical injury. Most epidermal cells do not contain chloroplasts.

The inner portion of the leaf normally consists of an upper layer of chloroplast-containing cells arranged in cylindrical columns, called *palisade mesophyll*, and a lower layer of more randomly shaped and arranged and loosely packed spongy mesophyll cells. The loose packing of the spongy mesophyll creates numerous air spaces, which allow the relatively free exchange of gases with the atmosphere by way of holes in the epidermis called *stomates*. Most stomates occur on the lower leaf surface to reduce water loss during gas exchange. The stomates are surrounded by guard cells, which can close the opening to further reduce water loss.

The bundle sheath contains two types of conducting cells—*xylem* and *phloem*. The xylem transport water, while phloem transport the nutrient products of photosynthesis. The ways in which xylem and phloem cells actually function to transport substances is not clear.

## Teaching Tips—Part I

### *Exploration*

1. Emphasize the importance of thin cross sections. Help the students with sectioning procedures if necessary. Do not allow students to see cross section drawings before they make their own observations, as this prohibits student inquiry and motivation.

2. *Kalanchoe blossfeldiana* should be used for one of the cross sections. *Kalanchoe* is a common blooming houseplant with succulent leaves. These leaves make an excellent cross section. If this plant is not available, try *Plectranthus* (creeping charlie) or *Ligustrum* (wax-leaf privet).

3. When collecting leaves for cross sections, choose thick, rather succulent leaves. Students will have more success finding the leaf layers on their own if they can work with these thicker leaves. If time is limited, you may wish to substitute commercially available prepared slides of leaf cross sections. These can be obtained from biological supply companies.

4. Stress the importance of the leaf as the photosynthetic organ in plants. Concise, carefully drawn leaves showing both external and internal anatomy is what the students should be producing on their data sheets.

### Term Introduction

5. Incorporate the class drawings to formulate a typical leaf on the board. Use this class model to begin the investigation of the different leaf tissues and to introduce names of the typical structures. Guide the class into pointing out the three most important regions of the leaf: outer covering of the leaf, middle of the leaf, and veins inside of the leaf. The terms *epidermis (upper and lower)*, *palisade mesophyll*, *spongy mesophyll*, *chloroplast*, *bundle sheath*, *vein (xylem and phloem)*, and *stomate* can be introduced to label identified structures.

6. Put the photosynthesis equation on the board, and remind students that the leaf is the primary site of photosynthesis.

7. Initiate a discussion of the function of the various parts identified. The discussion should include the following questions:
   Where might the $CO_2$ for photosynthesis come from?
   Where might the $H_2O$ come from?
   Where might the sugar be produced in the leaf?
   Where might the $O_2$ be released from the leaf?

8. Have students speculate about the function of each leaf layer, and list their ideas on the board.

### Concept Application

9. Divide the class into three sections. The groups in one section will design experiments to test hypotheses on "What Is the Function of the Outer Covering?" The groups of the second section will do "What Is the Function of the Inside Layers?" The third section groups will test hypotheses on "What Is the Function of the Leaf Veins?"

## Teaching Tips—Part II

1. Again, kalanchoe is a good leaf to use. The epidermis is relatively easy to remove, the stomates are quite visible, and the plant is easy to grow under light. If kalanchoe is not available, try other leaf succulents, such as jade plant, aloe, or ice plant.

2. The students design their own lab from the materials that you supply. Stress originality. If they have a better way of using other materials, let them try it if it seems the design will work.

3. Experimental design may vary, but most students should be removing the epidermis from one leaf, leaving the epidermis intact on another, and weighing moisture loss over a period of time. The experiment should be set up in a controlled fashion. Remember that students discuss the experiment with the teacher before doing it, so direct them into appropriate avenues of discovery.

4. Direct students to view under the microscope the leaf epidermis they remove. Have them make drawings of what they see. Use these drawings later on when discussing how $CO_2$ enters the leaf.

5. Students may cover the leaf epidermis with petroleum jelly; get them to think about how this might affect leaf photosynthesis.

## Teaching Tips—Part III

1.  Kalanchoe leaves work well in this experiment. Students can remove the epidermis carefully, without destroying the fleshy interior of the plant.

2.  In this experiment, the students should understand that:
    a.  they are testing only the middle part of the leaf;
    b.  they are testing to see whether this section is responsible for sugar formation in photosynthesis;
    c.  they will be working with light if photosynthesis is to take place;
    d.  they must make sure that the leaf does not dry out, because water is needed to make food in photosynthesis;
    e.  a carbon dioxide source must be present, presumably the air;
    f.  they will use a starch test to examine food production. When they get to this point, give them instructions for the starch test.

3.  Their experiments should involve some plant tissue in the dark and some plant tissue in the light.

4.  The students will need to keep the tissue in the dark for several days if a negative starch test is to result.

## Teaching Tips—Part IV

1.  Experimental designs may vary: Some students will want to cut veins in the leaf of a houseplant, and some students may want to measure the flow of colored water through leaves.

2.  Stress the idea of a controlled experiment with the students when they bring their designs to you.

3.  Potted houseplants can work well in this lab, particularly ones with obvious veins or thin leaves. Syngonium (arrowhead philodendron) is readily available, has visible veins, and dyes easily.

4.  Fresh celery stalks are a tried and tested plant for showing colored water transport in leaves. Impatiens also works well.

## Teaching Tips—Putting It All Together

1.  Gather experimental results and conclusions from the entire class.

2.  Put these results on the board or on transparencies. Review the results.

3.  Apply these conclusions to the typical leaf model. Ask, "Have we shown how each layer or tissue functions in the process of photosynthesis? Why or why not?"

| **Biological Terms** | **Thinking Skills** |
|---|---|
| chloroplast | describe nature accurately |
| epidermis | state causal questions |
| stomates | create alternative hypotheses |
| palisade mesophyll | generate logical predictions |
| spongy mesophyll | plan and conduct experiments |
| bundle sheath | organize and analyze data |
| vein (xylem and phloem) | draw and apply conclusions |

## Sample Test Questions

1. A plant that has leaves with a waxy cuticle covering would have some survival advantages in the
   - **a.** temperate forests.
   - **b.** deserts.
   - **c.** tropical rain forests.
   - **d.** pond communities.

2. Many species of flowering plants are able to grow in hot climates and in very dry soil. Which requirement must be fulfilled by such plants?
   - **a.** very deep root system to reach ground water
   - **b.** very large diameter in the tubes of the plant's water-transport system
   - **c.** increase in the number of roots of the plant to absorb water quickly
   - **d.** reduced leaf area to decrease water loss

3. The leaf layer with the most chloroplasts is found directly beneath the upper epidermis of the leaf. Explain why this is important for maximum photosynthesis in the plant. (The presence of many chloroplasts directly beneath the upper epidermis of a leaf suggests that the chloroplasts can receive the maximum amount of sunlight there.)

A student placed some leaves of a corn plant that had been exposed to light for 2 hours into a test tube and added a little water. To this tube, she added Benedict's solution, which turns red when in contact with a hot glucose solution. On heating the contents of the test tube to the boiling point, she found that the solution became red. She concluded that the leaves had produced glucose by the process of photosynthesis. To reach this conclusion, she made the assumptions below. Use the following key to classify her assumptions.

### KEY

A. a justifiable and necessary assumption

B. a justifiable but unnecessary assumption

C. an unjustified or irrelevant assumption

D. not an assumption; a restatement of results

4. Glucose is formed most abundantly in leaves.

5. Some other types of leaves will give the same results as those described.

6. Only green leaves will give the test for glucose.

7. The glucose will turn to alcohol by fermentation.

8. Benedict's solution will not turn red when boiled with pure water.

9. A glucose solution will not turn red spontaneously.

10. The color from the leaves did not affect the test for glucose.

11. The solution turned red after boiling.

*The next four items are based on the following information.*

Yucca is a plant of dry desert areas. Its leaves are long, narrow, and triangular in cross section. The water lily leaf floats on the surface of ponds, and its stem is completely submerged. When a yucca leaf and a water lily leaf are examined in cross section under a microscope, some differences that may be seen are:

| Water Lily | Yucca Leaf |
|---|---|
| • no fibrous supporting tissue | • much fibrous supporting tissue |
| • stomates only on the upper surface | • stomates on all sides |
| • many large air spaces | • no large air spaces |
| • few, small vascular bundles (phloem and xylem) | • many vascular bundles |
| • one layer of closely packed mesophyll beneath epidermis | • two or three layers of closely packed mesophyll beneath epidermis |
| • moderate cuticle | • heavy cuticle |
| • stomates at the surface of the leaf | • stomates sunken in pits in the epidermis |

12. The sunken stomates of the yucca aid its survival in the desert because the
    a. guard cells are shielded from the light.
    b. stomates are shielded from air currents.
    c. leaf is in a state of perpetual wilting.
    d. guard cells are protected from sand storms.

13. The supporting tissue in the water lily can be less than in the yucca because
    a. the lily is bigger than the yucca.
    b. yucca grows close to the ground.
    c. support of the lily is by vascular bundles.
    d. the water supports the lily.

14. The heavy cuticle of the yucca serves to
    a. protect it from insects.
    b. reduce water loss.
    c. increase photosynthetic rate.
    d. increase transpiration.

15. During periods of drought,
    a. the individual cells of the yucca might wilt, but the leaf as a whole remains intact.
    b. as the cells of the yucca wilt, the leaf would collapse.
    c. the water lily leaf would remain firm because of the large amount of stored water.
    d. the mesophyll of the yucca would prevent the penetration of the drying sunlight.

## Answers

| | | | |
|---|---|---|---|
| 1. | B | 9. | A |
| 2. | D | 10. | A |
| 4. | C | 11. | D |
| 5. | B | 12. | B |
| 6. | B | 13. | D |
| 7. | C | 14. | B |
| 8. | A | 15. | A |

# Plant Pigmentation • Chlorophyll• Light Waves • Photons

## Investigation 27     *What Colors of Light Are Used During Photosynthesis?*

## Synopsis

Students investigate the spectral nature of light and the absorption spectrum produced by a plant pigment and experiment to discover the effects of different colors of light on the photosynthetic rate of *Elodea*. They then use paper chromatography to discover whether more than one type of pigment molecule exists in spinach leaves. This is an empirical-abductive learning cycle.

## Suggested Time

Two class periods

## Background Information for the Teacher

Approximately 3 billion years ago, a unique process known as photosynthesis developed on Earth. This biochemical phenomenon markedly altered the nature of our planet. Photosynthesis produces carbohydrates and oxygen, both of which are essential for respiratory metabolism of plants and animals alike.

Depending on the quality of the spectroscopes or diffraction grating used, white light can be separated into the visible color wavelengths shown in the figure below.

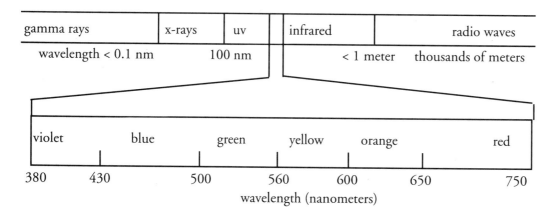

When spinach pigment extract is placed as a filter in front of the spectroscope or diffraction grating, the violet and red ends of the visible spectrum are dimmed the most. This is shown by the following graph of the absorption spectrum of chlorophyll a, the primary pigment present in the spinach pigment extract.

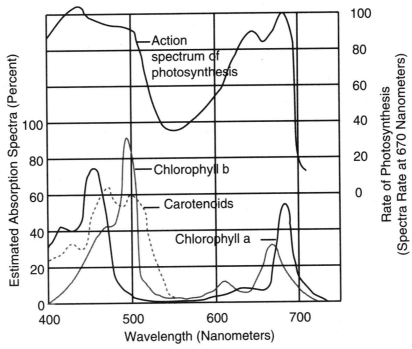

The different pigments shown in the graph are separated from the extract by paper chromatography. These pigments broaden the absorption spectrum of the pigment extract.

Use of primarily violet and red light for photosynthesis is demonstrated by isolating these color wavelengths and comparing the increased photosynthetic activity in *Elodea* with the lower rate observed with green and yellow light. This difference is apparent by the greater oxygen production when the elodea is subjected to violet or red light.

A water buffer (see step 5 below) may be needed to obtain good results because the water will limit the warming of the elodea by the lights (see graphs below), which in turn would reduce the level of photosynthesis.

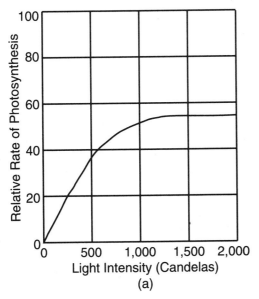

(a)

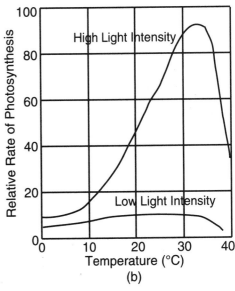

(b)

The primary objective of this investigation is to allow students to design and conduct experiments to discover the most effective colors of light for photosynthesis. Allowing students considerable freedom in the design of their experiments is an excellent way to produce varying results, which in turn will allow you to emphasize the need to control variables. Over 30 independent variables have been identified and listed by students who have done this investigation, including the following, which should be controlled: ability of investigator to count bubbles, distance light is from plant, temperature of water, direction of light, nutrient content of the water, amount of $CO_2$ in the water, length of plant, amount of water in the test tube, part of plant used, age of plant, and orientation of plant.

## Advance Preparation

Prepare plant pigment extract by boiling spinach leaves (available from a grocery store) in alcohol for several minutes. **CAUTION: Put the beaker containing alcohol and the spinach into a larger beaker or pan of water on a hot plate (to make a double-boiler); do not use an open flame.** Dilute the extract if it is too dark. Test by observing the absorption spectrum seen through a spectroscope.

Prepare a 0.25% $Na_2CO_3$ (dissolve 2.5 g sodium carbonate in 1 liter water) solution (source of $CO_2$) to keep the elodea in prior to lab day. Students may want to place their elodea samples into the solution during their experiments as well. Hornwort also works well if elodea is in limited supply. Elodea and hornwort may be purchased from local aquarium supply stores or ordered from Carolina Biological Supply Company, (800) 334-5551, or Ward's Natural Science Establishment, 5100 West Henrietta Rd., P. O. Box 92912, Rochester, NY 14623, (800) 962-2660.

Spectroscopes are available from Carolina Biological Supply Company, Powell Laboratories Division, Gladstone, OR 97027, (800) 547-1733.

Colored cellulose acetate is available from art supply stores; however, we have found it not to work well. Colored plastic filters that do work well are available from Cadillac Plastic and Chemical Company, 2625A East University Drive, Phoenix, AZ 85034, (602) 275-6295. We have used blue (#2045), green (#2092), red (#2100), and amber (#2422) filters.

Solvent solution (92% petroleum ether, 8% acetone) is available from Carolina Biological Supply. Paper chromatography kits including pigments, solvents, paper, and test tubes are available from Lab-Aids, Inc., 249 Trade Zone Drive, Ronkonkoma, NY 11779, (516) 737-1133.

## Teaching Tips

### Exploration

1.  Flat-sided bottles work best for observing the absorption spectrum (procedure step 1). This is seen easily as students look at a light source and pass the extract back and forth in front of the spectroscope.

2.  As students are completing the observations of the absorption spectrum, stop the class and orally survey the results. Ask the class to speculate about the possible importance of the observed effects of the pigment on the light spectrum and on photosynthesis.

3.  Have sufficient work stations set up to allow students to work in groups of two or three. Explain any of the quirks your particular equipment may have.

4. Have a large supply of healthy, growing elodea or hornwort on hand for procedure steps 6–9. If students do not see bubbles generated from the cut stem within 5 minutes, tell them to cut a new section.

5. Turn the classroom lights off while photosynthesis experiments are being performed. Books may need to be placed around the test tubes to keep out unwanted light from nearby setups. A water buffer may be needed to reduce the warming effect of the light as shown below.

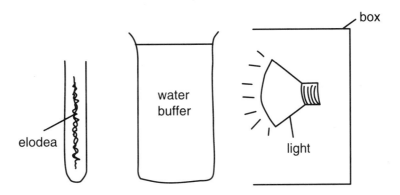

### Term Introduction

6. At the conclusion of Part I, have students report their results graphically on the board. Ask them to compare the various graphs and to look for similarities and differences and general patterns. Results of the experiments (red and violet produce the most bubbles and therefore presumably are the primary colors of light used to drive photosynthesis) should be related to results of the absorption observations (red and violet are most absorbed; green is reflected). Students should realize that the pigment appears green because green wavelengths are not absorbed, and if they are not absorbed, they cannot drive photosynthesis. Introduce the term *chlorophyll* to refer to the green pigment if you have not already done so.

7. You may wish to introduce the wave theory and particulate theories of the nature of light and the terms *wavelength* and *photon*. You may also wish to discuss theories of just how photons strike pigment molecules to transfer energy and presumably initiate the photosynthetic process.

### Paper Chromatography—Part II

8. As students are grinding their spinach, walk around the class with extra acetone to add to their mixtures, if necessary, due to excessive evaporation. Use a blender if available. Caution students not to inhale acetone, as the fumes are toxic. Keep the room well-ventilated or have students work under a hood where possible. When students have completed the activity, allow vessels containing acetone to air out thoroughly before washing. Place any paper towels that have contained acetone in a fireproof receptacle.

9. The smaller and finer the point of pigment on the chromatography paper, the better the quality of the chromatogram.

10. Any filter paper can be cut into strips 10 to 15 cm in length and used for chromatography paper.

11. Make sure test tubes or bottles are large enough for the paper strips.

12. Results of the paper chromatography experiment show the composite nature of the pigment extract. The idea that each pigment has its own absorption spectrum can be postulated at this point. State, however, that isolation and independent testing of these pigments would be needed for negation or support of this hypothesis. In Investigation 28, students actually isolate the pigment chlorophyll and test to see whether plants with chlorophyll are able to conduct photosynthesis while plants without it cannot.

### Concept Application

13. Investigation 28, *Is Chlorophyll Necessary for Photosynthesis?*, is a concept application activity for the concepts of plant pigmentation and photosynthesis.

---

**Biological Terms**

selective absorption
plant pigment
light wave
photon

**Thinking Skills**

describe nature accurately
state casual questions
create alternative hypotheses
generate logical predictions
plan and organize experiments
organize and analyze data
draw and apply conclusions

---

## Sample Test Questions

*The next 14 items refer to the following investigation.*

One hundred samples of several different plant parts were placed into each of five sealed containers of equal volume. The amount of $CO_2$ present in the containers at the beginning was 250 cm³ and at the end of 2 days was as shown in the table.

| Container | Plant Type | Plant Part | Color of Light | Temperature (°C) | $CO_2$ (cc) |
|---|---|---|---|---|---|
| 1 | myrtle | leaf | red | 15 | 100 |
| 2 | myrtle | leaf | red | 27 | 50 |
| 3 | myrtle | stem | blue | 21 | 200 |
| 4 | oak | root | blue | 27 | 300 |
| 5 | oak | leaf | orange | 27 | 150 |

Assume that the experimental conditions not listed are identical in all five containers.

1. On the basis of data in the table, one properly could compare the amount of $CO_2$ used per day at two different temperatures by comparing Containers
   a. 1 and 2.
   b. 1 and 3.
   c. 4 and 5.
   d. 2 and 3.

2. Compare Containers 1 and 2. What is the variable factor in the design of the experiment?
   a. kind of plant
   b. color of light
   c. temperature
   d. $CO_2$ present after two days

3. In which container was photosynthesis taking place at the fastest rate?
   a. 1
   b. 2
   c. 3
   d. 4
   e. 5

4. In which container was photosynthesis taking place at the slowest rate?
   a. 1
   b. 2
   c. 3
   d. 4
   e. 5

5. In which container was photosynthesis not occurring?
   a. 1
   b. 2
   c. 3
   d. 4
   e. 5

6. On the basis of data in the table, one could properly compare the amount of $CO_2$ used in 1 day by examining the data for
   a. myrtle leaves at 15°C and 27°C.
   b. myrtle stems and myrtle leaves.
   c. oak leaves and oak roots.
   d. oak leaves at 15°C and 27°C.
   e. oak leaves in orange light and in blue light.

7. The experimental data indicate that the oak leaves took up
   a. less $CO_2$ per day than did oak roots.
   b. more $CO_2$ at 27°C than at 15°C.
   c. the same amount of $CO_2$ per day as oak roots.
   d. more $CO_2$ per day than did oak roots.

*Use the following key to identify changes in the experimental design above that are described in the next five statements.*

**KEY**

The change described would

A. permit additional valid interpretations to be made.

B. permit fewer valid interpretations to be made.

C. neither improve nor worsen the experimental design.

D. improve the design somewhat but still not permit valid interpretations to be made.

8. Replace the oak root in Container 4 with a myrtle root.

9. Replace the orange light in Container 5 with a red light.

10. Change the temperature in Container 1 to 21°C.

11. Change the red light in Container 1 to orange light.

12. Change the temperature in Container 1 to 27°C.

13. Which of the following changes in the experimental setup would have to be made before one could properly compare the amount of $CO_2$ taken up in 1 day by an oak leaf and a myrtle leaf?
    a. lighten color in Container A to orange
    b. change temperature in Container A to 27°C
    c. lighten color in Container E to red
    d. lengthen the experiment to 3 days in all containers

*The next five items refer to the following graph and information.*

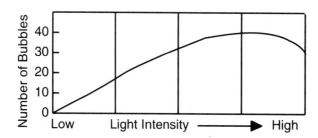

An immersed water plant was exposed to light of gradually increasing intensity over a period of several hours. At regular intervals, 1-minute counts were made of the number of bubbles released.

14. The number of bubbles released from the plant seems to be
    a. directly proportional to the light intensity throughout the investigation.
    b. the cause of the light becoming more intense as the investigation progressed.
    c. decreased halfway through the investigation.
    d. correlated with light intensity during most of the investigation.

15. The release of bubbles is most useful as the probable indication of the rate of
    a. fermentation.
    b. photosynthesis.
    c. growth.
    d. metabolism.

*For the next three items, use the following key.*

**KEY**

A. reasonable interpretation of the data

B. restatement of the data

16. The light could be increased to an intensity that would prevent photosynthesis.

17. A maximum of 35 bubbles per minute was recorded.

18. Light intensities for photosynthesis have an optimum range.

This diagram shows the relation between the rate of photosynthesis, amount of light, and $CO_2$ concentration.

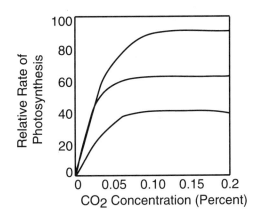

19. For maximum growth, these data indicate that plants should be grown in a $CO_2$ concentration of
    a. less than 0.5% and high light intensity.
    b. 0.10% or higher and medium light intensity.
    c. 0.2% and low light intensity.
    d. 0.10% and high light intensity.

20. Concentration of $CO_2$ in the atmosphere is normally 0.04%. If the data in the graph are correct, then plants in full sunlight are photosynthesizing
    a. at less than maximum rate.
    b. faster than they should.
    c. at maximum rate.
    d. faster than the plant in low light in the experiment.

21. If you wanted to prevent photosynthesis in a plant in full sunlight, it would be best to put the plant into a container with a $CO_2$ concentration of
    a. 0.0%.                          c. 0.10%.
    b. 0.05%.                         d. 0.2%.

*For the next two items, read the experiment and use the following key to evaluate each conclusion separately.*

### KEY

1. The conclusion is tentatively justified.

2. The conclusion is unjustified because it does not answer the question.

3. The conclusion is unjustified because the experiment lacks a control comparison.

4. The conclusion is unjustified because the data are faulty or inadequate, though a control was included.

5. The conclusion is unjustified because it is contradicted by the data.

An investigator wanted to determine whether light increased the rate of a certain reaction. On repeated tests, it was found that a certain amount of the original substance (X), after 1 hour, would produce 1 g of substance Y with 10 units of light, 2 g with 20 units, 4 g with 30 units, and 3 g with 40 units.

22.   Increased amount of light increases the rate of the reaction.

23.   Heat increased the rate of the reaction.

## Answers

| | | | |
|---|---|---|---|
| 1. A | | 13. C | |
| 2. C | | 14. D | |
| 3. B | | 15. B | |
| 4. C | | 16. A | |
| 5. D | | 17. B | |
| 6. A | | 18. A | |
| 7. D | | 19. D | |
| 8. D | | 20. A | |
| 9. A | | 21. A | |
| 10. C | | 22. 5 | |
| 11. B | | 23. 3 | |
| 12. B | | | |

# Role of Chlorophyll and Chloroplasts

## Investigation 28    *Is Chlorophyll Necessary for Photosynthesis?*

## Synopsis

Students test the hypothesis that chlorophyll is necessary for photosynthesis by growing normal and albino corn seedlings and then comparing their ability to produce starch. They also microscopically examine the intracellular structures of the normal and albino plants and elodea to discover the location of the chlorophyll molecules. This is a hypothetical-deductive learning cycle.

## Suggested Time

30 minutes to set up the growth activity; 10 minutes every third day for 3 weeks to gather growth results; 30 minutes to do Part II; one class period to do Part III; one class period to discuss final results

## Background Information for the Teacher

In certain types of corn, a recessive lethal gene for albinism may reveal itself in a homozygous recessive individual of the $F_2$ generation. Albinism is produced as the gene somehow inhibits the plants' ability to manufacture chlorophyll, the pigment molecule responsible for the green color of normal plants. Albino individuals will show some growth due to energy stored in the cotyledon. When this energy supply is depleted, however, the albinos will not be able to survive because they lack the chlorophyll necessary to capture the light energy needed to drive photosynthesis.

In this investigation, students test the hypothesis that chlorophyll is necessary for photosynthesis by comparing the ability of albino and normal corn plants to produce starch, a complex combination of sugar molecules that is produced during photosynthesis and that serves as a major food/energy source for plant respiration and growth. Support for the chlorophyll hypothesis is obtained as albino corn, which both macroscopically and microscopically appears to lack chlorophyll, tests negatively for starch in the iodine test, while normal green corn tests positively.

## Advance Preparation

Order the albino corn seeds ahead of time from a biological supply company. These seeds are an $F_2$ generation and germinate at a ratio of 3 normal green seedlings to 1 albino. Students can be asked to bring in egg cartons.

## Teaching Tips

### Exploration

1. Propose the hypothesis about the role of chlorophyll in a class discussion, along with any other student ideas. List all of the alternative hypotheses on the board.

2. Make sure that the growing plants get plenty of light from room windows, greenhouse, or artificial grow lights.

3. Remind the students that their plants need to stay moist, not wet. You may have to do some weekend watering.

4. Direct the students in designing their own appropriate data tables, taking measurements, making observations, and setting up graphs. It is important that they face the challenge individually, with as little help from the teacher as possible.

### *Term Introduction*

5. On about the tenth day, all seeds should have germinated and plants should all still be relatively healthy. Now is the time to do Part II. Students will have to sacrifice one seedling of each color for this activity unless you have them grow separate plants to run tests on. Use the students' observations to introduce terms to refer to structures found inside leaf cells (e.g., chloroplasts). Lead a discussion of their observations, and ask, "Do these observations help us test the hypotheses about the role of chlorophyll? If so, how? What additional evidence would be helpful?"

6. Do Part III on the day following Part II. Students will have to sacrifice two more corn seedlings. Plenty should still remain for use in the growth studies and in the Study Questions.

7. Note that the 3:1 ratio of normal to albino seedlings suggests that the trait is genetically determined. You may wish to introduce the idea of a lethal gene at this time because the inability of a plant to conduct photosynthesis is indeed lethal. Question students about how such lethal genes get passed from parent to offspring (as recessive traits).

8. Chapter 18 of the textbook should be assigned reading.

| **Biological Terms** | **Thinking Skills** |
|---|---|
| chlorophyll | describe nature accurately |
| chloroplast | state causal questions |
| | create alternative hypotheses |
| | generate logical predictions |
| | plan and conduct experiments |
| | organize and analyze data |
| | draw and apply conclusions |

## Sample Test Questions

Five geranium plants were treated as follows.

Placed in light:

| | |
|---|---|
| Plant I | Half of each leaf covered with foil to exclude light |
| Plant II | Upper and lower surface of leaves covered with petroleum jelly |
| Plant III | Placed in jar containing no carbon dioxide |

Placed in dark:

| | |
|---|---|
| Plant IV | Leaves removed and placed with petioles immersed in glucose solution |
| Plant V | No treatment |

After 2 days, leaves from each plant were removed and tested for starch content.

Results:

Plant I          Half exposed to light had starch

Plant II         No starch

Plant III        No starch

Plant IV        Starch, especially along veins of leaves

Plant V         No starch

*Use the following key to classify the statements below.*

**KEY**

Interpretation of the data is

A.  rejected on the basis of data presented.

B.  supported by data.

C.  reasonable, but the experiment is not designed to test it.

1.  The presence of starch indicates photosynthesis only if the leaf is deprived of an outside source of glucose.

2.  As starch may diffuse from its site of origin throughout a leaf, its presence is no indication of where it was formed.

3.  Light is necessary for starch formation in plants.

4.  Glucose is necessary for starch formation in plants.

5.  This experiment lacks a control.

6.  Plant II had no $CO_2$ intake because the stomates were covered.

7.  The roots of a plant may store starch.

8.  Which of the following is a predicted outcome of an experiment that can be used to test the hypothesis that chlorophyll molecules are necessary for photosynthesis?
    a.  Plants in the dark should not be able to conduct photosynthesis.
    b.  Albino plants should not produce starch once the energy in their cotyledons is depleted.
    c.  Lack of $CO_2$ will limit the rate of photosynthesis.
    d.  Albino plants should not be able to germinate.
    e.  Only plants with chlorophyll will be able to conduct photosynthesis.

9.  The independent variable tested in the experiment conducted with albino and normal corn plants to determine whether chlorophyll molecules are necessary for photosynthesis was the
    a.  amount of light shining on growing plants.
    b.  color of leaf after iodine solution is added.
    c.  type of corn plant.
    d.  ratio of albino to green corn plants.
    e.  amount of leaf material.

10.  Of the variables listed in item 9, which is the dependent variable to determine whether chlorophyll is needed for starch production?

11. Of the variables listed in item 9, which two variables should be held constant?

## Answers

| | | | |
|---|---|---|---|
| 1. | B | 7. | C |
| 2. | C | 8. | B |
| 3. | A | 9. | C |
| 4. | B | 10. | B |
| 5. | A | 11. | A, E |
| 6. | B | | |

# Water Transport and Transpiration

## Investigation 29    *What Causes Water to Rise in Plants?*

## Synopsis

Students design and conduct experiments to test alternative hypotheses about causes of water rise in plants by removing plant parts, by coating surfaces with petroleum jelly, and so on. This is a hypothetical-deductive learning cycle.

## Suggested Time

Two to three class periods

## Background Information for the Teacher

The stems of vascular plants contain xylem vessels, which conduct water that rises up from the roots to the leaves, where it is used for photosynthesis and other vital cell processes. But what causes water to rise against the physical force of gravity? Apparently, a number of factors are involved.

One force results from the osmotic movement of water into roots from the soil. This osmotic force, called *root pressure*, is generated at the bottom of the xylem and tends to push water upward. Evidence of this root pressure comes from cut stems that will "bleed" fluid for some time after they are cut.

Root pressure is also presumably responsible for the occasional appearance of drops of water on the tips of leaves at the leaf-vein endings when water loss due to evaporation (called *transpiration*) is low and the soil contains a lot of water. This "bleeding" is called *guttation.*

Root pressure alone, however, is not strong enough to account for the movement of water up a tall tree. Rather, another force or set of forces must be involved. One of these forces appears to be the cohesion of water molecules. The polarity of water molecules provides a strong attraction among water molecules; thus, a column of water molecules will stick together so that any "pull" on the top molecules will result in the rise of the entire column.

But what sort of a pull can exist at the top of the column? A number of popular textbooks suggest that the transpiration of water from the leaves will cause a partial vacuum that can "suck" the water up like sucking a milkshake through a straw. Clearly, however, this cannot be the case because "suction" as a force is nonexistent. The force that moves the milkshake up the straw is a push from below due to greater air pressure on the surface of the milkshake outside the straw than on the surface inside the straw. A number of your students will most likely hold this "suction" misconception.

What, then, provides the force? The best guess at this point appears to involve osmosis and goes as follows: Transpiration of water in leaf cells increases their concentration of solutes and therefore their osmotic pressure, resulting in movement of water into the cells from nearby xylem tubes. Because the column of water sticks together (due to cohesive forces of water molecules), the osmotic pressure at the top will cause the entire column to rise. This theory commonly is referred to as the *cohesion theory.*

Although the cohesion theory has gained acceptance among plant physiologists, it leaves a few problems unresolved. The theory requires the maintenance of the column of water in the xylem, yet breaks frequently occur. How the theory can accommodate this contradictory finding is not clear. Another puzzle is how the column of water is established in the first place. Perhaps it "grows" there as the plant grows.

The fact that no single theory solves all the problems should be viewed as a positive aspect of this lab. In a very real sense, this lab allows students to move quickly to the cutting edge of this area of research.

Expect a variety of hypotheses from your students at the outset. For example, the following alternative hypotheses were generated by students in a previous class: a) water evaporates from the leaves to create a vacuum that sucks water up, b) roots squeeze to push water up through one-way valves in the stem tubes, c) capillarity pulls water up like a paper towel soaking up water, and d) osmosis pulls water up.

Of course, equipment limitations will keep some ideas from being tested, but the "leaf evaporation" hypothesis can be tested by comparing water rise in plants with and without leaves (requiring the reasoning patterns involved in the isolation and control of variables). The "root squeeze" hypothesis can be tested by comparing water rise in plants with and without roots. The "one-way valve" hypothesis can be tested by comparing water rise in right-side-up and upside-down stems. Results allow rejection of some of the hypotheses but not others. The survivors are considered "correct," at least for the time being, just as in doing "real" science—which of course is precisely what the students will be doing.

## Teaching Tips

### *Exploration*

1.  Start by posing the problem and calling for alternative hypotheses. These should be listed on the board, followed by a discussion of how students might try to test them. Point out that the strategy they should attempt to follow is to negate hypotheses rather than to attempt to "prove" them. For instance, the "one-way valve" hypothesis leads one to predict that water will rise in a right-side-up stem but not in an upside-down stem. If water rises equally well in both stems, the hypothesis has been contradicted. Tell students to test as many hypotheses as they can in the time provided.

2.  Advise students to cut stems under water and to keep the stems in water for a minute before performing other manipulations. This prevents air-bubble blockage of the xylem.

### *Term Introduction*

3.  At an appropriate time, have students report their experimental designs and results to the class. This can be done in a variety of ways. Select the way that best suits your needs and the amount of time available. One successful approach is to have each group select a spokesperson to present a brief oral report (3 to 5 min) and to allow questions to be asked at the conclusion of each report. At the conclusion of all the reports, you can summarize the major findings and introduce or reintroduce such terms as *osmosis, transpiration, cohesion,* and *xylem.* Be prepared to deal with the notion of suction. You may wish not to tell students that no such thing as suction exists, but have them try to imagine what goes on at the molecular level when evaporation occurs. Ask them to try to imagine how a molecule escaping from the water surface possibly could pull those left behind.

### *Concept Application*

4. Because this lab concludes the set of learning cycles on plant physiology, no specific learning cycles have been included to allow the direct application of these biological concepts. The thinking skills involved here, however, will be applied in a number of the remaining labs.

5. Chapter 19 of the textbook should be assigned reading.

| **Biological Terms** | **Thinking Skills** |
|---|---|
| transpiration | describe nature accurately |
| xylem | state causal questions |
| osmosis | create alternative hypotheses |
| cohesion | generate logical predictions |
| root pressure | plan and conduct experiments |
| guttation | organize and analyze data |
| | draw and apply conclusions |

## Sample Test Questions

*Use the key to classify statements 1–6.*

### KEY

A. predicted by the root-pressure hypothesis

B. predicted by the transpiration hypothesis

C. predicted by the one-way-valves hypothesis

D. predicted by none of the hypotheses

E. predicted by two or more of the hypotheses

1. Water rises in plants that have no leaves.

2. Water rises only in stems placed right side up.

3. Water will not rise in plants that have no roots.

4. No return flow of water to the roots occurs.

5. Rates of water loss vary in different kinds of plants.

6. Water rises in segments of plant stems placed right side up and upside down.

*The next 11 items are based on the following experimental design:*

'The cut end of a stem is inserted into a glass tube filled with water. Movement of water into the plant is shown by a rise of water in the glass tube.

Four such transpirometers were made as follows:

Transpirometer A: Set up as shown, no further treatment

Transpirometer B: Set up as shown, placed in sunny window

Transpirometer C: Set up as shown, placed in the dark

Transpirometer D: Set up as shown, all leaves removed

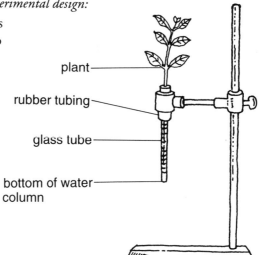

plant

rubber tubing

glass tube

bottom of water column

7.  The function of a transpirometer is to measure
    a.  the root pressure of a plant.
    b.  transpiration as it occurs in the intact plant.
    c.  the rate of transpiration.
    d.  the height of the water in the tube.

8.  Which transpirometer represents the control for the experiment?

9.  In which transpirometer would the rate of water loss be lowest?

10. Which transpirometer tests the hypothesis that light is necessary for transpiration?

11. In which transpirometer would the rate of water loss be greatest?

12. The effect of what independent variable can be tested by the experimental design?
    a.  number of leaves          d.  dark
    b.  kind of plant             e.  temperature
    c.  amount of water rise in the glass tube

13. Which of the variables listed in item 12 is the dependent variable?

14. A conclusion that could reasonably be drawn from data from the four transpirometers is that
    a.  the number of leaves is a major factor in transpiration.
    b.  temperatures above 30°C increase the transpiration rate.
    c.  photosynthetic rate influences transpiration.
    d.  sunlight is necessary if transpiration is to take place.

*Use the following key to interpret the results shown in the following statements about Transpirometer C.*

**KEY**

A.  The result is predicted, and the hypothesis is consistent with other data.

B.  The result is predicted, and the hypothesis is contradicted by other data.

C.  The result is not predicted, but the hypothesis is consistent with other data.

D.   The result is not predicted, and the hypothesis is contradicted by other data.

15.   The water column will become only slightly shorter because the stomates are closed in the dark.

16.   The water column will become much shorter because the plant makes food in the dark.

17.   The water column will become longer because water is produced during respiration.

18.   The water column will become much shorter because the stomates are open in the dark.

19.   The water column will become only slightly shorter because no photosynthesis is occurring.

## Answers

|     |     |     |     |
|-----|-----|-----|-----|
| 1.  | E   | 11. | B   |
| 2.  | C   | 12. | A   |
| 3.  | A   | 13. | C   |
| 4.  | C   | 14. | A   |
| 5.  | D   | 15. | A   |
| 6.  | B   | 16. | D   |
| 7.  | C   | 17. | C   |
| 8.  | A   | 18. | D   |
| 9.  | D   | 19. | A   |
| 10. | C   |     |     |

# Food Chains and Food Webs

## Investigation 30    *What Could It Be?*

## Synopsis

Students explore an unknown, ball-shaped, fuzzy object (an owl pellet) to determine its contents, and they generate hypotheses about its formation. They also use a simple key of skulls to identify the animals found in the object. The terms *predator, prey, trophic level, food chain, food web,* and *biological magnification* are introduced. Students then name other instances of food chains/webs and also collect, assemble, mount, and label a complete rodent skeleton. This is an empirical-abductive learning cycle.

## Suggested Time

Three class periods

## Background Information for the Teacher

An owl pellet is a fuzzy, ball-shaped object that is the regurgitated, nondigestible remains of an owl's prey. The typical owl pellet contains the hair and skeletons of several small rodents, bird bones and feathers, and insect exoskeletons. By collecting the remains of the prey from pellets, prey skeletons can be assembled and "keyed out," revealing the owl's food preferences. By using this information, plus previously known information regarding feeding relationships, one can infer community food chain and food web structure.

In addition to providing the students with an opportunity to improve their powers of observation and inference, this learning cycle allows you to introduce important biological terms related to community structure, as well as anatomical features of a variety of vertebrate skeletons.

The following general postulates of the theory of animal food chains and webs can be introduced:

1. The dependence of some animals on other animals as a source of food determines that animal species in a community will vary from small to large.

2. The ultimate source of food in animal food chains is green plants.

3. Many food chains exist in a community.

4. Commonly, predators eat animals that are smaller than themselves, so the largest predator in a community is at the top of one or more food chains.

5. Varying conditions and varying food choices of animals produce variations in the sequence of food chains.

6. The varying food chains usually create an interlocking network of chains called a food web.

7. Feeding patterns may result in dangerously high concentrations of nonbiodegradable molecules in the bodies of animals at or near the top of food webs (biological magnification).

The learning cycle also represents a good concept application activity related to biological classification (Investigation 2) because it requires students to identify prey remains by use of a dichotomous key.

## Advance Preparation

Owl pellets can be ordered from Creative Dimensions, P .O. Box 1393, Bellingham, WA 98227, (206) 733-5024,  and from most biological supply houses. Pellets sold for study have been fumigated to make handling safe for students.

Students should work in pairs for this activity.

## Teaching Tips

### Exploration

1. Introduce the lesson by having the students imagine that while taking a walk in a forest they spot a fuzzy, ball-shaped object lying on the ground beneath a large pine tree. After picking it up and carefully looking it over, they conclude that it is something they have never seen before. Show the students one of the owl pellets (without identifying it), and ask them to guess what it might be and to cite reasons for their guesses if possible. Do not be disturbed if someone correctly guesses that the object is an owl pellet. Simply accept the guess as a reasonable, but not necessarily correct, one. Challenge the students to observe the objects carefully to try to discover which, if any, of their ideas is correct.

2. You may have to provide some students with an additional pellet if their first one contains only bird bones.

3. After hypotheses about the object's origin have been generated and skulls have been keyed out, lead a discussion in which students attempt to evaluate the validity of their ideas with reference to their observations and/or any additional information they may have. You may want to offer the hint that mice are nocturnal (hence the predator also must be nocturnal).

### Term Introduction

4. Have the students diagram on the board all the feeding relationships implied by their observations, using arrows pointing from the prey to the predator (mouse → owl).

5. After diagramming the feeding relationships, introduce the biological terms listed below, writing them on the board and defining them in terms of the present context.

### Concept Application

6. Ask the students for other examples of predator-prey relationships, food chains and webs, and biological magnification.

7. Students may be motivated and should be encouraged to do some library research on the organisms found in the owl pellets. They may want to construct a complete skeleton of one or more of the organisms, such as those shown in the diagrams on page 194.

8. Investigations 31–35 allow for further applications of the terms introduced here.

## Biological Terms

predator
prey
food chain
food web
producers
primary and secondary consumers
trophic level
biological magnification

## Thinking Skills

describe nature accurately
state causal questions
generate alternative hypotheses

## Sample Test Questions

*The next ten items are based on this diagram of a food web.*

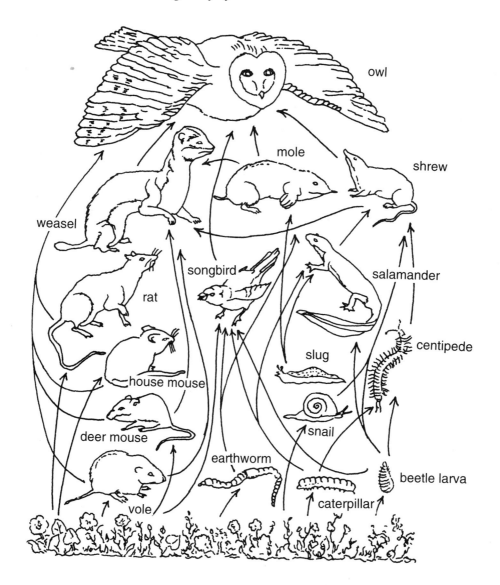

*Use the key to classify the statements.*

**KEY**

A. supported by the diagram

B. contradicted by the diagram

C. neither supported nor contradicted by the diagram

1.  In this food web, voles are producers.

2.  Salamanders feed on material that comes indirectly from fruits and flowers.

3.  If the owl population increased for some reason, the weasel population would increase.

4.  The greatest amount of food energy is consumed by the mammals.

5.  Voles are primary consumers.

6.  If mice store larger supplies of food than usual, a long and severe winter will be coming.

7.  If hunters shoot many more owls than usual, the shrew population will be reduced.

8.  Snails are primary consumers.

9.  Songbirds can be classified as primary and secondary consumers.

10.  The greatest amount of food energy exists at the producer level.

## Answers

1. B

2. A

3. B

4. C

5. A

6. C

7. B

8. A

9. A

10. A

## Complete Skeleton and Skulls Mounted on Cardboard

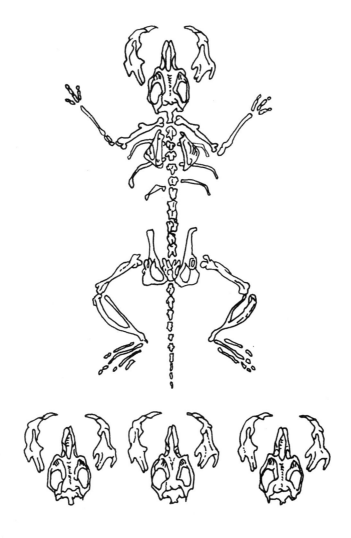

## Complete Skeleton and Skulls Mounted Upright

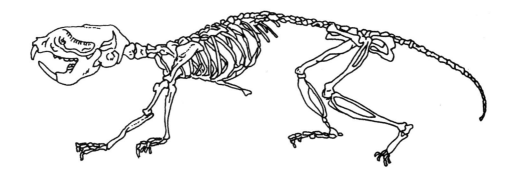

# Biogenesis • Biological Decomposition

> ## Investigation 31  *What Happens to Dead Organisms?*

## Synopsis

Students conduct factorial experiments to test the effects of three variables on the rate of breakdown of dead organisms. Experimental results are analyzed, and the term *biological decomposition* is introduced. Microbial disease is then discussed, as are methods of food preservation. This is an empirical-abductive learning cycle.

## Suggested Time

One class period for setup; 10 to 15 minutes every second or third day for 1 to 2 weeks for observation; one class period for term introduction; one or more class periods for concept application

## Background Information for the Teacher

Under favorable environmental conditions, the complex organic molecules found in the bodies of dead organisms are absorbed and used as food by such microbes as molds and bacteria, which grow from spores and resting cells found virtually everywhere in the environment. The result of this process, called *biological decomposition*, is the growth of microbe populations and the eventual disappearance of the dead organisms. Of course, when the dead organisms are gone, so is the microbes' food source, so they too die. The result is that the original complex organic molecules of the dead organisms are broken apart into smaller organic and inorganic molecules, which are left in the surrounding soil, air, and water. These are then available as raw materials (fertilizer) for the growth of plants.

The rate at which decomposition takes place varies directly with the rate at which decomposer populations increase. Consequently, the degree to which the environment favors the growth of decomposer populations determines the rate at which a dead organism will decompose. A number of environmental variables and substances can be shown to influence the rate of decomposition.

a. Amount of water: Decomposers, like all organisms, require water; therefore, if no water is available, no decomposers will grow and biological decomposition will not occur.

b. Temperature: Increasing temperature increases the metabolic rate of the decomposers and thus increases the rate of decomposition.

c. Amount of sugar or salt: These substances inhibit the growth of decomposers (and the rate of decomposition) by creating an osmotic gradient that causes water to diffuse out of their cells.

d. Amount of vinegar: Vinegar lowers the pH of the environment below the tolerance of many decomposers; thus, it kills them and stops decomposition.

e. Amount of alcohol and other antiseptic solutions: These solutions are toxic to decomposers in a variety of ways; thus, they kill the decomposers and stop decomposition.

f. Amount of light: Light inhibits the growth of some decomposers by inhibiting certain necessary chemical reactions; thus, it reduces the rate of decomposition.

## Advance Preparation

The following film loops can be obtained from Kalmia Co. Inc., Department A2, 71 Dudley St., Cambridge, MA 02140, (617) 864-5567. Microgardening—six color loops from Education Development Center: 81-4442 Alternaria; 81-4459 Rhizopus; 81-4467 Fusarium; 81-4483 Trichoderma Growth Rings; 81-4491 Rotting Pear; 81-4509 Mushroom Growth and Reaction; Complete set of all six film loops 89-2638.

## Teaching Tips

### *Exploration*

1. Use the introduction in the student manual as a point of departure for this investigation. You may want to bring in a fresh piece of fruit, hold it up, and ask, "Is this dead? Why or why not?" The discussion should allow you to note briefly that death must be looked on as a cellular phenomenon; that is, a part of the fruit may be alive, part of it dead, depending on whether the cells in that part of the fruit are still active. Eventually, that activity stops, and death results. Then what happens?

2. Avoid using the term *decomposition* during the exploration phase. Use the term *breakdown* instead.

3. After student groups have selected variables to be tested and have tried to figure out ways to design their experiments, lead a class discussion of their ideas. Guide students to the discovery of the strengths and weaknesses of the various designs proposed.

4. Most of the student designs will test the effect of each variable independently (and in a controlled fashion) but will usually not test the effect of all combinations of the three variables. To lead them to the desired factorial design, ask, "What would happen if it turns out that water is necessary for breakdown? Will an experiment comparing hot and cold conditions tell us anything if water is not added to each container?" Because we really don't know what the effects of the variable will be, students should realize the need for generating all possible combinations in their designs. After the students have struggled with this problem for a while (and some have developed a workable design), you may wish to have them consider whether the following experiment is satisfactory.

### Variables Tested

a. amount of water (0 mL vs. 50 mL)
b. amount of salt (0 g vs. 15 g)
c. temperature (35°F vs. 75°F)

### Proposed Factorial Design

|  |  | Amount of Salt | |
|  |  | None | Some |
|---|---|---|---|
| **Amount of Water** | **None** | 1<br>No water<br>No salt<br>35°F | 2<br>No water<br>Salt<br>35°F |
|  | **Some** | 3<br>Water<br>No salt<br>35°F | 4<br>Water<br>Salt<br>25°F |

|  |  | Amount of Salt | |
|  |  | None | Some |
|---|---|---|---|
| **Amount of Water** | **None** | 5<br>No water<br>No salt<br>75°F | 6<br>No water<br>Salt<br>75°F |
|  | **Some** | 7<br>Water<br>No salt<br>75°F | 8<br>Water<br>Salt<br>75°F |

Point out to students the dishes that may be compared. For instance, Dishes 1–2, 3–4, 5–6, and 7–8 test the effect of amount of salt. Dishes 1–3, 2–4, 5–7, and 6–8 test the effect of amount of water. Dishes 1–5, 2–6, 3–7, and 4–8 test the effect of temperature.

5.  Make sure all groups cover their petri dishes with the covers and keep them in a well-ventilated area when not being observed. Tape can be used to seal the lids. Caution students to avoid inhaling air above opened dishes.

6.  You may wish to leave the fish and meat used by your students uncovered outside for a few minutes (after thawing). This allows adult flies to lay eggs in the meat. If maggots appear, you will have a wonderful opportunity to discuss the notion of spontaneous generation, because some students are likely to invoke the idea to explain the maggots' appearance.

7.  Have your students make observations of their dishes for 10 to 15 minutes every few days. After 1 to 2 weeks, or when you think the breakdown has gone far enough, have a discussion to analyze class data.

### Term Introduction

8.  List all the tested variables on the board, and ask each group what their result was for each variable. Use a + if an increase in the values of the variable increased the rate of breakdown, use a – to indicate the opposite, and use a *0* if no effect was apparent. Have your students copy the class data from the board and write conclusions about the effects of the various variables.

9.  After you have discussed the effects of the variables on breakdown, ask the students what they think actually caused the breakdown. Most likely they will simply repeat the list of variables found to be positively correlated with the rate of breakdown (e.g., water, temperature), but they should be encouraged to think further. Did they see or smell anything growing on the dead organism? If so, what might this be? Could this have anything to do with the breakdown? Someone in class should be able to offer the hypothesis that the "stuff" on the dead organism is actually alive and growing and is the actual cause of the breakdown because it "eats" the dead organism. If no one does, you will have to suggest this idea yourself. Once the idea has been advanced, discuss students' results to see whether they support the hypothesis. Students should be able to see that the results indeed support the hypothesis, because certain chemicals and lack of water would kill the microbes, just as they would familiar organisms. Likewise, increasing temperatures would increase the metabolic rate of the microbes just as it does for familiar cold-blooded organisms.

After you have developed and supported this hypothesis, introduce the term *biological decomposition* and identify specific decomposer populations (bacteria, fungi).

### Concept Application

10.  The idea of microbial growth and biological decomposition can be extended to many topics, such as diseases, food poisoning, food preservation, and public sanitation. To lead into these topics, you may wish to make an assignment: Have your students go to a grocery store and make a list of ten different types of food. Have them use labels and the knowledge they have learned from the investigation to figure out what types of preservation technique are used to keep these foods from spoiling.

11.  You now may want to ask your students where they think the fungi and bacteria came

from initially. After speculation on their part, show them one or more of the film loops mentioned in the Advance Preparation section and see whether they want to modify their ideas. Another strategy would be to discuss the experiments of Redi, Spallanzani, and Pasteur. Students then could recreate these experiments. A final strategy would be to have your students pick a hypothesis (spontaneous generation, biogenesis) and redesign their experiments to test it.

12. Chapter 20 of the textbook should be assigned reading.

---

### Biological Terms

decomposition
decomposer
food spoilage and preservation
spontaneous generation
biogenesis

### Thinking Skills

describe nature accurately
state causal questions
create alternative hypotheses
generate logical predictions
plan and conduct experiments
organize and analyze data
draw and apply conclusions

---

## Sample Test Questions

*Identify the following statements, using the following key.*

**KEY**

A. a hypothesis

B. a prediction

C. an observation

D. a question

E. a conclusion

While walking around a lake one day, you find two dead fish lying about 3 m apart on the shore. One of the fish you recognize as a bluegill, the other a bass. The bluegill is lying within 30 cm of the lake water on a moist, muddy area. The bass is resting on a dry, sandy area 2 m from the water. On returning to the area 2 weeks later, you find the bluegill tissue is almost completely decomposed, whereas the bass is just beginning to decompose.

1. Several fly maggots can be seen crawling in and on both fish.

2. The bass might have tougher tissue.

3. The difference in decomposition may be due to the amount of available moisture.

4. If a dead bluegill and a dead bass are placed within 30 cm of the lake, they would decompose at similar rates.

5. Because the fish were different types and they were exposed to different types of soil and different amounts of water, we can't say for sure why they are decomposing at different rates.

6. Why is the bluegill more decomposed than the bass?

7. Two hikers crossed a desert. On the way, they noticed a dead coyote. Two weeks later, they passed the body again and were surprised to find that it had not yet decayed.
   a. Generate a hypothesis concerning why the coyote had not decayed.

    **b.** Generate a prediction (expected outcome) based on your hypothesis and an experimental design.

    **c.** Provide evidence in support of your hypothesis in terms of the data gathered from Investigation 31, *What Happens to Dead Organisms?*

*Evaluate statements 8–15 according to the following key.*

**KEY**

A.   Correct: The data alone are sufficient to show that the statement is correct.

B.   Probably correct: The data indicate that the statement is probably correct.

C.   Insufficient: No data indicate whether the statement is true or false.

D.   Probably incorrect: The data indicate that the statement is probably incorrect.

E.   Incorrect: The data alone are sufficient to show that the statement is incorrect.

Analyses were made of the vitamin C content of red ripe and green tomatoes. Mature green tomatoes were stored at the temperatures indicated. Those that ripened by the end of the first week were analyzed for their vitamin C content; those that ripened at the end of the second week were analyzed at the end of the second week, and so on. In addition, some mature green tomatoes were analyzed each week.

| Condition When Taken From Field | Temp. When Stored | No. of Weeks Stored | Stage of Ripeness When Analyzed | Vitamin C mg/100 g |
|---|---|---|---|---|
| mature green | not stored | 0 | mature green | 15.0 |
| red ripe | not stored | 0 | red ripe | 16.2 |
| mature green | 21.1°C | 1 | red ripe | 14.4 |
| mature green | 21.1°C | 2 | red ripe | 12.9 |
| mature green | 21.1°C | 3 | red ripe | 8.2 |
| mature green | 26.7°C | 1 | red ripe | 14.0 |
| mature green | 26.7°C | 2 | red ripe | 9.8 |
| mature green | 26.7°C | 3 | red ripe | 7.1 |
| mature green | 21.1°C | 1 | mature green | 10.0 |
| mature green | 21.1°C | 2 | mature green | 7.2 |

  **8.** Tomatoes ripened at 32.2°C would have less vitamin C after 3 weeks than those stored at 26.7°C.

  **9.** Tomatoes could not be stored at 32.2°C because at this high a temperature they would decompose.

**10.** The lower the temperature at which tomatoes are stored, the less is the breakdown of vitamin C.

**11.** Heat directly and/or indirectly causes a breakdown of the vitamin C molecule.

**12.** After 4 weeks of storage, tomatoes stored at 21.1°C would contain less than 7 mg/100 g of vitamin C.

**13.** Some mature green tomatoes ripen in storage within a week.

**14.** The green tomatoes that did not ripen in a week had lost about the same amount of vitamin C as those that ripened during the week.

15. Vitamin C is manufactured elsewhere in the plant and then is stored in the fruit.

16. Grass clippings from a recently mowed lawn were mixed in the soil of one flower bed but not mixed in the soil of a second flower bed located on the other side of the house. After 2 weeks, the flowers in the first flower bed were much greener than those in the second bed. The most reasonable hypothesis to explain this is that
    a. the first flower bed received more water.
    b. the grass molecules were broken down by decomposers and absorbed by the roots of the flowers in the first bed.
    c. the flowers in the first bed ate the grass clippings.
    d. the flowers in the first bed absorbed blades of grass through their roots.
    e. the flowers in the second bed absorbed a yellow substance through their roots.

17. The actual cause of the color difference of the flowers in the two flower beds is not possible to determine without further testing because
    a. the flowers are not the same color.
    b. the weight of the soil was not measured.
    c. distilled water was not used to water the flowers.
    d. the grass was not mixed in the soil of both beds.
    e. the two flower beds differ in more than one way.

18. Diagram a factorial experiment to test the effect of amount of grass clippings, amount of sunlight, and amount of fertilizer on the color of flowers.

## Answers

| | |
|---|---|
| 1. C | 4. B |
| 2. A | 5. E |
| 3. A | 6. D |

7. a. Bacteria could not grow because the hot sun caused water and fluids to evaporate.
   b. A piece of dead coyote with water will decompose, but a dried-out piece will not.
   c. Dried bread did not decompose, but wet bread did.

| | |
|---|---|
| 8. B | 13. A |
| 9. C | 14. D |
| 10. A | 15. C |
| 11. B | 16. B |
| 12. B | 17. E |

18.

**Amount of Sunlight**

| | None | Some |
|---|---|---|
| **None** | color of flowers | color of flowers |
| **Some** | color of flowers | color of flowers |

Amount of Grass Clippings

**No Fertilizer**

**Amount of Sunlight**

| | None | Some |
|---|---|---|
| **None** | color of flowers | color of flowers |
| **Some** | color of flowers | color of flowers |

Amount of Grass Clippings

**Some Fertilizer**

# Population Dynamics • Limiting Factors

## Investigation 32  *What Is the Pattern of Population Growth and Decline?*

### Synopsis

Students graph the growth and decline of yeast populations under differing environmental conditions. The graphs are compared, and a general pattern of population growth and decline is noted. The teacher introduces such relevant terms as *S-shaped growth, carrying capacity, limiting factors,* and *population crash.* Students then apply these concepts to the human population. This is an empirical-abductive learning cycle.

### Suggested Time

One class period for setup; portions of two to four class periods to record data; one to two class periods for discussion and concept application

### Background Information for the Teacher

Under ideal conditions, populations have an inherent ability to produce offspring in tremendous numbers. For example, one pair of houseflies starting to breed in April could have 191,010,000,000,000,000,000 descendants by August if all their eggs hatched and if all the young survived to reproduce. Such an exponential growth pattern is common in populations with high biotic potentials in unlimited environments. The rate of increase increases. For example, two offspring can produce 4, then 8, 16, 32, 64, 128, 256, 512, and so on (see Figure 1).

No real population can increase in size indefinitely, however, due to disease, lack of food, space, and water, and the like. Such limiting factors act to produce a growth curve that looks more like that for the yeast population shown in Figure 2. The yeast population growth curve shows an S-shaped growth pattern. Initial increase is slow, but growth rate accelerates rapidly until deaths start to outnumber births when limiting factors begin to assert themselves. The population stops growing when a balance is struck between the population's biotic potential and the environment's ability to support the population. The number of births equals the number of deaths, and the population has reached the environment's carrying capacity.

Figure 1

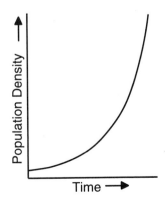

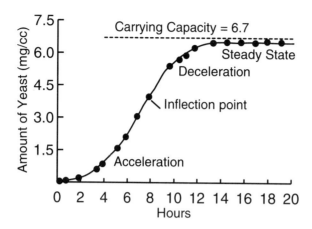

In environments where necessary raw materials and energy are continually resupplied, a population may remain near the carrying capacity indefinitely. Otherwise, the population will decline rapidly as resources are depleted. The population may crash completely, as is the case of the yeast populations growing in a closed system in this lab activity.

In summary, the general postulates of a theory of population growth are as follows:

1. An environment presents a population with a range of conditions.

2. Generally, too little or too much of a specific environmental factor (e.g., too cold/too hot, too dry/too wet, too little salt/too much salt) adversely affects individual survival and hence limits population growth. Each environmental factor has an optimum range.

3. A small population of any species in an appropriate environment grows rapidly and soon reaches its intrinsic natural rate of increase (biotic potential).

4. Growth of a population in a limited environment constantly changes that environment.

5. Growth continues at the intrinsic rate until competition for resources and/or some effect of the environment, such as predators, reduces the rate.

6. Population growth stops when the birth rate equals the death rate.

7. If an environment adversely changes and/or necessary raw materials are not resupplied, its populations will crash.

## Teaching Tips

### *Exploration*

1. In addition to or instead of yeasts, fruit fly populations can be used for this learning cycle. Initial populations of approximately ten flies are satisfactory, provided that both males and females are present.

2. As a lead-in activity, you might want to show students a test tube containing about 5 mL of yeast culture and to ask them what they think will happen to the yeast population over the next few days. Draw possible growth curves on the board. After they have come up with several possibilities, ask what effect adding 2 mL of sucrose solution might have on the population. Ask them what other environmental variables might affect the yeast population growth. After they have named several variables, tell them they are to select a single variable and design an experiment to test its effect on the growth of the yeast population.

3. Use one package of baker's (not brewer's) yeast added to 1 L aged tap water. Further dilute with water if cells are too numerous to count under the microscope.

4. Stir the culture before pouring.

5. Use fine-tipped droppers of uniform size to help standardize data.

6. Students probably should make at least three separate high-power field counts and average them when calculating the yeast population.

7. After students have worked for about 5 minutes with the problem of calculating the population size, lead a class discussion to pool ideas and to develop a workable procedure. This will involve a series of multiplications based on something like those in the sample calculations below. This procedure involves proportional reasoning, which will give many of your students difficulty. Try to let them generate as much of the procedure as possible, because telling them prior to their own efforts will do little to help them understand the process.

### Sample Calculations

The class should come up with something like the following steps for calculating the yeast populations in the test tubes:

Average Number of Yeast in High-Power Field

×

Number of High-Power Fields on Slide (1 drop)

×

Number of Drops in 1 mL

×

Number of mL in Test Tube

×

Number of Dilutions, if any

- It does not matter whether you calculate the number of high-power fields in a coverslip or estimate this number (numbers from 500 to 1,000 are well within reason). As long as the whole class uses the same number, the data obtained should be a reliable representation of what is happening to the yeast population.
- Some students may wish to calculate the diameter and area of their high-power field and divide this into the area of the coverslip to be more accurate.
- If low power on the microscope is 100X and the field of vision is 2 mm (directly measured by a transparent ruler under low power), then a 500X field will be $\frac{1}{5}$ as wide, or 0.4 mm. The area of a circle is $\pi r^2$; therefore, using 3.14 as the value of $\pi$, the area of the high-power field is about 0.5 mm$^2$.
- If low power on the microscope is 100X and the field of vision is 1.5 mm, then a high-power magnification of 430X will be $\frac{10}{43}$ as large, or 0.35 mm. The area of this high-power field then would be $3.14 \times (0.35 \text{ mm})^2 = 0.38 \text{ mm}^2$.
- If your coverslips are 22 mm × 22 mm, the area of a coverslip = 484 mm$^2$. With 500X and a 0.4-mm field, the number of high-power fields in the coverslip area is 484 mm$^2$/0.16 mm$^2$ = 3,025. A conversion factor of 3,000 could be used by the students for the number of high-power fields in a coverslip.

- In the case of dilutions, multiply by 10 for every dilution of 10:
  e.g.,      2 dilutions of 10 = × 100
               3 dilutions of 10 = × 1,000
  Each dilution of 10 = 1 mL yeast, 9 mL water.

### Term Introduction

8. After having the students graph their results on the board, ask them to find a general pattern most of the yeast populations seem to have gone through and to draw it on their paper. With reference to the pattern, introduce the terms listed under Biological Terms, using student data as operational definitions wherever possible. Have them list factors that influenced growth patterns, as well as factors they think may have limited growth. Write the word *limiting factors* at the head of this list as a means of introducing this term.

### Concept Application

9. Ask your students what phase they think the U.S. population currently might be in. Have them plot the U.S. population data and then draw a dotted line to indicate what they think the population of the United States will be by the year 2010.

An alternative application activity that would involve your students in the ethics and morals of the world hunger problem would be to have your students read "Living on a Lifeboat," an interesting and controversial paper by Garrett Hardin. This paper is available in the textbook *Biological Science Interaction of Experiments and Ideas*, commonly called *BSCS Black*, complete with editorial comments and discussion questions.

10. Chapter 21 of the textbook should be assigned reading.

| **Biological Terms** | **Thinking Skills** |
| --- | --- |
| lag phase | describe nature accurately |
| growth phase | state causal questions |
| S-shaped growth pattern | create alternative hypotheses |
| stationary phase | plan and conduct experiments |
| declining phase | organize and analyze data |
| limiting factors | draw and apply conclusions |
| exponential growth | |
| carrying capacity | |

## Sample Test Questions

Draw two graphs showing what the growth of yeast populations in two different environments might look like. In the first environment, the yeasts will be grown in a test tube of sugar water in a lab. In the second environment, the yeasts will be grown on a bunch of grapes (a normal environment for yeasts) outdoors in California in the spring.

1. Discuss reasons why your graphs look similar or different.

2. List as many possible limiting factors as you can think of in both situations. Explain why each would be a limiting factor.

*The next 12 items refer to the following graph and information about cell counts made from a culture medium incubated at 22°C.*

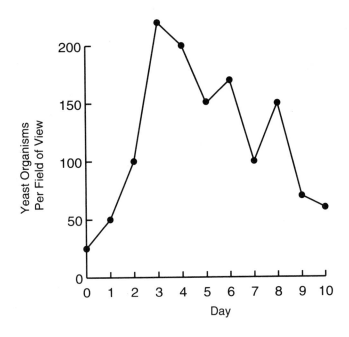

3. The tube from which the count is to be made must be shaken vigorously to
   a. break off the yeast buds.
   b. see individuals.
   c. get an even distribution of yeast.
   d. get the maximum number of individuals in the dropper.

4. If the culture medium had been incubated at 30°C, the
   a. yeast organisms would freeze.
   b. food supply would last for a longer period of time.
   c. organisms could not grow or reproduce.
   d. growth curve might peak on day two.

*Use the following key to answer the next four items.*

**KEY**

A. a hypothesis

B. a prediction

C. data

D. an assumption

5. the dots on the graph

6. a reading from a part of the line between the dots

7. an explanation (based on the graph) of changes in population density of the yeast

8. an expectation, based on the graph, of what would occur at a higher temperature

*Use the graph of the yeast population and the following key to answer the next six items.*

**KEY**

A. The statement is a restatement of the data.

B. The statement is a reasonable interpretation of the data.

C. The statement is contrary to the data.

D. Insufficient evidence exists to evaluate the statement.

9. The change in temperature of the culture caused the decrease in the population.

10. The maximum number of yeast organisms was on about the third day.

11. The population reached a steady state on the fifth day.

12. The population probably will decrease and eventually die out.

13. A limited supply of nutrients probably is one factor that caused a decline in the yeast population.

14. Some other organism got into the culture and ate the yeasts.

Four microscopes are set up in the laboratory as follows:

| Microscope # | Objective | Ocular |
|:---:|:---:|:---:|
| 1 | 10X | 5X |
| 2 | 20X | 10X |
| 3 | 40X | 5X |
| 4 | 45X | 15X |

15. If a slide showing microorganisms is examined with each of the microscopes, in which two microscopes will the microorganisms appear to move with the same degree of rapidity?
    - **a.** 1 and 2
    - **b.** 1 and 4
    - **c.** 2 and 3
    - **d.** 3 and 4

16. With which microscope would you expect to observe the greatest number of microorganisms at any given instant?
    - **a.** 1
    - **b.** 2
    - **c.** 3
    - **d.** 4

17. With which microscope would you expect to observe the fewest microorganisms at any given instant?
    - **a.** 1
    - **b.** 2
    - **c.** 3
    - **d.** 4

*Assume that the diagram on the next page represents the nosepiece and objectives of a microscope. Under low-power magnification, 100 yeast cells can be counted side by side along the diameter of the field.*

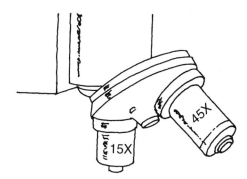

18. About how many of these same yeast cells will you see when you turn the nosepiece to high power?

    a. 3
    b. 33
    c. 130
    d. 145
    e. 300

19. With a 10X eyepiece, the yeasts under high power will be magnified

    a. 10X.
    b. 55X.
    c. 150X.
    d. 450X.
    e. 675X.

20. If the microscope fields were square instead circular, and about 1,000 yeast cells could be seen in the entire field under low power, about how many cells would be seen when you turn the nosepiece to high power?

    a. 100
    b. 250
    c. 500
    d. 667
    e. 4,000

21. A drop of liquid is taken from a thoroughly mixed 100-mL yeast culture and placed under a microscope. Approximately 1,000 cells are visible. Suppose the 100-mL yeast culture then is diluted by adding 400 mL of sugar solution. About how many yeast cells would be visible when this culture is viewed under the same lens?

    a. 200
    b. 250
    c. 700
    d. 1,300
    e. 5,000

## Answers

| | | | |
|---|---|---|---|
| 3. C | 8. B | 13. B | 18. B |
| 4. D | 9. D | 14. D | 19. D |
| 5. C | 10. A | 15. C | 20. A |
| 6. D | 11. C | 16. A | 21. A |
| 7. A | 12. B | 17. D | |

# Balance of Nature • Predator-Prey Relationships • Intraspecific Competition • Interspecific Competition

## Investigation 33 *What Causes Population Size to Fluctuate?*

## Synopsis

Students play the roles of predators, prey, and abiotic environmental components in a simulation game and graph data to reveal population fluctuations across time. With reference to the simulation and graphed data, the teacher introduces the terms *predator-prey relationship* and *intraspecific competition* and discusses possible causal relationships involved. The phrase balance of nature also is introduced. Students then graph and discuss Hudson Bay Trapper data and other instances of population control. This is an empirical-abductive learning cycle.

## Suggested Time

Two to three class periods

## Background Information for the Teacher

The graph below shows one of the classic examples of predator-prey population fluctuations. The Hudson Bay Company of Canada contracted with trappers across Canada and the northern United States Territories to buy their pelts. The company then shipped the pelts to England, where they were marketed. Since the early 1800s, the Hudson Bay Company has kept accurate records of all the pelts their fur trappers have taken each year. These data now can be used to indicate population sizes for the fur-bearing animals taken.

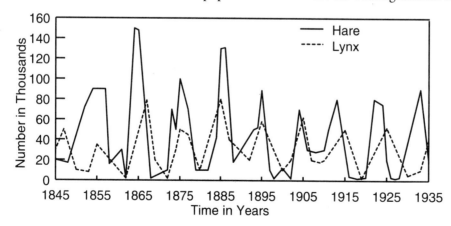

From the graph, one can see that the lynx population peaks on an average of every 9.6 years. During these fluctuations, the hare population seems to exhibit the same pattern, only the extremes are wider and the peaks seem to occur slightly before (though these same data could be interpreted as following later) the lynx peaks. In this type of predator-prey interaction, the general explanation usually goes something like the following: As the hare prey population increases, the lynx predators have unlimited food and their numbers increase tremendously. As the population of the prey continues to increase (usually exponentially), it soon approaches or reaches the carrying capacity of the environment, food supply usually being the limiting factor. With the habitat being depleted, intraspecific competition increases and the prey population crashes, followed shortly thereafter by the crash of the predator population for the same reason.

The data seem to suggest some cause-and-effect relationships, and in other studies this hypothesis has been supported. Yet, interestingly, studies in areas where the snowshoe hare does not have any predators seem to indicate that the hare population undergoes fluctuations of a similar period on its own. Certainly, intraspecific competition for food and shelter would increase in the hare population as its numbers increase. The following example of the Kaibab deer population makes this point clear.

In 1906, President Theodore Roosevelt created the Grand Canyon National Game Preserve to help develop a large deer population on the Kaibab Plateau (North Rim area of the Grand Canyon). Deer hunting was prohibited. Domestic grazing animals were there, mostly sheep and some cattle, but their numbers were decreasing at this time. Partially as a part of the game preserve plan and partially in response to pressure from ranchers, hunters, and the general public, a predator removal program was started in 1906 to protect the deer herd. Over a period of 25 years (1906–1931), 6,254 predators (mountain lions, wolves, coyotes, and bobcats) were removed by hunting and trapping. During the years 1931–1939, public hunting of mountain lions for sport, and both coyotes and bobcats for fur, removed 2,843 more predators. By 1931, no more wolves were left in the area, and other predators' numbers had been greatly reduced.

The plan to create an ideal habitat seemed to be a success. During this time, the deer population increased from an estimated 3,000 to 4,000 in 1906 to over 100,000 in 1924. At this point, the carrying capacity of the environment had been exceeded. With no place to migrate to and the natural forage of the area all but wiped out, intraspecific competition among the deer population increased tremendously over the next 14 years and 90,000 deer died on the Kaibab. Of the 90,000, only 14,000 were killed by hunting (again permitted since 1924); the other 76,000 died mostly from starvation and malnutrition-related causes.

Because no one theory seems to account for all of the evidence regarding population change, the major postulates of three alternative theories are presented.

### Nicholson's Theory

1. Animal populations are normally in a state of balance, and though they fluctuate, they do so in a restricted manner.

2. This situation is brought about only by factors that depress the population at high densities and increase it at low densities.

3. Reproductive rate, mortality due to predation, competition, disease, self-regulating behavior such as territorial fighting, and lack of food are the chief density-dependent factors (factors whose importance depends on the density of the population).

### Andrewartha and Birch's Theory

1. Most animal populations fluctuate irregularly through factors that act independently of density, notably those linked with climate.

2. Many populations become extinct, and many populations persist, through chance.

3. The ability of animals to migrate and thus to recolonize is of special importance.

**Wynne-Edwards's Theory**

1. Animal populations are regulated by density-dependent factors.

2. Food shortage is the ultimate limiting factor.

3. Animal populations normally regulate their own density far below the limit set by food through dispersive behavior and restraints on reproduction.

In the simulation activity in this learning cycle, students generate population-size fluctuations in a deer population and in a mountain lion population. Analysis of data allows for discussion of causes and introduction of relevant terms.

## Advance Preparation

If you plan to do the simulation outdoors, warn your students 1 or 2 days before the simulation to wear suitable shoes and clothes.

You will need to prepare the data table (see Table 1 on page 153 of the student manual) listed under Materials and referred to in procedure steps 10 and 13 (student page 151).

## Teaching Tips

### Exploration

1. Use the introductory material and procedure step 1 to initiate a discussion of population size fluctuation to lead into the simulation. Ask students for any reasons they can think of to account for population-size fluctuations, but do not provide feedback at this point concerning the merits or demerits of their ideas. Use this time as a brainstorming session. An evaluation of the various ideas comes after the data have been collected.

2. When in the area where you will conduct the simulation, tell the students that they are about to participate in an activity that emphasizes the most essential things that animals need to survive. Ask your students what might be some important variables the habitat of deer must supply for them to survive. Tell them that for the sake of simplicity they will be looking only at food, water, shelter, and (later on) predators.

3. Have the students read the procedures, and go over any questions. Emphasize that all students must know all the directions because every student will eventually be in all components of the simulation.

4. Strictly define boundaries for the students to stay within. If you choose to stay indoors, simply clear the center of the room of tables and chairs and have groups form at the front and back of the room. The simulation also could be modified to be played across a long table if the teacher wishes to have less of a run-and-chase atmosphere. In the latter case, you may wish to make colored cards for the various habitat components. The deer and habitat students then could choose their cards secretly and place them on the table, concealing them with their hands until the teacher gives a signal, at which time all students reveal their cards for that round. The deer then could "consume" their habitat choices or die, and students could move around the table to become a new condition for the next round.

5. Hesitancy on the part of the students to participate in the simulation can be kept to a minimum by emphasizing the following points:
   - The simulation is an attempt to model a process that occurs in nature.
   - The simulation is used by college students and adults to help them visualize a process that usually is seen only in population data tables after years of research.
   - You want students to think about the simulation as they participate so that at the end of the simulation they can answer questions about how the simulation was like nature and how it was different from nature.

6. Make sure the students in the deer group do not watch the habitat group choose signs and vice versa.

7. The students should not change signs once they declare what they are or what they are looking for that round. If they are unable to resist the temptation, you may want to substitute a more permanent method of designating their goal. For example, have blue cards represent water; green, food; and brown, shelter. A deer then picks a blue card and tries to find a habitat person with a blue card, and so on.

8. Allow the habitat students to confer to set up habitat conditions they think are best for the first round. After the first round, habitat conditions should be generated individually. If you wish, you may allow students within groups to confer about being all shelter or all food in any one round, because these situations may occur sometimes in nature.

9. You may wish to assign students to record data for the simulation.

10. Keep the pace of the simulation brisk.

11. After you have completed ten or so rounds of the simulation, you may wish to introduce one or two mountain lions to see the effect of a predator on the deer population. You also might have the students experiment with different environmental situations. Allow the simulation to run through four or five rounds after each experiment.

### Term Introduction

12. After the students have completed their questions and graphs, draw the graph of the class data on the board or an overhead. Then involve the class in a discussion to analyze the data, and introduce the biological terms involved.

### Concept Application

13. Tell the students about the Hudson Bay Trappers and their 100-year data. Ask them what they think the predator-prey graphs for these data would look like. Then have them graph the data and answer the Study Questions.

14. You may now wish to discuss predator-prey relationships in more detail. You could present the first part of the Kaibab Plateau deer population data and have the students then make predictions about the next few generations and then compare their predictions with what actually happened.

15. Chapter 22 of the textbook should be assigned reading.

| **Biological Terms** | **Thinking Skills** |
|---|---|
| cyclic oscillations | state casual questions |
| predator-prey oscillation | create alternative hypotheses |
| balance of nature | organize and analyze data |
| interspecific competition | |
| intraspecific competition | |

## Sample Test Questions

Draw a graph that shows a typical predator and prey population relationship.

Describe the short-range and long-range effects on the ecosystem if the prey species suddenly was exposed to a deadly, highly contagious viral disease. (If prey species was depleted due to virus, it would either cause the crash of the predator species or the predator would need to find an alternative food supply. In the long run, the lack of the prey would probably result in a rise in the food supply used by the prey and an increase in a virus-resistant population of organisms, that occupy the same, or a similar, niche to invade. This would set the stage for the introduction of a new predator species or the old one could reenter the area, assuming they still existed in nearby areas. In the long term, the ecosystem may not be changed much. Of course if the virus was too successful, it could wipe out the entire area for years.)

*The next four items refer to the following graph.*

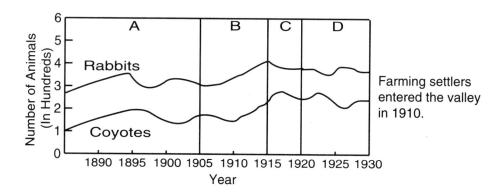

Farming settlers entered the valley in 1910.

1. The sections of the graph indicated by A and D are similar because the
   a. coyote population is rising.
   b. rabbit population is rising.
   c. mean rabbit population is the same in A and B.
   d. rabbit and coyote population are in dynamic equilibrium.

2. The change in the rabbit population at B could be explained by
   a. a decrease in the coyote population.
   b. an increase in the coyote population.
   c. presence of more plants grown by settlers who moved into the valley.
   d. a disease that drastically lowered the coyote population.

3. The mean rabbit population
   a. increased between 1917 and 1922.
   b. decreased between 1898 and 1900.
   c. increased generally between 1905 and 1930.
   d. decreased generally between 1900 and 1920.

4. The change in the rabbit population between 1905 and 1916 could best be accounted for by a(n)
   a. decrease in predators.            c. decrease in rabbit food.
   b. increase in rabbit food.          d. increase in predators.

*The next four items refer to a pond environment.*

Animal X was in abundance in a small freshwater pond. Animals Y and Z were introduced into the pond. Y preys on X, and Z preys on Y. The following graph represents the populations of these animals sampled over a period of time. Use the key that follows the graph to answer the items.

**KEY**
I
II
III

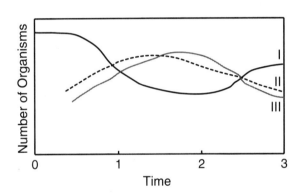

5. Which animal functions as a predator, as well as prey, in this pond?

6. Which line represents Animal X?

7. Which line represents Animal Y?

8. Which line represents Animal Z?

## Answers

| | | | |
|---|---|---|---|
| 1. D | | 5. II | |
| 2. C | | 6. I | |
| 3. C | | 7. II | |
| 4. B | | 8. III | |

# Ecosystem • Biological Community

## Investigation 34  *How Do Organisms Interact With Their Environment?*

## Synopsis

On a field trip, students measure physical features of the environment and observe feeding relationships among organisms. Data along a transect from the center of an arroyo or stream to 60 meters into the surrounding area are gathered to reveal variations in plant type and frequency. Alternative hypotheses are proposed to explain observed variations. *Ecosystem, biological community*, and related terms are introduced. Biotic and abiotic features of other ecosystems are discussed, and students attempt to construct a self-sustaining aquatic ecosystem. This is an empirical-abductive learning cycle.

## Suggested Time

2-to-3-hour field trip, plus four to five class periods

## Background Information for the Teacher

Living organisms and their nonliving (abiotic) environment are inseparably interrelated and interact with each other. Any system that includes all of the organisms in a given area (biological community) interacting with the abiotic environment so that energy flows from the plant populations (producers) to the herbivores (primary consumers) to the omnivores and carnivores (secondary and tertiary consumers) to the bacteria and fungi (decomposers) is called an *ecological system* or *ecosystem*.

Energy input to communities must be sustained because energy is lost as it passes from one level to the next. Inorganic substances (C, N, $CO_2$, $H_2O$, etc.), however, recycle through the decomposer populations back to the producers, to the consumers, to the decomposers, and so on.

It is convenient to recognize the following components of all ecosystems: 1) inorganic substances involved in material cycles, 2) organic compounds (proteins, carbohydrates, lipids, and humic substances) that link biotic and abiotic, 3) climate (temperature and other major physical factors), 4) producers (organisms that are able to manufacture food from simple inorganic substances using light energy), 5) consumers (animals that ingest other organisms as their food/energy source), 6) decomposers (organisms that directly absorb complex compounds of dead organisms and release inorganic nutrients that are usable by the producers. Items 1 through 3 comprise the abiotic components, while 4 through 6 constitute the biomass (living weight).

From the point of view of ecosystem functioning, the following categories provide insight: 1) energy transfers, 2) food chains/webs, 3) diversity patterns in time and space, 4) nutrient cycles, and 5) development and evolution. The field trip allows you to introduce many aspects of ecosystem structure and functioning as students gather data relevant to at least four of these five categories.

## Advance Preparation

Preselect a suitable area for the exploration activity. Variety in land form is a major consideration, and presence of an arroyo or stream is necessary to conduct the transect study.

Be aware of any local management practices of the area regarding municipal, county, state, or federal parks or land regulations.

Check with school officials with regard to parental permissions, transportation, liability, and health conditions of students before planning the field trip.

## Teaching Tips

### *Exploration*

1. Stress to students appropriate behavior and etiquette while studying natural areas.

2. Group size will determine the number of transect lines used; however, actual study teams probably should be only two or three students.

3. When performing the quadrat studies, note the relative abundance of some plants and the scarcity of others. When assigning teams to quantify individual plant species, be sure to adjust team size with density of plant. For example, mesquite trees will be counted quickly, whereas grass species will take much longer and require more people. Be flexible and creative about what will work best with your group size and capability.

### *Term Introduction*

4. Prior to the introduction of terms, have students plot class results of plant distribution on a large pictorial cross section of area in the class. For example:

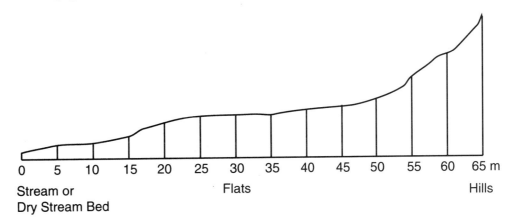

5. Direct the discussion to discover observable patterns, and explain why they might occur and how they relate to individual plant adaptations. Similarly, produce a class ecosystem chart derived from the field data. Emphasize the flow of energy and the recycling of materials through the use of arrows (e.g., sage → rabbits → hawks → decomposers → raw materials → sage). Following construction of the chart, introduce the term *biological community* to refer to the collection of biotic relationships. Then have students cite evidence of relationships among the abiotic environment and specific organisms (e.g., sunlight → sage). Diagram these on the chart, and introduce the term *ecosystem* to refer to all of the biotic and abiotic relationships within the area. If observed, such other relationships as *symbiosis*, *parasitism*, and *competition* can be pointed out and named at this time.

### *Concept Application*

**6.** Prior to assigning the Study Questions, discuss the variety of ecosystems present on our planet and how they relate to the biome concept.

**7.** Chapter 23 of the textbook should be assigned reading.

---

**Biological Terms**

ecosystem
biological community
adaptation
energy transfer
food chain/web
material cycling

**Thinking Skills**

describe nature accurately
state causal questions
create alternative hypotheses
organize and analyze data
draw and apply conclusions

---

## Sample Test Questions

**1.** If carbon dioxide ($CO_2$) were withdrawn from the atmosphere, which organisms would experience negative biological effects first?
  **a.** primary consumers          **c.** secondary consumers
  **b.** producers                   **d.** decomposers

**2.** It is easily seen that nonproducers are dependent on producers and other consumers. We can say, however, that producers are dependent on other organisms because
  **a.** they are green.
  **b.** they obtain energy to produce cellular materials from the sun.
  **c.** they depend on decomposers for such essential compounds as nitrates.
  **d.** their energy is made from minerals in the soil.

*The next 11 items are based on the following information.*

In temperate areas, mountain slopes facing south receive more direct sunlight than slopes facing north. As a result, the south-facing slopes are hotter and drier.

Use the key to identify the statements, which are inferences about north-facing and south-facing slopes.

### *KEY*

A. north-facing slopes only

B. south-facing slopes only

C. both slopes

D. neither slope

**3.** After a storm, snow melts faster on these slopes.

**4.** Snow accumulation usually is greater on these slopes.

**5.** In early spring, these slopes are the first to provide food for primary consumers.

**6.** Much open space can be found on these slopes.

**7.** These slopes support a food web of primary and higher-level consumers.

8. Vegetation on these slopes is lush.

9. Drought-tolerant grasses often are abundant on these slopes.

10. Decomposers are absent from the food webs on these slopes.

11. Shade-tolerant flowers are abundant on these slopes.

12. On these slopes, matter cycles and energy flows.

13. The climax community usually is a rain forest.

14. A small group of people is stranded on a barren island with 1,000 bushels of wheat and 1 cow. To survive for the greatest length of time, the people should
    a. eat the cow and then eat the wheat.
    b. feed the wheat to the cow and drink the milk.
    c. feed the wheat to the cow, drink the milk, and then eat the cow.
    d. drink the milk, eat the cow when milk production ceases, and then eat the wheat.

15. Which of the following would reduce the amount of food available for human use?
    a. increased production by producers
    b. increased efficiency of energy use in herbivores eaten by humans
    c. increased number of consumer levels between producers and humans
    d. decreased number of consumer levels between producers and humans

16. Within any community, which would have the smallest total mass?
    a. producers
    b. primary consumers
    c. secondary consumers
    d. decomposers

17. Which of the following does not recycle in an ecosystem?
    a. carbon
    b. oxygen
    c. water
    d. phosphorous
    e. energy

## Answers

1. B
2. C
3. B
4. A
5. B
6. B
7. C
8. A
9. B
10. D
11. A
12. C
13. D
14. A
15. C
16. C
17. E

# Succession

## Synopsis

Students observe and graph successional changes in a temporary pond to determine the sequence of events and create alternative hypotheses to explain their observations. The terms *pioneer* and *climax species, succession,* and *competition* are introduced in the context of the students' observations, and students discuss examples of succession in other settings. This is an empirical-abductive learning cycle.

## Suggested Time

30 minutes the first day; 30 minutes every third day for 2 weeks

## Background Information for the Teacher

When water returns to the site of a previous pond, a succession of changes occurs in the new ecosystem that develops. A variety of organisms becomes evident in a predictable order as spores, cysts, and eggs that were residual in the soil develop on time schedules peculiar to each species. The pioneer species are the first to appear. These are algae and other autotrophs, which are referred to as producers because of their ability to produce their own food.

Primary consumers, which are dependent on the producers for food, are next to become apparent. These are principally ciliated protozoa. Finally, the secondary consumers, rotifers, appear. At this point, a relatively stable climax community exists.

During succession, ecosystems tend to develop greater complexity. This complexity is reflected in longer food chains and more complex food webs involving more species of smaller populations, hence greater diversity and greater biomass. These structural changes during succession are accompanied by functional changes in the ecosystem. Early stages of succession show high rates of production of organic matter; production is greater than community respiration ($P/R > 1$). As succession progresses, this $P/R$ ratio approaches 1. In other words, the amount of production is approximately equal to the community respiration; therefore, biomass no longer accumulates.

Although no succession will take place in the laboratory "temporary pond," in the sense of new organisms colonizing the pond, the relative abundance and number of species in encystment stages will change and diversity and biomass increases should be apparent.

General postulates of a theory of temporal succession are as follows:

1. Temporal succession of species occurs in some specific localities and under some specific conditions.

2. In general, a typical consumer succession accompanies each kind of producer succession.

3. Long-term successions are largely due to changes in the environment caused by producers, but they are also due in part to changes wrought by consumers.

4. Short-term successions, common in microbial populations and rare in higher consumer populations, are largely due to a shifting supply of food as modified by consumer activity.

5. In most cases, the consumer climax is determined by the producer climax.

## Advance Preparation

Use a child's wading pool for your pond if possible. If not, battery jars or aquariums will work. Soil should be gathered from the top 2 cm of any dry temporary pond. Remember, this is the source of life (eggs and spores) for your pond. About 4 L of soil will be sufficient for 200 L of water.

*Pond Life* (1967), by G. K. Reid, is available from Golden Press, New York.

## Teaching Tips

### Exploration

1. Soil and water should be added as a class activity with some discussion about where the soil came from.

2. Put the pond in full sun if possible. If not, artificial light will serve as a satisfactory substitute.

3. The first observation of the pond should be done as a class activity, providing an opportunity for you to stimulate questions about useful observations and measurements. Subsequent observations should be made at least twice a week. These continuing observations and samplings can be made by students individually or in small groups.

### Term Introduction

4. After students have compiled and graphed their data (2 to 3 weeks), have one member from each group put his or her graph on the board. A typical graph will display time along the horizontal axis and the number of each type of observed organism along the vertical axis. The graph will present a series of superimposed line graphs, each showing the rise (and possible decline) of a different population over time.

5. With reference to the students' data, ask students to identify the first type of organism observed. Introduce the term *pioneer species* to name this organism. Introduce the term *succession* to describe the orderly changes that have been observed. After students have been encouraged to speculate about the kind of interaction that may have occurred, reintroduce the term *competition* as any interaction that is mutually detrimental to both participants, and discuss its possible role and the role of changes in physical factors in the observed succession. You may want to have students discuss similarities and differences in this competition and that observed in Investigation 31. Finally, you can use this opportunity to introduce the term *climax stage*, defined as a stable stage in succession in which the numbers and kinds of organisms remain relatively unchanged. In temporary ponds, a climax stage may not be attained, or it will last only as long as sufficient water remains in the pond.

6. The question of where the organisms initially came from may elicit a discussion of spontaneous generation. Students should not be told that this idea is wrong without reference to the series of experiments (e.g., Redi, Spallanzani, Pasteur) that contradicted the hypothesis.

### Concept Application

7. You may wish to use a series of slides, the student text, or a filmstrip without the audio-tape, showing succession in different settings and under different circumstances. Through class discussion, students should describe what is taking place and attempt to generate an explanation for the changes.

8. Chapter 24 of the textbook should be assigned reading.

| Biological Terms | Thinking Skills |
| --- | --- |
| pioneer species | describe nature accurately |
| succession | state causal questions |
| climax stage | create alternative hypotheses |
| | organize and analyze data |
| | draw and apply conclusions |
| | proportional reasoning |
| | probability (random repeated sampling) |

## Sample Test Questions

The following items refer to the forests of the Pacific Northwest. Douglas firs, cedars, and hemlocks are the principal trees of the region. Characteristics of each are listed in the table.

| Douglas Fir | Cedar and Hemlock |
| --- | --- |
| Seedlings die in shade. | Seedlings grow in shade. |
| Seedlings grow well on ashes. | Seedlings do not grow well on ashes. |
| Seeds are winged. | Seeds are not winged. |

1. When an old Douglas fir tree dies in a dense forest, its place will be taken by
   a. Douglas fir seedlings only.
   b. cedar seedlings only.
   c. a mixture of cedars and hemlocks.
   d. hemlock seedlings only.

2. The effect of a fire in this area should be to increase the number of
   a. Douglas firs.
   b. cedars.
   c. hemlocks.
   d. pines.

*Classify the next six items, using the following key.*

### KEY

A. observation

B. logical prediction

C. illogical prediction

3. The normal climax of a Douglas fir, cedar, and hemlock community should be a Douglas fir forest.

4. The seeds of the Douglas fir are winged.

5. After a fire in this community, the Douglas fir seedlings should enter, grow well, and crowd out other seedlings.

6. The young Douglas fir trees will not grow in mature Douglas fir forests.

7. If no fires occur in the forests, the Douglas firs will disappear when the present trees die out.

8. Openings that allow the growth of cedars and hemlocks are created by fires.

*The next two items are based on the figure below.*

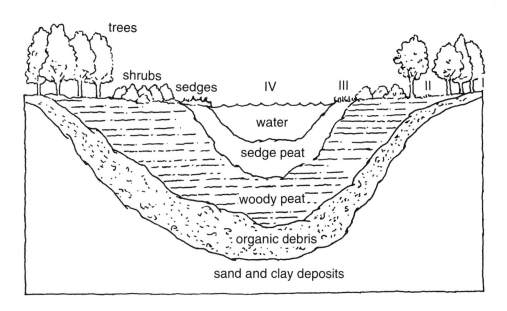

9. Which of the following concepts is represented by the figure?
   a. matter flows
   b. succession
   c. energy
   d. spontaneous generation

10. The next layer deposited at Position III probably will be
   a. clay.
   b. water.
   c. woody peat.
   d. sand.

## Answers

| | |
|---|---|
| 1. C | 6. B |
| 2. A | 7. B |
| 3. C | 8. C |
| 4. A | 9. B |
| 5. B | 10. C |

# Organic Evolution

## Investigation 36    *What Changes Have Occurred in Organisms Through Time?*

## Synopsis

Students explore fossils found in six rock layers of the Grand Canyon, representing different periods in geologic time, to determine characteristics of the fossils and to search for patterns in the history of life on Earth. Trends in the fossil record are discussed, and various hypotheses to account for these trends are proposed and evaluated by the students. Terms relating to evolutionary patterns and Earth history are introduced (e.g., *organic evolution, adaptive radiation, extinction*). This is an empirical-abductive learning cycle.

## Suggested Time

One to one-and-one-half class periods for exploration of the fossils; one-half period for students to find patterns, class discussion, and creating and discussing hypotheses; one-half period for introducing terms; one or more periods for concept application

## Background Information for the Teacher

The theory of organic evolution (the idea that species change across time) represents a cornerstone of modern biology because it conceptually ties together numerous and varied observations. The idea that species evolved had been suggested by others prior to publication of Charles Darwin's *The Origin of Species*, yet Darwin was the first to clearly spell out major postulates of evolutionary theory as follows:

1. All life evolved from one simple kind of organism.

2. Each species, fossil or living, arose from another species that preceded it in time.

3. Evolutionary changes were gradual and of long duration.

4. Each species originated in a single geographic location.

5. Over long periods of time, new genera, new families, new orders, new classes, and new phyla arose by a continuation of the kind of evolution that produced new species (adaptive radiation).

6. The greater the similarity between two groups of organisms, the closer is their relationship and the closer in geologic time is their common ancestral group.

7. Extinction of old forms (species, etc.) is a consequence of the production of new forms or of environmental change.

8. Once a species or other group has become extinct, it never reappears.

9. Evolution continues today in generally the same manner as during preceding geologic eras.

In *The Origin of Species*, it is clear that Darwin recognized that he was describing two theories: "evolution or descent with modification" and "natural selection." In this lab, you can introduce the theory of evolution. Investigation 38, "How Do Species Adapt to Environments?," allows you to introduce the theory of natural selection.

## Advance Preparation

Included at the end of this teacher material are illustrations of fossils to use in the six fossil layers necessary for this investigation. If it is not possible to obtain the fossil kits, you can cut up these layer sheets and allow the students to use them instead (with the names and dates removed). The fossil kits are preferred, and the 50 plastic fossil molds that make up the kits can be obtained from various biological and earth science suppliers.

Each fossil kit has fossils representing six geological time periods. The fossils selected for this investigation demonstrate characteristics true of the fossil record. In general, these fossils reflect (from oldest to youngest):

- a progression from simple to complex
- a general size increase of fossils
- a general increase in diversity
- continuity of some life forms through several time periods
- disappearance or extinction of some life forms
  These patterns are revealed in Figure 1. (See page 229.)
  Copies of the following will need to be made:
- Figure 2 for Activity A (See page 231.)
- Figure 3 for Activity B (See page 232.)
- Pictures of the fossils for procedure step 5

Each fossil picture is identified by a letter set in the lower left corner (L–A). This represents the layer (L) and the set the fossil belongs to (A). (See pages 233–236.)

## Teaching Tips

### Exploration

1. Assign students to work in groups according to the number of fossil kits you have for the class.

2. Call students' attention to the diagram of the rock strata in the student manual, and explain that the fossils in the kits were found in the six corresponding rock layers. Also point out that no fossils were found in the seventh and bottom layer (layer G).

3. Have students obtain the kits and begin their observations. You may want to call their attention to the list of questions at procedure step 3 before they begin.

4. When students begin procedure step 3, you may need to explain what is meant by a family tree and provide an example.

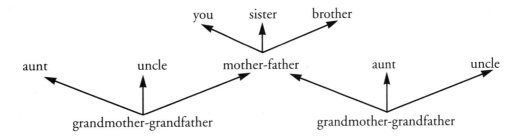

*Ask the students to make a "fossil family tree," following this pattern.*

### Term Introduction

5. With reference to the students' diagrams on the board, engage the class in a discussion of their data.

6. Ask students which layers they believe to be the youngest and the oldest and why. Introduce the terms *superposition, relative dating, fossilization,* and *extinction,* with reference to the data. Tell students that scientists have performed radioactive isotope dating on the rock strata to determine absolute dates.

7. Now ask the class what patterns they found by comparing the different life forms found in the respective layers. Students may have noted several of the patterns listed under Advance Preparation. If not, you may have to lead them a little. These patterns should be diagrammed on the board.

8. Ask students to propose hypotheses to account for why these patterns exist in the fossil record. If they do not understand, lead them with questions like, "What are some possible ways to account for how these organisms got here (on Earth)? What are some ways to account for their appearance or disappearance in the fossil record at these times?" List all suggested hypotheses on the board.

9. Ask the class to consider each of the hypotheses one at a time and to evaluate how well each is supported or weakened by the data from the fossil record. Introduce and discuss the term *organic evolution.*

### Concept Application

10. You may wish to show a filmstrip or cover some of the other areas of evidence that support the theory of organic evolution, notably comparative anatomy, comparative embryology, comparative biochemistry, and chromosomal similarities. *The Land,* a film produced by Shell Oil Company, gives an overview of Earth's geologic history.

11. Another approach you may wish to consider is to explain how scientists "test a theory" by making predictions concerning what they will find when they do experiments or research in new areas. Have your students make some predictions based on what patterns they think they would find if they could compare the proteins, DNA, or internal anatomy of closely related organisms and distantly related organisms.

12. If you do not choose to cover other areas of evidence at this time, you may want to try one or more of the following as an application:
    • View the film loop *Fossil Interpretation* (Biological Science Curriculum Study).
    • Have your students research the evolutionary sequence of an organism that is living today (e.g., horse, human, elephant).
    • Arrange for a field trip to a local fossil bed or museum.

13. Included below are two pencil-and-paper activities that also can be used as applications.

### Activity A

Figure 2 (page 231) illustrates geometric forms from eight successive layers. The oldest, at the base, represents the lowermost layer in the sequence and contains the simplest shapes. Younger layers yield newer or specialized figures. The youngest figures are encountered in the topmost layer (H). This investigation shows the ideas of divergent evolution, parallel evolution, convergent evolution, and radiation. In several cases, no single answer is correct.

### Examples:

A.   Begin with the oldest layer (A) and work upward, connecting by pencil lines the likely related figures, layer by layer.

B.   Cut the figures apart, rearranging them into patterns.

C.   Connect the various figures with arrows to show trends. Indicate which organisms became extinct, changed, or remained constant.

### Activity B

Figure 3 (page 232) shows ten geologic layers of graptolite fossils, with the oldest at the bottom and the youngest at the top. The entire sequence represents fossils found in the Upper Cambrian or Lower Ordovician rocks and continues into the Devonian. Graptolites are an extinct group whose exact relationship to modern animals is not known but whose characteristics evolved rapidly through geologic time.

A.   Establish possible lineages for the various graptolites shown with a series of arrows connecting related fossils or by cutting the sketches apart and rearranging them into related sequences. Be careful to keep the fossils in their correct layer when rearranging.

B.   Locate with numbers and letters possible examples of parallel evolution, convergent evolution, or divergent evolution.

14.   Chapters 25 and 26 of the textbook should be assigned reading.

---

## Biological Terms

organic evolution
speciation
adaptive radiation
sedimentation and rock dating
extinction
convergent evolution
divergent evolution
parallel evolution

## Thinking Skills

describe nature accurately
state causal questions
create alternative hypotheses
generate logical predictions
organize and analyze data
draw and apply conclusions

---

## Sample Test Questions

*The next six items refer to the following chart. The width of each screened area indicates the number of kinds of vertebrates.*

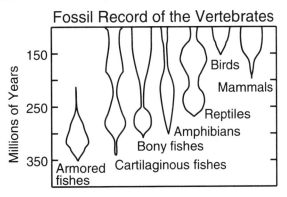

Fossil Record of the Vertebrates

1. What is the basis for this chart?
   a. the age of fossil mammals
   b. the origin of life
   c. carbon dating of the earth's strata
   d. numbers and geologic ages of fossil species

2. "After an animal group has originated, it tends to develop many kinds." This statement would be classed as
   a. a problem.                   c. a result.
   b. data.                        d. an interpretation.

3. What appears to be the most recent group of animals to have come into existence?
   a. reptiles                     c. bony fish
   b. mammals                      d. birds

4. The number of kinds of organisms in a group is a measure of successful adaptation. Which group of fish appears to have been the most successful?
   a. armored fishes               c. bony fish
   b. cartilaginous fish           d. all groups equally successful

5. On the same basis, which group appears to have been the least successful?
   a. bony fish                    c. birds
   b. armored fish                 d. mammals

6. If one were to assume that species do not change, one would expect to find
   a. the simplest fossils in the oldest rocks.
   b. the simplest fossils in the newest rocks.
   c. the same kind of fossils in old and new rocks.
   d. no fossils in any rocks.

*The next seven items are based on the following diagram. The diagram shows sedimentary rock layers and certain organisms found in them. The layers in Locality I were found several kilometers away from those in Locality II. The labels* a–d *and* 1–4 *refer to the different strata.*

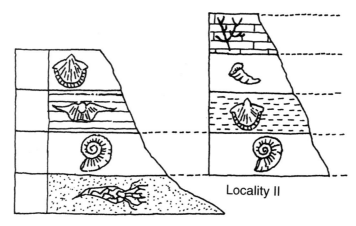

Locality II

Locality I

7. What is the evidence that these are sedimentary rocks?
   a. the fossils
   b. the layers
   c. both of these
   d. neither of these

8. The increase in complexity of organisms through time
   a. is clearly shown here.
   b. is indicated by their positions in the rock strata.
   c. cannot be inferred from this diagram.
   d. is not possible.

9. If no geological shifts have taken place, the organisms in
   a. Stratum a are the simplest.
   b. Stratum d are the simplest.
   c. Stratum a are the oldest.
   d. Stratum d are the oldest.

10. Which stratum in Locality II might be continuous with Stratum d in Locality I?
   a. Stratum 2
   b. Stratum 3
   c. Stratum 4
   d. none of the strata

11. Which of the following can be inferred from the study of the fossils in the various strata?
   a. Organisms have changed through time.
   b. Organisms change structurally from simple to complex.
   c. The relative geologic ages of two specific fossils can be determined.
   d. The organisms in the diagram are the only ones that were living in the area when the fossils were formed.

12. The reason Stratum c does not occur in Locality II may be because
   a. no record of volcanic activity is shown in Locality II.
   b. erosion may have washed away Stratum c.
   c. it is actually above those shown here.
   d. it is in Stratum 4 of Locality II but is not shown.

13. Assume that no disturbance of the strata has occurred. One would expect to find the organisms in Locality II, Stratum 3, and also in Locality I,
   a. Stratum d.
   b. the stratum just above Stratum d.
   c. Stratum c.
   d. the stratum just below Stratum a.

14. Over many years, the uplifting of a mountain range separates a species into two separate populations. After many generations, when the members of the two populations are again brought together, they no longer are able to interbreed. This process is called
   a. parallel evolution.
   b. convergent evolution.
   c. convergent radiant evolution.
   d. retrogressive evolution.
   e. divergent evolution.

## Answers

| | |
|---|---|
| 1. D | 8. C |
| 2. D | 9. C |
| 3. D | 10. A |
| 4. C | 11. C |
| 5. B | 12. B |
| 6. C | 13. B |
| 7. C | 14. E |

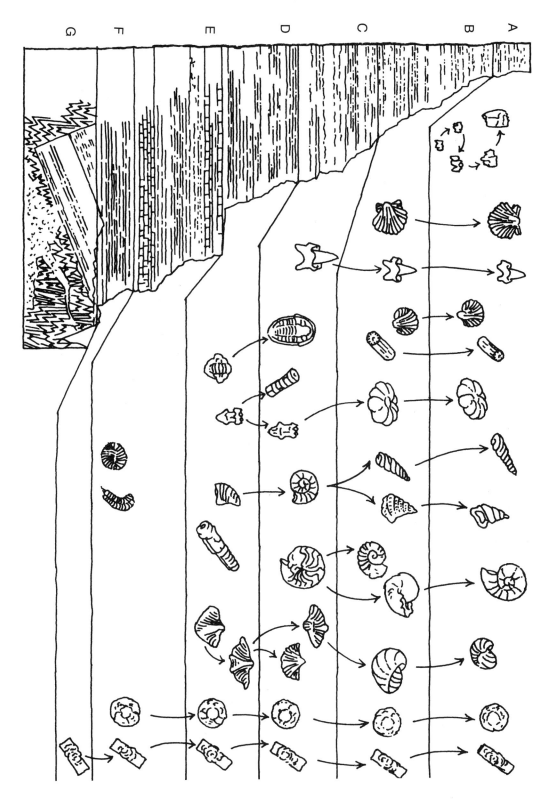

Figure 1.

| Layer A |
| --- |
| These are organisms from the present geologic period. |
| The horse evolution occured during this period and is represented by the teeth (A). |
| $A^1$ *Equus*—Quaternary to Present—$1 \times 10^6$ years ago |
| $A^2$ *Pliohippus*—Pliocene—1 to $10 \times 10^6$ years ago |
| $A^3$ *Merychippus*—Meiocene—13 to $25 \times 10^6$ years ago |
| $A^4$ *Mesohippus*—Oligocene—25 to $36 \times 10^6$ years ago |
| $A^5$ *Hyracotherium*—Eocene—36 to $58 \times 10^6$ years ago |

| Layer B |
| --- |
| Two major groups of snails became distinct during this layer (B). |
| One of the branches of nautilus either converged with the other or became extinct (C). |
| Bony fish appeared (D). |

| Layer C |
| --- |
| The trilobite sequence ends here showing extinction (F). |
| Echinoderms show divergent evolution (E). |

| Layer D |
| --- |
| Diversity of organisms in this layer. Trend is generally from simple form (snail) to more complex. |
| Trilobite starts in this layer and shows an INDEX SPECIES (G). |

| Layer E |
| --- |
| Pre-Cambrian fossils from Australia show only soft-bodied organisms, some of which carry through to today (I). |

| Layer F |
| --- |
| Only fossil evidence of life during this layer's history are algae and bacteria. |

**Activity A**

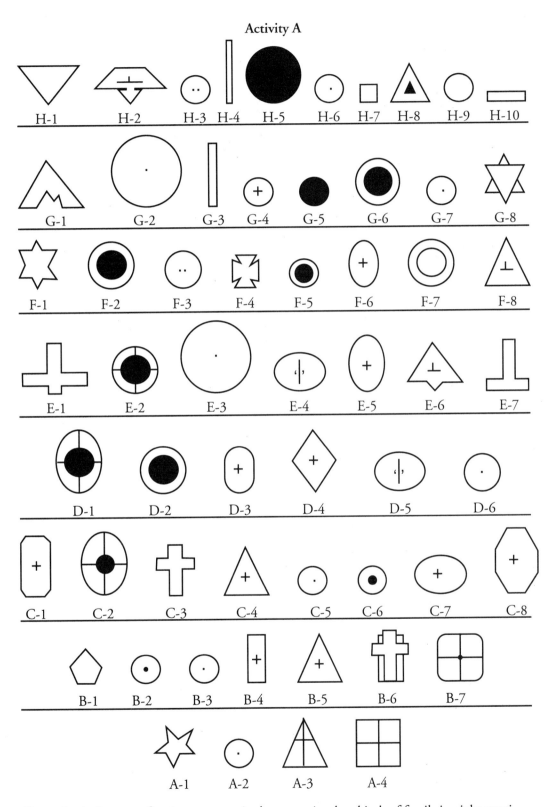

Figure 2. A diagram of various geometric shapes to simulate kinds of fossils in eight stratigraphic intervals, to be used in a problem showing evolutionary patterns and phylogenic trends.

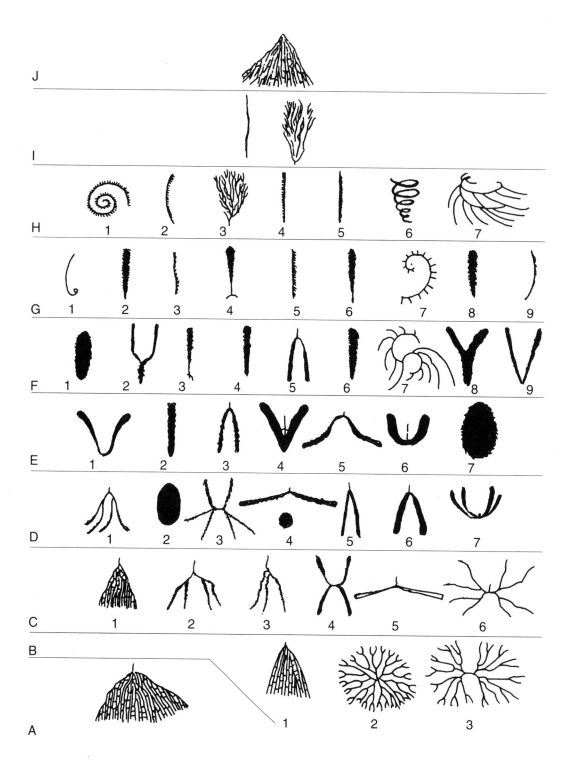

Figure 3. A diagram of graptolite occurences for ten successive stratigraphic horizons, a problem in reconstruction of phylogenic trends.

## Fossil Layer A

| **Collenia**<br>Algae-Bacteria<br>(Cenozoic)<br><br>L-A | **Carcharodon**<br>CHORDATA, Pisces<br>(shark tooth; Tertiary-Miocene)<br><br>L-A | **Medusian**<br>Jellyfish<br>(Cenozoic)<br><br>L-A | **Merychippus**<br>CHORDATA, Mammalia<br>(horse tooth; Tertiary-Miocene)<br><br>L-A$_3$ |
|---|---|---|---|
| **Equus**<br>CHORDATA, Mammalia<br>(horse tooth; Quaternary)<br><br>L-A$_1$ | **Tetragramme agassizi**<br>ECHINODERMATA, Echinoidea<br>(sea urchin; Cretaceous)<br><br>L-A | **Turritella alticostata**<br>MOLLUSCA, Gastropoda<br>(Tertiary)<br><br>L-A | **Venericardia robustus**<br>MOLLUSCA, Pelecypoda<br>(clam; Tertiary-Quaternary)<br><br>L-A |
| **Pecten jeffersonius**<br>MOLLUSCA, Pelecypoda<br>(scallop; Teriary-Quaternary)<br><br>L-A | **Littorina**<br>MOLLUSCA, Gastropoda<br>(snail; Paleozoic to Recent)<br><br>L-A | **Hyracotherium**<br>CHORDATA, Mammalia<br>(horse tooth; Eocene)<br><br>L-A$_5$ | **Lytoceras**<br>MOLLUSCA, Cephalopoda<br>(Jurassic-Cretaceous)<br><br>L-A |
| **Oleneothyris hariani**<br>BRACHIOPODA<br>(Cretaceous)<br><br>L-A | **Fish Bone**<br>CHORDATA<br>(Quaternary)<br><br>L-A | **Pliohippus**<br>CHORDATA, Mammalia<br>(horse tooth; Pliocene)<br><br>L-A$_2$ | **Mesohippus**<br>CHORDATA, Mammalia<br>(horse tooth; Oligocene)<br><br>L-A$_4$ |

## Fossil Layer B

| | | | |
|---|---|---|---|
| **Collenia**<br>Algae-Bacteria<br>(Tertiary)<br><br>L-B | **Carcharodon**<br>CHORDATA, Pisces<br>(shark tooth; Tertiary-Miocene)<br><br>L-B | **Tetragramme agassizi**<br>ECHINODERMATA, Echinoidea<br>(sea urchin; Cretaceous)<br><br>L-B | **Medusina**<br>Jellyfish<br>(Cretaceous)<br><br>L-B |
| **Turritella alticostata**<br>MOLLUSCA, Gastropoda<br>(Tertiary)<br><br>L-B | **Venericardia robustus**<br>MOLLUSCA, Pelecypoda<br>(clam-Tertiary-Quaternary)<br><br>L-B | **Meekoceras gracilitatis**<br>MOLLUSCA, Cephalopoda<br>(Triassic)<br><br>L-B | **Pleurotomaria**<br>MOLLUSCA, Gastropoda<br>(snail; Jurassic)<br><br>L-B |
| **Acanthoscaphites**<br>MOLLUCSCA, Cephalopoda<br>(Cretaceous)<br><br>L-B | **Oleneothyris hariani**<br>BRACHIOPODA<br>(Cretaceous)<br><br>L-B | **Fish Vertebra**<br>CHORDATA, Bony Fish<br>(Triassic)<br><br>L-B | **Pecten jeffersonius**<br>MOLLUSCA, Pelecypoda<br>(scallop; Tertiary-Quaternary)<br><br>L-B |

## Fossil Layer C

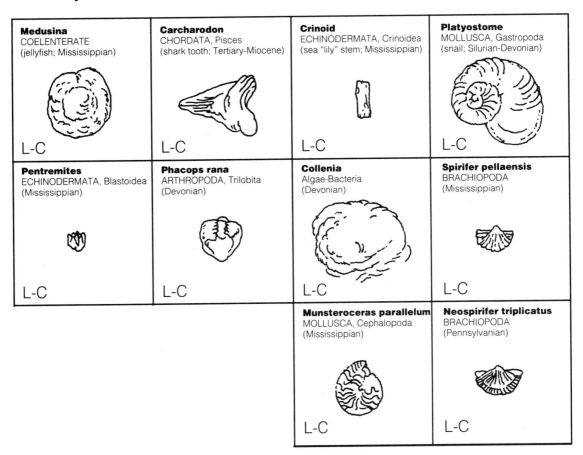

**Medusina**
COELENTERATE
(jellyfish; Mississippian)

L-C

**Carcharodon**
CHORDATA, Pisces
(shark tooth; Tertiary-Miocene)

L-C

**Crinoid**
ECHINODERMATA, Crinoidea
(sea "lily" stem; Mississippian)

L-C

**Platyostome**
MOLLUSCA, Gastropoda
(snail; Silurian-Devonian)

L-C

**Pentremites**
ECHINODERMATA, Blastoidea
(Mississippian)

L-C

**Phacops rana**
ARTHROPODA, Trilobita
(Devonian)

L-C

**Collenia**
Algae-Bacteria
(Devonian)

L-C

**Spirifer pellaensis**
BRACHIOPODA
(Mississippian)

L-C

**Munsteroceras parallelum**
MOLLUSCA, Cephalopoda
(Mississippian)

L-C

**Neospirifer triplicatus**
BRACHIOPODA
(Pennsylvanian)

L-C

## Fossil Layer D

**Michelinoceras sociale**
MOLLUSCA, Cephalopoda
(Ordovician)

L-D

**Mucrospirifer
thedfordensis**
BRACHIOPODA
(Devonian)

L-D

**Medusina**
COELENTERATA
(jellyfish; Devonian)

L-D

**Flexicalymene meeki**
ARTHROPODA, Trilobita
(Silurian)

L-D

**Maclurites**
MOLLUSCA, Gastropoda
(snail; Ordovician)

L-D

**Eospirifer radiatus**
BRACHIOPODA
(Silurian)

L-D

**Collenia**
Algae-Bacteria
(chirt; Devonian)

L-D

**Codaster**
ECHINODERMATA
(blastoid; Silurian)

L-D

## Fossil Layer E

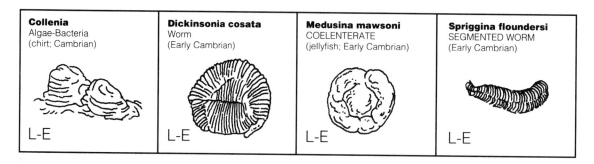

| **Collenia** Algae-Bacteria (chirt; Cambrian) | **Dickinsonia cosata** Worm (Early Cambrian) | **Medusina mawsoni** COELENTERATE (jellyfish; Early Cambrian) | **Spriggina floundersi** SEGMENTED WORM (Early Cambrian) |
|---|---|---|---|
| L-E | L-E | L-E | L-E |

## Fossil Layer F

**Collenia**
Algae-Bacteria
(chirt; Pre-Cambrian)

L-F

## Fossil Layer G

No fossils found in this layer

L-G

# Geologic Time • Adaptive Radiation

## Investigation 37  *Have Humans Been on Earth for a Long Time?*

## Synopsis

Students plot the relative location of historical, archeological, geological, and astronomical events on a single-scale time line. Difficulties encountered in constructing the time lines are discussed as a means of introducing the vast amount of time available for evolution and the relatively brief period of time humans have been on Earth. This is a descriptive learning cycle.

## Suggested Time

One to two class periods

## Background Information for the Teacher

The fossil record reveals a vast diversity of life forms that have evolved, adaptively radiated, and, in some cases, become extinct over billions of years—about 3.4 billion years, according to the best estimates currently available. In this activity, students construct time lines noting the relative positions of important events in Earth's history and in the evolution of life. If they attempt to construct their time lines using 1 m to represent 1 billion years, they will discover that only 1 mm of their 5.5-m line is devoted to the events associated with humankind, almost two-thirds of the events given on their data table. As it is clearly not possible to record all of these events in such a small space, a new scale will have to be selected. Unfortunately, a scale large enough to accommodate human historical events will produce a line many kilometers long. This discovery by the students will help them realize that humans have been on Earth a very short time relative to Earth's history. Thus, vast periods of time have existed for organisms to evolve from earlier forms and to adaptively radiate into vast and diverse more recent forms.

## Advance Preparation

Paper strips for the time lines can be made inexpensively by using a band saw to cut rolls of paper towels into 3-to-5-cm-wide strips. Adding machine paper rolls also work well. The activity can be conducted outdoors along a long sidewalk or field.

## Teaching Tips

### Exploration

1. Students may find it helpful if you provide an example time line using important dates from a student's life. Ask a student volunteer for specific events, such as: year of birth, year first went to school, and so on. Draw a time line on the board, using a single scale, and plot these events. Emphasize the importance of using a single scale for all of the events.

2. Help students get started by suggesting that they list all dates chronologically before starting their time lines.

3. Some groups may need hints from other groups or from you to select a reasonable scale and to use the proportional reasoning needed to place events in their correct position along the time line.

4. A major problem students will have is getting all of the archeological and historical events on their lines; these will be too close together to list separately. Students should expand their lines to cover at least several meters if they have not already done so. Following this, they should be allowed to change scales to list these events, provided they indicate precisely where on the original scale the events begin and end.

### Term Introduction

5. Have a few of the completed time lines taped to the board for comparison. Discuss any difficulties encountered, and emphasize the vast amount of time available for evolution and the relatively brief time humans have been on earth. The phrase *geologic time* can be introduced to refer to this time perspective. Reintroduce the phrase *proportional reasoning* to help emphasize the quantitative reasoning patterns used in locating positions along the time lines. You may also want to introduce and discuss methods of radioactive dating at this time.

### Concept Application

6. You may wish to discuss adaptive radiation as suggested in the Study Questions. Investigation 38 provides for additional applications. This would be an excellent place to include an activity or discussion on endangered species.

| **Biological Terms** | **Thinking Skills** |
|---|---|
| geologic time | organize and analyze data |
| adaptive radiation | draw and apply conclusions |

## Sample Test Questions

The discoverers of fossil humans have tended to give new genus and species names to almost every bone fragment discovered. The differences between many of these forms, however, are no greater than the differences between modern human races. Dobzhansky devised the following method of tabular classification to overcome some of the difficulties of the older systems. Use the table below to classify the following statements. All species listed belong to the same family as modern humans.

A = genus *Australopithecus*

H = *Homo*

**Human Origins**

| Species and Subspecies | Locality | Approximate Age in Thousands of Years | Brain Size (cc) |
|---|---|---|---|
| *A. afarensis* ("Lucy") | S. Africa | 3,800–3,000 | 450–500 |
| *A. africanus* | Africa | 3,000–2,200 | 450–500 |
| *A. robustus* | Africa | 2,000–1,800 | 450–500 |
| *A. boisei* | Africa | 2,000–1,200 | 450–500 |
| *H. habilis* | Africa | 2,000–1,500 | 700 |
| *H. erectus* | Africa, Europe Asia, China | 600–300 | 800–1200 |
| *H. sapiens neanderthalensis* | Africa, Europe Asia | 300–40 | 1400–1700 |
| *H. sapiens cro-magnon* | Africa, Europe Asia | 90–34 | — |
| *H. sapiens sapiens* | All continents | 60–Present | 1300–1600 |

1. A major advantage of this system of classification over that of giving each bone fragment a separate generic and specific name is that it
   a. is simpler.
   b. reveals possible relationships.
   c. reduces the number of names.
   d. is more consistent with proper nomenclature.

2. The data suggest that humans originated in
   a. Africa.
   b. Asia.
   c. Australia.
   d. Europe.

3. Could a *Homo sapiens* male and a *Homo sapiens neanderthalensis* female have produced fertile offspring? Why or why not?
   a. Probably yes, because they belong to the same genus.
   b. Probably yes, because they belong to the same species.
   c. Probably no, because they belong to different subspecies.
   d. Probably no, because they had different brain sizes.

4. If a hand weapon were found with fossils of one species, which of the following inferences is most reasonable? The weapon
   a. was used by the human species.
   b. belonged to a member of an apelike species that hunted the human species.
   c. was made by a form with a brain size greater than 1300 mL.
   d. was used to make iron spear points.

5. From the data in the chart, the best estimate of the brain size of a subspecies of *Homo erectus* called *heidelbergensis* is
   a. 600 mL.                              c. 900 mL.
   b. 750 mL.                              d. 1300 mL.

6. The fossil skulls of humans show a trend that brain size
   a. has gotten smaller.                  c. has generally increased.
   b. has remained constant.              d. has no importance.

7. If you constructed a time line in which 1 cm represented 500 years, about how long would your line be (in kilometers) if the present were at one end and the origin of life (2 billion years ago) were at the other end? Note: 100 000 cm = 1 km.
   a. 1 km                                 d. 40 km
   b. 10 km                                e. 100 km
   c. 20 km

8. About how far from the end of your time line (in item 7 above) would the first "true" humans appear? Note: To simplify matters, assume that the first "true" humans appeared about 1 million years ago.
   a. 500 cm                               d. 50 km
   b. 20 m                                 e. 100 km
   c. 1 km

## Answers

1. B          5. C
2. A          6. C
3. B          7. D
4. A          8. B

# Natural Selection

## Investigation 38    *How Do Species Adapt to Environments?*

## Synopsis

In this activity, the process of natural selection is simulated by students playing the role of predatory birds feeding on "mice" made of paper chips. After the students gather, graph, and discuss the data, the teacher introduces the term *natural selection* to refer to the simulated process. Students then are challenged to apply this idea to explain changes in Galapagos tortoise and peppered moth populations over time. This is a descriptive learning cycle.

## Suggested Time

Two class periods

## Background Information for the Teacher

The backbone of modern biology is the theory of evolution (descent with modification) and Darwin's theory of natural selection. Darwin's theory represents the first theory to explain satisfactorily how evolution occurs. It is generally accepted today even though refinements and additions to it continue to be made. The theory consists of the following seven basic postulates.

1. Populations of organisms have the potential to increase at a geometric rate (biotic potential).

2. In the short run, the number of individuals in a population remains fairly constant because the conditions of life are limited (limiting factors exist).

3. Individuals in a population are not all the same; they have variations (variable characteristics).

4. A struggle for survival exists such that individuals having favorable characteristics will survive and produce more offspring than those with unfavorable characteristics.

5. Some of the characteristics responsible for differential survival and reproduction are passed from parent to offspring (they are heritable). Hence, a natural selection for certain favorable characteristics occurs.

6. The environments of many organisms have been changing throughout geologic time.

7. Natural selection causes the accumulation of favorable characteristics and the loss of unfavorable characteristics to the extent that new species may arise.

This lab activity simulates the process of natural selection and allows you to review Postulates 1, 2, 3, and 6 with your students and to introduce Postulates 4, 5, and 7.

## Advance Preparation

Select a variety of brightly colored, strongly patterned fabrics. Floral or leaf prints are good.

Paper chips may be cut with a standard hole punch (four at a time.).

Paper thickness may vary. This introduces a second variable, which you may find desirable.

## Teaching Tips

### *Exploration*

1. It is important that exactly 25% of the paper chips remain after selection. This prevents exponential growth of the population. If three students act as predators, each will select 25 chips. If two or four students act as predators, they must still remove 75 chips as prey. Verify that the students have determined how they will split up the total of 75 chips.

### *Term Introduction*

2. After the data have been gathered and graphed, instruct one student from each group to put his or her graph on the board. In a class discussion, the students should be asked to summarize the data. For example, "What patterns or trends do the data reveal? What colors have been eliminated? What colors have reproduced in greatest numbers? Are these the same for all environments?" Following this discussion, introduce the term natural selection. To do this, point out that some colors have been "selected for," others "selected against." Because this selection was done by nature (predators), we call the process *natural selection.* The terms *adaptation* and *survival of the fittest* should be introduced and defined. The roles of variation, biotic potential, heredity, and limiting factors should be identified in the simulation.

3. You may need to discuss the theory of inheritance of acquired characteristics and to compare it with the theory of natural selection. Many students will hold this erroneous idea and not be aware that it is contradictory to the idea of natural selection.

### *Concept Application*

4. To reinforce these ideas, you may wish to discuss other instances of natural selection, such as the case of *Biston betularia* (the peppered moth) and instances of artificial selection such as domestic plant and animal breeding. The film loop *Galapagos Tortoises* (Ealing Film Loops) may be shown in which the students observe two "types" of Galapagos tortoises (a highland type with short neck and legs, and a lowland type with long neck and legs) and are challenged to explain observed differences using the theory of natural selection.

5. Chapter 27 of the textbook should be assigned reading. Students should also review Chapter 5.

| **Biological Terms** | **Thinking Skills** |
|---|---|
| natural selection | state causal questions |
| adaptation | organize and analyze data |
| survival of the fittest | draw and apply conclusions |

## Sample Test Questions

*The next six items refer to a tropical island heavily infested with mosquitos. The island was sprayed with DDT over a period of several months. Daily accounts of population size gave the information shown in the graph.*

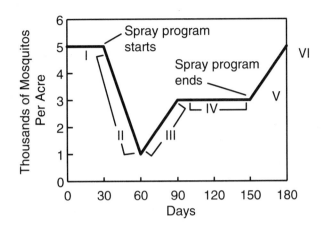

1. After looking at these data, someone made the statement, "DDT caused a reduction in the mosquito population." This statement would be classified as a
   a. hypothesis.
   b. prediction.
   c. conclusion.
   d. question.

2. The most probable reason for the decreasing effectiveness of the spraying as the summer progressed was that the
   a. mosquitos became immune to the DDT.
   b. mosquitos resistant to DDT lived and produced offspring.
   c. DDT was used at irregular intervals.
   d. the DNA of the mosquito population was not affected.

3. Which process is chiefly responsible for the change represented in section II of the curve?
   a. repopulation
   b. overpopulation
   c. variation
   d. selection

4. The best explanation for some mosquitos surviving the first spraying is that
   a. the weather early in the summer was probably rather cool.
   b. most of the mosquitos were adults.
   c. environmental factors varied slightly as the summer progressed.
   d. natural variation existed within the population.

5. The best hypothesis to explain the increase shown in section V is reproduction by mosquitos that are
   a. migrating to the island.
   b. mutants.
   c. not resistant.
   d. females.

6. If insecticides are no longer as successful in killing flies as they were in the past, it is probably because
   a. insecticides are made differently.
   b. susceptible flies have been eliminated.
   c. the flies are avoiding the insecticides.
   d. insecticides loose their power.

7. How does the theory of natural selection differ from the theory of inheritance of acquired characteristics? (According to the theory of natural selection, characteristics that are genetically derived may give individuals an advantage in survival, thus these individuals survive and pass the characteristics to the next generation. Individuals with

unfavorable characteristics do not survive to reproduce, thus those unfavorable characteristics are eventually deleted from the population. The theory of the inheritance of acquired characteristics argues that favorable characteristics that are acquired during ones lifetime are passed to offspring, hence over time the population in general acquires more favorable characteristics. Both theories lead to the same end but do so in different ways. Unfortunately for the second theory, biologists have not found that characterisitcs acquired during ones lifetime can be passed to their offspring.)

8. How does natural selection differ from artificial selection? Cite some instances of artificial selection. (The only major difference is the agent of selection, i.e., nature vs. humans. Varieties of dogs have arisen via artificial selection as have several breeds of domestic farm animals and several crops, e.g., corn, wheat, cotton.)

*The next 9 items refer to the following information about insects.*

Assume that in a certain strain of insects, dark color is dominant to light color. Ten pairs of dark insects with heterozygous genotypes were released in a plot covering 5,000 m² of a white, sandy area. They could not escape from the area.

If the heterozygous insect lives and breeds through two or three generations, you could expect the hybrid cross results to have 1 BB : 2 Bb : 1 bb, or 3 dark for each light form. During the next few years, the actual proportion of dark forms decreased and the proportion of light ones increased. After a few years, the ratio of the insects was 1 dark : 3 light.

An interesting question raised by this observation is: why did the ratio of dark to light insect change?

*Use the key to identify each of the next nine items.*

**KEY**

A. a reasonable hypothesis

B. an unreasonable hypothesis and/or contradicted by the data

C. not a hypothesis but a restatement of the data

D. a reasonable prediction

9. There are more white insects now because light color is dominant to dark color.

10. Predators did not like the taste of light-colored insects.

11. Light-colored insects were not as visible on the white sand as the dark insects.

12. After a few years, there were more light insects than dark insects.

13. The color of the light ones helped protect them from predators.

14. You could expect a continued shift in the gene frequency of the population.

15. Natural selection in this environment favored the light-colored insects.

16. The white sand caused dark insects to become light, and these then produced light insects.

17. Many of the dark ones moved out of the plot to some other area.

## Answers

1. C
2. B
3. D
4. D
5. C
6. B
9. B
10. B

11. B
12. C
13. A
14. D
15. A
16. B
17. B

# Answers to Study Questions

## Investigation 2

1. Living things are made of cells, grow, reproduce, die, respond to stimuli, are chemically complex, and are highly organized.

2. People classify for several reasons. First, classifying provides a way of organizing and keeping track of several complex and diversified things. This facilitates use and allows for easier access. Second, by classifying, people can more easily see relationships and shared characteristics. This allows for ease of identification. Finally, classification allows for simplification. Creating specific categories gives order and structure, which simplifies the complex nature of large collective groups.

3. Libraries use classification schemes for books categorized from broad to narrow categories. Within each broad category, books are grouped according to topic. Related topics are given similar numbers. At the lowest level, individual books are individually identified with a number. This scheme enables people to find books and to identify related books. In auto-parts shops, parts are similarly classified into broad to narrow categories. Within each category are numbers for the category of the part and its specific function. This classification speeds identification of specific parts and identification of their functions.

4. to describe and organize them to facilitate their identification and study; to determine evolutionary relationships among them

5. at the highest level—i.e., the kingdom level; Here, organisms are grouped under the broadest categories, with the fewest similarities.

6. at the lowest level—i.e., the species level; Here, the organisms must be most similar, i.e., be enough alike to be able to mate and produce fertile offspring.

7. Since species are operationally defined as able to reproduce viable offspring, one would allow the two mice to mate and observe the offspring that results. If the offspring are viable, then the mice are of the same species; if they are not viable, then the two mice may not be of the same species or they may simply not have been able to mate and produce viable offspring for some unknown reason.

## Investigation 3

1. A population is a group of organisms of the same species living together in a particular area. In this context a sample is a small subset of those organisms that hopefully is representative of the larger population.

2. Answers will vary. The following is one possible answer: Assign each student a number and then select a subset of those numbers using a table of random numbers. List all students alphabetically and then select every fourth student from the list.

3. A normal distribution is the pattern that typically occurs when the values of a continuous variable are plotted on a frequency distribution. It is called *normal* because it occurs often.

4. There may be a variety of genetic and/or environmental factors that cause normal distributions, but the most likely cause in most cases is that the variation in the characteristic under consideration is caused by genes that distribute themselves randomly from the parents to the offspring; thus any value for a particular offspring is partially the product of

chance. The probability of certain genetic combinations occurring dictates that some values will be expressed more often than others.

5. Genes are small segments of chromosomes; genes are located in the nucleus of most cells.

6. The gene that is expressed over another gene for the same value or characteristic is called the *dominant gene*. The gene that is masked by the dominant gene is said to be recessive.

7. The basic problem is that in most cases the genes and the environment both vary from individual to individual; thus it is not possible to tell which caused any observed difference between individuals (i.e., it is a control-of-variables problem). If you could find identical twins (same genes) who were reared apart (different environment), then any observed differences could be attributed to the environment.

8. The different types of gametes possible are:
   a. D, d.
   b. DE, De, dE, de.
   c. DEf, Def, dEf, def.

9. The probability of getting the gamete de is:
   a. no chance of getting de.
   b. there is a 50% chance (50/50) of getting de.
   c. there is a 100% chance of getting de (will always get de).

10. The probability of getting a given genotype is:
    a. there is a 50% chance of getting Dd.
    b. there is a 25% chance of getting Dd.
    c. there is a 25% chance (2 in 8) of getting DdEe.
    d. there is a 1 in 16 chance (6.25%) of getting DDEE.

11. a. The kitten has a 50% chance (2 in 4) of carrying the recessive "no color" gene.
    b. The chance that the kitten will have no color is 25% (1 in 4).

12. a. The genotype ratios of the heterozygous bean plant offspring would be 1:2:1 (LL:Ll:ll). The phenotype ratios of the beans would be 3:1 (3 large pods to 1 short pod).

13. a. Assume that P is the gene for purple eyes and O is the gene (of the pair) for orange eyes. When these combine (PO), the result is a white-eyed Gronk. So a male PO mated with a female PO could produce all three offspring types (PP, PO, and OO).
    b. Purple (PP) × white (PO) would produce offspring genotypes of PP and PO in a 1:1 ratio.

## Reasoning Module 1

1. 50%

2. 16.7%

3. 20%

4. 1/36 = 2.8%, 6/36 = 1/6 = 16.7%

5. a. 25; 4/5

**b.** 80%

**c.** 80%

6. **a.** 5/75 = 6.7%

   **b.** 6.7%

7. **a.** 23/28 = 82%

   **b.** 18%

   **c.** No, because this class is not likely to be representative of the school's population with respect to the sex of the students.

**Brain Bender**—Answers will vary. For example: Assume that the probability of finding a needle in a 1-cubic-foot haystack in one hour is about 1. Assume that the probability decreases with an increase in size of stack (i.e., the probability would be 1/2 with a 2-cubic-foot stack). A five-foot-tall stack would contain about $(5 \times 5 \times 5) \div 2 = 62.5$ cubic feet of hay. Therefore, the probability would be about 2 out of 62.5. Variables may include visual acuity, size of needle, shape of haystack, etc.

## Investigation 4

1. The term *variable* refers to a characteristic, property or feature that has been found to have different values in a sample of objects and/or organisms. The terms *characteristic*, *property*, and *trait* all mean the same and refer to some observable feature of an object or group of objects.

2. Eye dominance: left-eyed or right-eyed
   Sex: male or female

   Hair on back: present or absent
   Hair color: brown or black

3. A *constant* is a characteristic whose values do not change or vary within the sample of objects under consideration.

4. The discontinuous variables are sex, handedness, eyedness, and tongue-rolling ability. The continuous variables include height, weight, quickness, and arm span. Handedness depends on how it was determined.

5. Sex, handedness, eyedness, and tongue rolling are probably all traits that are determined by a single gene pair. They are discontinuous traits—either "on" or "off," "yes" or "no"— so their expression probably depends on the presence or absence of one genetic "switch." Height, weight, arm span, and quickness are probably controlled by a number of gene pairs because they are continuous traits. Their expression varies over a wide range with many intermediate values in between, so there is not simply one switch that controls their expression. It is likely that many gene pairs work together to influence the final expression of these characteristics.

6. **a.**

|  | Number of Spots | |
|---|---|---|
|  | Many | None |
| Big | 3 | 9 |
| Small | 3 | 12 |

   (Size)

   **b.** The above data do not suggest a correlation between size and number of spots because the ratio of small spotty worms to small plain worms is the same as the ratio of large spotty worms to large plain worms: 1:3. If size and spottiness were correlated, or linked in some way, then the ratio should change as the size changes.

7. **a.** The variables are crossed dominance, uncrossed dominance, and equal sight in both eyes. Players with crossed dominance had higher batting average than those with uncrossed dominance. Players who saw equally with both eyes had the highest batting averages. Researchers explain their results by comparing batting averages.
   **b.** Answers will vary.

## Reasoning Module 2

1. **a.** Yes, it shows a correlation between the speed of the auto was traveling and the distance the auto traveled on one gallon of gasoline. The slower the speed the auto went the further it traveled and likewise the faster the auto traveled the shorter the distance the auto would cover.
   **b.** Point #5 may be an exception.
   **c.** The car could have been a different make, wind could have played a role, a different type of fuel could have been used, or some other force might have acted upon the auto. There are an infinite number of reasons why the exception might have been produced.

2. 
|          | Small Frogs | Large Frogs |
|----------|-------------|-------------|
| Spots    | 7           | 8           |
| No Spots | 13          | 2           |

Yes, there is a correlation. Most of the small frogs (13/20 = 65%) are not spotted, but most of the big frogs are spotted (8/10 = 80%). It appears that there is a greater chance of being spotted if you are a large frog.

3. Yes, most of the smokers died of lung cancer (5/7 = 71%) while most of the nonsmokers died of something else (5/6 = 83%).

4. **a.** the number of aspirin consumed and the risk of heart attack

   **b.**
   |                   | Heart Attack | No Heart Attack |        |
   |-------------------|--------------|-----------------|--------|
   | Aspirin Taken     | 104          | 10,933          | 11,037 |
   | No Aspirin Taken  | 189          | 10,845          | 11,034 |

   The data indicates a correlation. The risk of heart attack among the aspirin takers is 104/11,037 = 0.94%, while the risk among the non-aspirin takers is 189/11,034 = 1.71%.
   **c.** Yes, aspirin is believed to act by inhibiting the aggregation of platelets.
   **d.** Yes, there seemed to be an excess in the number of people dying of strokes in the group of people taking the aspirin. The aspirin may have assisted in the hemorrhages in the brain in a few cases. There were more cases of strokes in the aspirin-taking group than in the group that did not take the aspirin.

5. **a.** income and blood pressure
   **b.** inverse; As the income goes up, the blood pressure goes down.

c. No, the relationship is stated as a correlation, not a cause and effect. One would need to generate hypotheses (possible causes) to explain the correlation. For example, it could be that low income keeps people from buying the proper food. Poor nutrition then causes high blood pressure. Or perhaps low income causes people to worry. Perhaps worry, in some way, causes high blood pressure. Clearly the causal links have not been worked out.

6. Answers will vary.

## Investigation 5

1. The back teeth are probably used for grinding food since they are flat and provide a large chewing surface—excellent for breaking up grasses and plants.

2. The front teeth are fangs or tusks possibly used for fighting or perhaps for rooting out plant material stuck in the mud. They are probably not used to help eat meat because the other teeth do not appear to be sharp enough to cut the meat.

3. This animal is probably a herbivore since its back teeth are designed for chewing plants. The front teeth are probably tusks used for fighting, not eating as mentioned. However, if these teeth could be used to eat meat, then the animal would be an omnivore.

4. The eyes are on the top of the head and positioned to the side. This is good for peripheral vision, perhaps to keep an eye on potential predators. The fact that they are on the top might allow the animal to see when partially submerged in water.

5. Some bottom fish have eyes on top like this, as do frogs and toads. Many prey animals, such as deer, have eyes pointed to the side.

6. This animal may be terrestrial or perhaps amphibious since its eye sockets are elevated from the surface to the skull—allowing it to see over the surface of the water when the rest of its body is submerged. It appears to be much too heavy to be able to fly.

7. It may be a hippopotamus, as they are large plant eaters that live in and/or near ponds/lakes and spend much of their time submerged.

## Investigation 6

1. Hyperventilation—rapid, deep breathing—can be dangerous if it is done prior to holding one's breath because it enables one to hold his or her breath for a longer time than may be safe, i.e., one may faint before he or she starts breathing again. If you faint while underwater you could drown. Hyperventilation releases $CO_2$ and $H^+$ from the blood. As one holds his or her breath the $O_2$ drops and the $H^+$ level builds up. The increasing $H^+$ level signals the brain to start breathing again but the level may not rise fast enough to send the signal prior to the $O_2$ level from dropping too far, which causes the fainting.

2. When a person is suffering from carbon monoxide poisoning most of his hemoglobin is bound to the carbon monoxide instead of to normal oxygen. The paramedics will administer a mixture of the gases to first replace the carbon monoxide with oxygen to nourish the cells and the carbon dioxide to increase its level in the blood stream and stimulate the nerve cells to send a message to the brain, which in turn sends a message to respiratory muscles to increase the breathing rate. When the carbon dioxide level returns to normal, then the breathing rate will return to normal.

3. The atmospheric pressure of oxygen is lessened as a person ascends. As the air pressure decreases so does the alveolar pressure of oxygen in the body. This will lower the concentration of oxygen in the blood causing the body to increase its respiratory rate and heart rate to compensate for the lack of oxygen. This condition is known as altitude sickness. Its symptoms are shortness of breath, nausea, and dizziness. The heart rate needs to increase in order to supply the surrounding tissues with enough oxygen to survive.

4. most definitely; The higher the respiration rate, the higher the heart rate. Likewise, the lower the respiration rate, the lower the heart rate. These changes can be due to internal as well as external factors such as hyperventilation and exercise. As metabolism increases, carbon dioxide increases in the bloodstream. This increase stimulates nerve cells to send messages to the brain to increase the respiratory rate to rid the body of the unwanted carbon dioxide. This, in turn, causes the heart rate to increase—showing a strong correlation between the two.

5. In a hypothermic condition the body slows its metabolic rate and reduces the oxygen needs of the tissues. This will allow less tissue to be damaged due to oxygen deprivation so the recovery possibility will be greatly increased. The knowledge of the slowing of metabolism has given doctors the ability to perform open heart surgeries and heart transplants. The bodies are cooled during the operations to minimize the oxygen need to the tissues and allow for a better chance of survival.

6. Guttation, turgor pressure, and transpiration are a few examples of homeostatic controls in plants. Guttation happens when the water absorbed by the roots creates pressure on the inside of the plant. This pressure forces water droplets out of the leaves until a relief in the pressure is compensated. Turgor pressure controls the amount of water inside the cells of the plant. This pressure forces the cytoplasm and the cell membrane against the cell wall and the cell becomes rigid. Transpiration is the evaporation of water vapor from stems and leaves during the day. This process is controlled by guard cells.

7. Organisms need to have their internal environment at equilibrium. In order for the cells inside of the organism to survive they need to have their fluids precisely maintained at all times. When this equilibrium is disrupted the cells will have an excess or will be missing out on something needed to survive. If the equilibrium is not restored in a timely manner then death might occur in the cell. All cells need a system of checks and balances in order to function.

8. *Homeostasis* refers to living systems by definition, therefore, strictly speaking, nonliving homeostatic relationships do not exist. Nevertheless, a thermostat is similar in that a decrease in room temperature causes the thermostat to turn on a heater while the resulting increase in temperature will cause the heater to shut off. The result is that the room maintains a fairly constant internal temperature.

9. a. assume person's heartbeat is 70 beats/minute
   b. assume person lives to 70 years old
   c. multiply 70 beats/minute × 60 minutes = 4,200 beats in 1 hour
   d. multiply 4,200 × 24 hours = 100,800 beats in 1 day
   e. multiply 100,800 × 365 days = 36,792,000 beats in 1 year
   f. multiply 36,792,000 × 70 years = 2,575,440,000 beats in this person's lifetime

## Investigation 7

1. **a.** The two variables being tested are the amount of light and amount of moisture.
   **b.** For the variable amount of light, there is a lot of light or very little light.
       For the variable of moisture, there is dry and wet.
   **c.** To test for the amount of light variable, the amount of moisture has to be held constant. To test for the amount of moisture the amount of light has to be held constant.
   **d.** Boxes II and IV
   **e.** The location of the mealworms in Box II suggests that they are attracted to light, but it could also mean that the worms were moving away from the wet side of the pan. We can't tell which variable affected the movement of the worms because this was not a controlled experiment.
   **f.** Box II, because the moisture is the same throughout the pan (dry); The experiment seems to support the hypothesis that the worms are attracted to light since most of them are on the light side of the box.
   **g.** Box III tells me that mealworms respond to the amount of moisture variable as well as to the amount of light variable. If they did not respond to moisture, then they should be at the lighted end. But they are not at the lighted end. They are in the middle. Therefore, they do respond to moisture. They "prefer" light and dry conditions according to these data.
   **h.** I would not draw the conclusion that mealworms prefer light to dark because not enough worms were used to show a clear trend. If only one of the worms that ended up in the lighted end went the other way, the results would be 2 to 2, or half in one end and half in the other. Such a result would indicate that the amount of light had no effect.

2. Answers will vary but here is an example:

   Does the size (diameter) of a wheel affect how fast and far a wheel will roll?

   To test this you would need two wheels, one large and one small. The wheels would roll down a ramp and the distance they traveled would be measured from the bottom of the ramp. The speed of the wheels would be measured by timing them with a stopwatch from the bottom of the ramp to a set mark (~ 6 ft).

   The independent variable would be the size of the wheel and the dependent variable would be the distance and speed of the wheel.

   The variables that must be held constant are: the masses of the wheels (Styrofoam® wheels work well because the mass difference between an 8-cm wheel and a 16-cm wheel is basically negligible), the ramp angle and length, how the wheels are released, how speed and distance measurements are taken.

   To be sure that differences are not due to chance we would repeat the experiment several times and then try some runs with wheels of different materials or of different sizes.

## Reasoning Module 3

1. $H <^H_T$   $T <^H_T$   1/4 = 25%

2. 1/36 = 2.7%

**3.** **a.** 3/4 = 75%

   **b.** 9/16 = 56.25%

**4.**   2/4 = 50%

**5.**   1/100 = 1%

**6.** 10/32 = 31.25% of the time this result will occur due to chance alone. Set up a tree diagram. The diagram will show 32 possible results. Ten of the results will show three left turns and two right turns (e.g., LLLRR, LRRLL, LRLLR).

**7.** **a.** 1/2

   **b.** 1/2 = 50%

   **c.** If we ignore the people who could not tell the difference we get 3 people who prefer Brand X and one who prefers Brand Y. A tree diagram analogous to the one for the four mealworms shows that there are 16 possible results. Out of these 16, four of them show three Brand X choices and one Brand Y choice (i.e., XXXY, XXYX, XYXX, YXXX). Therefore, the probability that this result is due to chance alone is 4/16 = 1/4 = 25%. If you concluded that the results indicates that people, in general, prefer Brand X to Brand Y, you stand a 25% chance of being wrong and a 75% chance of being right.

**8.** **a.** Although 4 of 5 = 80% is a high percentage, we do not know what else these people might have eaten. Perhaps 4 out of 5 people who had cherry pie also came down with the illness. The banana cream pie may be the cause but other possible causes have not been ruled out.

   **b.** No, we need to know what percentage of the non-banana cream pie eaters got stomach pains and nausea.

### Brain Bender

**1.** Assume that a plate can contain from 1 to 7 letters or digits chosen from 26 letters and 10 digits, or 36 characters. Assume that any one or more of those characters can be blank, with the exception of all blanks (a plate must contain at least one letter or digit). Then there are $37^7 - 1$ possible plates.

**2.**

| | Possibilities | |
| Door 1 | Door 2 | Door 3 |
| --- | --- | --- |
| (1) CAR | PIG | PIG |
| (2) PIG | CAR | PIG |
| (3) PIG | PIG | CAR |

(1) If the car is behind door 1 (1st option above), and you switch to door 2, you lose.

(2) If the car is behind door 2 (2nd option above) and you switch to door 2, you win.

(3) If the car is behind door 3 (third option above) and we assume that the host, knowing what is behind each door, opens door 2 to show you a pig, and you switch to door 3, then you win.

Therefore, switching leads to winning in 2 out 3 cases. If you do not switch, you win in only 1 out of 3 cases. You should switch!

## Investigation 8

1. The fly is caught with the tongue and taken into the mouth where saliva starts the digestion process. The fly then passes through the esophagus to the stomach. Digestive juices are released into the stomach where most of the digestion takes place. From the stomach, the fly travels to the intestine where nutrient uptake occurs followed by water absorption. The remaining material passes into the cloaca where it mixes with products from the urogenital tract. This combined waste is discharged out the vent.

2. In the frog, surface area in the digestive system is increased by folds on the inner wall of the intestine and by having a long intestine. A long intestine provides more overall surface area and folds within the intestine greater area for absorption within a relatively small area.

3. Arteries are tubes that transport oxygenated blood to the body. Veins are tubes that transport deoxygenated blood back to the heart. Capillaries are small beds of tubes with porous walls through which exchange of nutrients, gases and wastes can occur between the blood supply and individual cells.

4. The respiratory system supplies the circulatory system with oxygen and takes away excess waste gases from the circulatory system.

5. The digestive system supplies the circulatory system with nutrients for the body and disposes of solid wastes from the body. The urogenital system filters the blood to remove excess wastes from the body, temporarily stores these wastes, and then excretes them from the body.

6. An organ is a group of related tissues that work together to perform a specific function. A system is a group of organs that work together to maintain a particular homeostatic aspect of an organism. An organism is a self-contained, living unit that interacts with the external environment.

7. Answers will vary. The following is one example: The kidneys are thought to filter blood to remove excess wastes so as to maintain specific concentrations of different molecules in the blood. One test of this hypothesis would involve testing the amount of wastes in the kidney discharge before and after the addition of specific wastes into the bloodstream. The amount of waste in discharge should decrease if the hypothesis is correct.

## Investigation 9

1. Living organisms are composed of small units called cells. This distinguishes them from nonliving things.

2. The microscope shows an inverted mirror image.

3. The tissues of a large number and variety of organisms would need to be observed under the microscope and found to be composed of cells; no

4. Age of cells, ability to obtain nutrients, function, certain environmental influences could increase or decrease cell size, amount of stored materials, ability to get rid of wastes, etc.

5. By looking through the microscope, it is apparent that plants have a "fatter" border—the cell wall. There also are organelle differences between the two, such as the chloroplasts in plants. Also plant cells generally have large open spaces not generally found in animal cells.

## Investigation 10

1. A tissue is made up of similar cells (in most cases, identical cells) that provide a common function. Usually we will see that the cell's structure and function are directly related to the type of tissue involved (e.g., plant tissue responsible for water transport is made up of hollow cells that allow water to pass through).

2. Cells can differ in size, cell-wall thickness, shape, complexity of structures within the cell, color, mobility/activity, and location within the tissues.

3. Cell size and shape are important for function and mobility. We would expect to see larger, thicker, and "squarer" shaped cells when tissue is needed for support and rounder shaped cells for easy transport through vascular systems. Cells that are used for protection against outside environmental factors would need tough cell walls (such as in plant leaves) or might be thin and stackable for replacement upon damage as in skin cells. The complexity of structures inside the cell would most likely attest to the amount of chemical processing needed by the cell. We would not expect a sperm cell to have complex intracellular structures since its purpose is only to transport chromosomes.

## Investigation 11

1. It is necessary to use the electron micrographs to observe the cell organelles because light microscopes do not magnify enough times.

2. Membranes are found throughout the cell and appeared to be connected to each other in many places.

3. The nuclear membrane, the ER, and the Golgi body are all connected at some point.

4. The ER consists of long channels through the cytoplasm and is connected to other organelles. This structure is ideal for a transport system much like highways connected to many cities.

5. Mitochondria release energy to the cell. Muscle cells need more energy and, therefore, have more mitochondria.

6. Mitochondria and lysosomes may move through the cell in order to provide benefits to the entire cell. For instance the mitochondria may move around to supply energy to a

greater portion of the cell, while lysosomes may move around to digest waste material in the cell. By being able to move around they may also reduce the number necessary for the cell's operation.

7. The folding of the inner mitochondrial membrane may provide more surface area for chemical reactions to take place. As a result, fewer mitochondria may be needed in order to meet the cell's energy requirements.

8. The ER might be important in the islets of Langerhans. Its function might be to transport insulin out of the cells. Or perhaps, Golgi bodies would be abundant as they might actually secrete the insulin.

9. The cell organelles perform specific functions necessary to the survival of the cell just like the way organs perform specific functions necessary to the survival of the organism.

10. Nucleus—would direct these processes.

    ER—could transport necessary materials for the processes.

    Ribosomes—could reuse the amino acids to make proteins.

    Lysosomes—could actually break down the old organelles.

    Golgi bodies—could package and transport the materials to needy sites.

    Mitochondria and chloroplasts—could provide the energy for breaking the old organelles down in order to make new organelles.

## Investigation 12

1. The fact that the yeast cells in solution caused a blue solution of BTB to turn yellow supports the hypothesis that the cells produce $CO_2$. The fact that the cells did *not* cause a blue solution to turn yellow contradicts the hypothesis that the yeast cells intake $CO_2$ and produce $O_2$.

2. In this experiment, the independent variables were solution type, amount of light, temperature, and color of BTB solution at the start of the experiment. The dependent variable was the color of the BTB solution at the end of the experiment. Only one independent variable at a time should be allowed to vary. All others should remain constant. This is the only way to determine whether or not any particular independent variable produces a change in the dependent variable.

3. Answers will vary.

4. Based upon these results yeast have both plant and animal characteristics. The asexual budding appears to be typically a plant characteristic. However, the results of the experiment suggest animal-like respiration in that the yeast cells appear to take in $O_2$ and release $CO_2$ because the blue BTB solution changed to yellow. Likewise, the yellow BTB solution remained yellow indicating that $CO_2$ was not being converted to $O_2$. Also, the evidence that the amount of light did not affect the results, indicates more of an animal characteristic than a plant characteristic.

## Reasoning Module 4

1. yes; If all of the variables were held constant except for the one being tested, it is safe to say that a fair test has been conducted. Therefore, the result is tied to the one variable being tested.

2. the height the balls bounced

3. the height from which the balls were dropped; the surface on which the balls were dropped; how the balls were dropped.

4. the number of push-ups that could be performed

5. where the push-ups were performed (land vs. water)

6. jars #1 and #5, because all other variables in these two jars were kept constant (plant type, plant part, color of light); The only variable that was different was the temperature.

7. **a.** The swimming coach recorded the swimmers' heights and their respective times for the 50-yard freestyle. She then plotted the data on a graph to see if there was a correlation between height and time.
   **b.** Although the distance and the stroke performed were constant, other variables such as the lanes the swimmers each swam in (inside lanes may have an advantage over outside lanes) were not considered. Nevertheless, the experiment is most likely as controlled as possible. The experiment could be repeated several times each time switching lanes to make it more "fair."
   **c.** the speed/time of the swimmers
   **d.** What independent variables do you think are important in this situation? distance; stroke performed; experience, condition, technique, quickness of each swimmer, and lane the swimmer is in

8. **a.** distance (miles) the car could be driven
   **b.** speed at which the automobiles were driven
   **c.** road conditions; type of car driven; tire pressure; weather conditions
   **d.** amount of gasoline (one gallon)
   **e.** speed at which cars were driven
   **f.** Use the same car driven on the same road for each speed. Check tire pressure often and keep it constant. Repeat the experiment several times.

### *Brain Bender*

**a.** Although the experiment was run the same way for all 15 people, it is not controlled because that white cup always was first and orange second following the cracker. To be "fair," the order would have to be randomized and the cracker added before each or before none.

**b.** possibly because it was given first when they were thirstier, or because the cracker "spoiled" the taste of the second cup, or because people prefer white (it looks cleaner or cooler, etc.), or perhaps the result was due to chance; The list of possibilities is endless.

**c.** No experiment can "prove" anything because alternative explanations can always be found. This is especially true in this experiment.

**d.** Randomize the order. Eliminate the cracker. Repeat at least 100 times.

# Investigation 13

1. Time spent in mitosis divided by the generation time is proportional to the number of cells in mitosis divided by the total number of cells observed. This is expressed as:

$$\frac{t_m}{t_g} = \frac{N_m}{N_0} \cdot \text{Solving for time spent in mitosis we have } t_m = \frac{N_m \times t_g}{N_0}.$$

$N_0 = 100 \quad t_g = 3 \text{ hr} \qquad N_m = 50 \qquad t_m = \frac{50 \times 2}{100} = 1$

2. **a.** Onion root tip cells spent 0.55 hours in mitosis.

$$t_m = \frac{16 \times 22}{642} = 0.55 \text{ hr or } 33 \text{ min. } 0.55 \text{ hr} \times 60 \text{ minutes/hour} = 33 \text{ minutes}$$

   **b.** $\dfrac{0.55 \text{ hr}}{22 \text{ hr}} = 0.025$ or 1/40 of their life in mitosis.

   **c.** $0.025 = 2.5\%$

3. The difference between animal cell replication and plant cell replication is the formation of a cell plate in plants and a furrow in animals during the telophase. Also, asters (radially arranged fibers) from centromeres in the metaphase appear in animal cells but are not seen in plants.

5. Reduce the chromosome number of each parent by dividing each cell in half and then joining two of these halves.
   **a.** The number of chromosomes is reduced by 1/2.
   **b.** Two chromosome divisions occur on meiosis.
   **c.** Four new cells are produced in meiosis.
   **d.** Chromosome replication occurs during the interphase.
   **e.** Each individual receives one pair of chromosomes from the father and one from the mother so they have two of each type of chromosome.

6. If we put equally spaced ink marks on a growing root tip, we should expect the spaces between these marks to increase and be more pronounced toward the zone of elongation.

7. Arrangements will vary. Some possible arrangements would include pairing like chromosomes, placing them in descending order, or both, which is similar to the technique used by geneticists to determine karyotype. (The karyotype is the student lab manual is for a male.)

# Reasoning Module 5

1-6. Answers will vary.

7. Applied research is conducted with the goal of solving a practical problem. Pure research is conducted to further understanding of a particular phenomenon—to explain something to satisfy one's curiosity.

8. **a.** Why does grass grow under tree A but not under tree B?

   **b.** One alternative hypothesis would be that the leaves are more scarce on tree A, so the sun is getting through to the ground and the grass is growing. A second hypothesis is, the soil under tree B is too acidic, so grass does not grow under tree B. A third hypothesis could be, no water is getting close to tree B, so grass cannot grow there.

A fourth hypothesis would be, grass was never planted under tree B.

c. To test hypothesis one, the branches could be cut off tree B permitting more sunlight to hit the ground.

d. If the hypothesis is correct, the grass should now grow under tree B, all other things being equal.

9. h     11. d     13. g     15. a

10. f     12. e     14. c     16. b

17. Statement #13 could be considered to be a hypothesis prior to experimentation and data collection. Depending upon how the experiment turns out, it could also be a conclusion. A medical doctor might incorrectly diagnose a disease and tell someone they have disease X when they really do not. The MD's statement is really a hypothesis and should be stated as such, i.e., I think you have disease X. Instead, it was stated as a fact (i.e., a conclusion). This would lead to the wrong treatment and a failure to cure. The treatment is the experiment.

### Brain Bender 1

a. Turn over the *E* card because an odd number on the other side would break the rule.

b. Do not turn over the *K* card because we have no rule about consonants.

c. Do not turn over the *4* card because neither a vowel nor a consonant will break the rule.

d. Turn over the *7* card because a vowel on the other side would break the rule.

### Brain Bender 2

1. can't tell, because no information about this possible trip as given can be inferred

2. yes; They can travel from Fish to Bird with a stop at Bean.

3. no; If travel between Fish and Snail were possible, then travel would be possible from Bird to Snail (via Bean and Fish) but this is not possible, according to the second clue—therefore travel between Fish and Snail is not possible.

## Investigation 14

1. Answers may vary.

2. The heart generally is visible first.

3. The egg tooth appears to be used to break the shell.

4. a. As new cells arise they appear to take on different sizes and shapes.

   b. The differentiating cells take on different functions necessary for the organisms to survive and compete in its environment.

5. Answers may vary. There is an interesting issue here. If cell differentiation is controlled by genes and if mitosis gives rise to exact duplicate copies of genes, then how can it be possible for cells to differentiate?

6. It suggests that the environment has some influence on gene expression.

7. Answers will vary. Here are some examples:

   The chick embryo uses the calcium for growth and differentiation.

As hatching time approaches, the egg shell loses calcium and becomes thinner and weaker to make it easier for the new chick to break out of the shell.

The warmth/heat of the incubator reduces the amount of calcium in the shell.

Growth rather than differentiation is more prominent during this final stage of development and thus more calcium is needed by the embryo.

8. yes; Answers will vary. Here are two alternatives.

   a. To exchange gases/wastes with the environment.

   b. Allows for easier breakage when hatching.

   To test hypothesis *a* you could seal the shell (wax or plastic wrap) and see if the embryo is able to develop. If *a* is correct, normal development should stop. Several waxed and unwaxed eggs should be used and all treated the same way except for the wax coating.

9. Both human and chicken embryos undergo the same stages of development (cleavage, gastrulation, neurulation etc.). Cleavage, however, looks very different in different animals. This is because the amount of yolk in the egg determines how cleavage occurs. Chick eggs contain quite a lot of yolk compared to human eggs.

## Investigation 15

1. Presumably nothing but mixing occurred. No chemical reaction took place because the indicator did not change color.

2. Iodine—The iodine solution indicates starch is present.
   Benedicts—This solution indicates the presence of sugar.
   Paper—A simple test for fats is the formation of a greasy spot.
   Biuret—A test for proteins.
   Limewater—Indicates $CO_2$.
   BTB—Indicates $CO_2$.
   Phenolphthalein—Indicates pH.

3. Answers will vary. Several foods and beverages give positive reactions with more than one indicator suggesting that they contain more than one type of molecule.

4. Structures will vary. Sugars contain C, H, and O usually in small units of $C_6H_{12}O_6$ ratios. Starch molecules usually consist of linked sugar subunits. Lipids/fats also consist of C, H, and O atoms but may also contain other elements, particularly P and N. They have a much smaller proportion of O than found in sugars and starches. Proteins are more complex than the previous molecules. They consist of C, H, and N atoms. Most contain some S. Proteins consist of one or more units called *amino acids*. Amino acids have the form:

$$H_2N - \underset{\underset{H}{|}}{\overset{\overset{R}{|}}{C}} - C \overset{\displaystyle O}{\underset{\displaystyle OH}{\phantom{=}}}$$

The *R* indicates one of several side groups of varying complexity. The evidence for these structures comes primarily form two types of experiments. In the first type samples of the unknown material are put into a hot flame and burned. When different elements burn, they give off different colors; thus, the color of the flame is an indication of the type of atoms present. The second type of experiment involves the collection of materials given off during chemical reactions. The amounts of such materials as $CO_2$, $H_2$, $O_2$, $H_2O$, or $NH_3$ given off will provide an indication of the amounts of atoms present in the initial molecules.

5. During a chemical reaction the molecules break apart and recombine to form different combinations. This does not happen when molecules are simply mixed. The color of light reflected by a material is a function of the nature of its molecules; thus, when a chemical reaction takes place, the color of the materials involved changes. A rise or decrease in temperature, the formation of bubbles, or the formation of precipitate may also indicate a chemical reaction.

6. a. true
   b. true
   c. false
   d. true
   e. false
   f. cannot determine
   g. false

## Investigation 16

1. If the hypothesis that saliva breaks down some foods but not others is being tested in question 3, then certain results can be predicted. If the saliva breaks down protein, then when the biuret test is conducted, the color will remain pinkish. If there is no breakdown, then the color will turn purple. If the saliva breaks down starch, then when the iodine test is conducted, the color will remain orange. If there is no breakdown, then the color will change from orange to blue-black. Also, if the saliva breaks down starch, then when the Benedict test is conducted, the color will change from blue to green to yellow to orange in the cracker-saliva and the potato-saliva solutions. If there is no breakdown, then the color will remain the same as at the start. If the saliva breaks down fat, then when the paper test is done on the container consisting of fat and saliva, there will be a water spot as opposed to a greasy spot on the paper. If there is no breakdown, then the spot will be greasy. If conflicting results are obtained, then the experimental design should be changed. If class results are consistent, then the hypothesis that saliva breaks down some foods but not others will be supported.

2. Based on the results of this lab, it can be concluded that evidence supports the hypothesis that saliva starts to break down starch into simpler glucose molecules but does not affect proteins or fats.

3. Answers will vary.

4. The major independent variable is the amount of saliva used (some versus none). The dependent variables are the reactions of the various mixtures. The amounts of the food substances, amount of mixing, and the order of mixing should be controlled.

5. Chemical breakdown differs from mechanical breakdown in that during chemical breakdown, the molecular subunits are actually altered. By contrast, whereas in mechanical breakdown, there is little molecular splitting. Instead, aggregates of like molecules are broken apart. In biological breakdown, the molecules are changed into different substances via both chemical and mechanical breakdowns. The processes are similar in that the original substances are being made smaller.

6. Answers will vary. Here is an example.

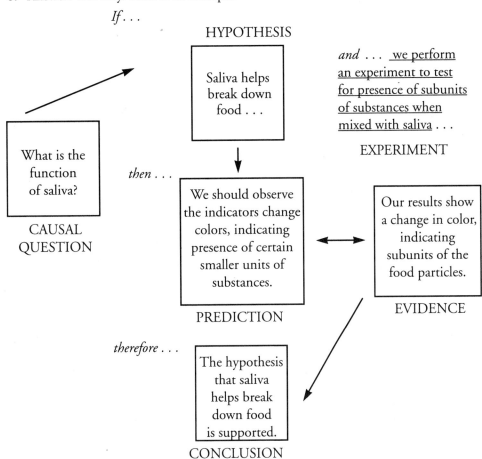

*If . . .*

HYPOTHESIS

Saliva helps break down food . . .

*and* . . . we perform an experiment to test for presence of subunits of substances when mixed with saliva . . .

EXPERIMENT

What is the function of saliva?

CAUSAL QUESTION

*then* . . .

We should observe the indicators change colors, indicating presence of certain smaller units of substances.

PREDICTION

Our results show a change in color, indicating subunits of the food particles.

EVIDENCE

*therefore* . . .

The hypothesis that saliva helps break down food is supported.

CONCLUSION

## Investigation 17

1. *Alternative Hypotheses Tested*
   a. The liver cells break down but the hydrogen peroxide remains the same.
   b. The liver cells remain the same but the $H_2O_2$ breaks down and changes.
   c. Neither are changed.
   d. Both are changed.

   *Expected Results*
   a. If the liver cells break down (are changed) but the $H_2O_2$ remains unchanged, then following a reaction the used $H_2O_2$ should react only on new liver cells and not on old liver cells.
   b. If the liver cells remain the same but the $H_2O_2$ breaks down (is changed), then used $H_2O_2$ should not react with either old or new liver cells and new $H_2O_2$ should reach with both.
   c. If neither are changed, then the reaction should continue endlessly. All possible combinations should result in a reaction.
   d. If both are changed, then no combinations of old or new $H_2O_2$ with old or new liver should result in a reaction.

2. The data reveal the following:
   a. new liver + new $H_2O_2$ = reaction
   b. old liver + new $H_2O_2$ = reaction
   c. old liver + old $H_2O_2$ = no reaction
   d. new liver + old $H_2O_2$ = no reaction
   Of the four alternatives proposed, the data seems to support the hypothesis that the liver cells remain the same while the $H_2O_2$ has changed. This is supported by the fact that old liver with new $H_2O_2$ results in a reaction here as new liver with old $H_2O_2$ does not.

3. Although our hypothesis is strongly supported by the evidence we still can not be sure that there are no other factors involved which have not yet been identified.

4. The reaction may have converted $H_2O_2$ to water and oxygen gas. The molecules of oxygen gas hit the side of the test tube at a more rapid rate than a liquid (Kinetic Theory) and causes the sensation of heat due to increased molecular motion.

5. The experiment was controlled in that:
   a. All liver was derived from the same source.
   b. Environmental conditions of the room were the same.
   c. The same enzyme was used in each test.
   d. Only one variable was changed per the two tests.

6. The dependent variables in this experiment were the amount of bubbles and heat produced. The independent variables were the condition of the liver and $H_2O_2$ (whether new or used).

7. A catalyst is a substance that speeds up a chemical reaction but is itself unchanged when the reaction has ended. It does this by decreasing the activation energy needed for a reaction to take place by increasing the number of reacting molecules with enough energy to react. An enzyme is a protein catalyst that increases the rate of specific chemical reactions. They are produced and secreted by living things. In nonenzymatic reactions, two or more molecules react (or don't) and are changed in the process. In enzymatic reactions the substrate molecules are changed but the enzyme remains unchanged. In enzymatic reactions the enzyme can react over and over again which is not the case for either molecule involved in a nonenzymatic reaction. Also, enzymes speed up the reaction where as chemical reactions can proceed very slow.

8. In a chemical reaction the two (or more) molecules are interacting to form some new product whether enzymes are involved or not. In a mixture of two substances the two substances retain their own identities and do not react.

9. Answers will vary.

## Investigation 18

1. Light molecules would move faster because it takes less of a push to get light things moving than heavy things. Diffusion is caused by pushes from other objects.

2. The increase of salt concentration in the extracellular fluid causes water to flow out of the body cells.

3. Temperature rise should increase diffusion rate because temperature rise indicates more rapid motion of molecules. The faster molecules move, the further they will travel in any period of time.

4. **b.** gain water and burst, because water will diffuse from higher water concentration on the outside of the cells to a lower concentration of water on the inside

5. **a.** The volume of liquid inside will probably decrease due to diffusion of water out of the cell.

   **b.** The concentration of dextrose will probably stay the same because it is probably too large to get into the cell. However, if it could get into the cell, the concentration inside would increase due to diffusion of dextrose from high to low concentration.

6. Independent variables were molecule size, molecule concentration, and where the molecules were placed (inside or outside the cells). Dependent variables were bag weight and any color change of a solution when an indicator was added. Any and all independent variables except the one being tested should be held constant.

7. Answers will vary.

8. It could have been bumped into or perhaps a positive or negative attractive force (i.e., like a magnet) could force it in. If the movement is down, the force of gravity could be involved.

9. The forces mentioned in question 8 could be involved; however, if only mechanical forces of diffusion are involved, the movement from high to low concentration will occur due to random collisions with other molecules. In high-concentration areas the relative number of collisions with like molecules will be greater than with unlike molecules, therefore, the net movement that results from these collisions will be directed away from the group of like molecules.

10. Answers will vary.

## Investigation 19

1. Adenine must be attached to thymine, and cytosine must be attached to guanine. You can look at the percentages of adenine and thymine and compare them. The two should be the same. This is also true for cytosine and guanine. If the percentages are the same then the model is probably correct. But one cannot be absolutely sure, because something else might be going on that could lead to this same prediction.

2. Answers will vary.

3. Answers will vary; however, if student percentages are similar to those in the table from clue set 3, then they support the students' models.

4. During the early stages of pregnancy there are a limited number of copies of the original DNA and these must direct many subsequent cell divisions. If they were to be broken apart during this time then the embryo might lose some vary valuable information needed to grow and survive. Once this information is lost it can never be replaced and the pregnancy may be terminated or the child could be born with severe birth defects.

5. Genes could be altered in such organisms as bacteria to produce many kinds of molecules that could then be used to fight diseases. If a disease is caused by a defective gene, that gene could be altered or replaced with a normal gene.

6. The molecule will have to open at several spots along the helix to expose the base pairs. When the base pairs are exposed, new bases will fill in the gaps according to the sequence specified. As the base pairs fill in the openings, the helix will continue to twist and

unwind until a complete copy has been produced. Within each new strand of DNA there will be one old strand and one new strand to ensure that the original information is not lost in the copying process.

## Investigation 20

1. Three factors that might limit the population of adult brine shrimp are the salinity of the water, the temperature of the water, and the concentration of adult brine shrimp. High or low salinity may shrink or burst the eggs and render them nonviable. Temperature extremes may kill the eggs or fry. The concentration of adult brine shrimp may affect the fertilization of eggs. Too few adults could lead to a low rate of fertilization. Salinity levels at or near that of sea water are probably the ideal levels as the adults are normally found at this salinity level. Room temperatures of 70 to 80°F appear to result in a good hatch rate of the eggs. This temperature range is likely to be the same encountered by the adults during their breeding season. Higher concentrations of adult shrimp should lead to a higher fertilization rate of the eggs as opposite sexes will have an easier time of encountering each other.

2. Answers will vary.

3. To make 1X solution, add 90 ml of water to 10 ml of 10X sample.

   To make 2X solution, add 80 ml of water to 20 ml of 10X sample.

   To make 3X solution, add 70 ml of water to 30 ml of 10X sample.

   To make 1/3 X solution, add 96.7 ml of water to 3.3 ml of 10X sample.

   To make 2/3 X solution, add 93.3 ml of water to 6.7 ml of 10X sample.

4. To make 1X solution, add 60 ml of water to 10ml of 7X sample.

   To make 2X solution, add 25 ml of water to 10ml of 7X sample.

   To make 3X solution, add 13.33 ml of water to 3.3 ml of 7X sample.

   To make 1/3 X solution, add 67.7 ml of water to 3.3 ml of 7X sample.

   To make 2/3 X solution, add 63.3 ml of water to 6.7 ml of 7X sample.

5. Four independent variables that should be held constant in this experiment are water temperature, the number of eggs put into the vials, the size of the vials, and the amount of water provided. The amount of hatching of the eggs is the dependent variable.

## Reasoning Module 6

1. a. 24 mutations
   b. 6.4 mutations

2. 128 kph, 74 kph

3. 2.67 cups of milk and 3.33 eggs

4. 14 years old

5. $\dfrac{\sqrt{720\,A}}{\sqrt{370\,B}} = \dfrac{6 \text{ seconds}}{x \text{ seconds}}$  $x = 4.3$ seconds

6. The second store would save you about 1¢/pair. If you need the 8 pairs, shop at the second store. If you only need 6 pairs, shop at the first store and save $1.25.

7. amount of oil and amount of gasoline; proportional relationship

8. velocity and distance from each other; constant difference

9. shadow length and time of day; proportional

10. 56 kilometers

11. 195 cm or 1.95 m

12. 21 francs

### Brain Bender 1

$$\frac{12 \text{ banded frogs}}{72 \text{ frogs}} = \frac{55 \text{ banded frogs}}{x} \qquad x = 330 \text{ frogs}$$

### Brain Bender 2

$$\frac{7°}{360°} = \frac{800 \text{ km}}{x} \qquad x = 41{,}142.9 \text{ km}$$

## Investigation 21

1. There are such things as male-only flowers, female-only flowers, and flowers that have both male and female parts. Male flowers would have stamens only; female flowers would have pistils. The other flower parts could be present in both types of flowers. Members of the pepper and sycamore families have unisexual flowers. Members of the magnolia and lily families have bisexual flowers.

2. The petals are usually colorful and large. Two possible functions of the petals are attraction for pollination purposes, and protection. An experiment to test the attraction hypothesis would be to first get several flowers. Next we could clip off the petals of some of the flowers. As time elapses, we would observe to see if the flowers without the petals still attract pollinators. We would predict that the flowers without the petals would not attract pollinators, and the flowers with petals would attract pollinators. If this did occur, it would support the hypothesis that the function of the petals is to attract pollinators.

## Investigation 22

1. A bell pepper produces about ten flowers per plant.

2. Answers will vary. One typical answer would be: My bell pepper contained 40 seeds.

3. Forty new individual pepper plants could be produced from a single fruit.

4. Four hundred pepper plants could be produced from a single pepper plant.

5. The number of peppers that could be produced per acre in one growing season can be calculated by the following method: number of old pepper plants per hectare × number of pepper flowers per plant = number of new pepper plants.

6. To calculate the number of new plants that could be produced if all the seeds from the above harvest were planted can be calculated as follows: number of new plants = number of pepper plants per hectare × number of peppers per plant × number of seeds per pepper plant.

7. Many factors can affect the biotic potential of the bell pepper plants, e.g., available nutrients, space, water, presence of disease, presence of herbivores, parasitism. All of these may be limiting factors that may control population size and growth. For example if nutrients are not available, many of the plants will not grow and reproduce.

8. The fruits with the highest biotic potential are the ones containing the most seeds. Among them are tomatoes, bell peppers, sunflowers, wild oats, pumpkins, squash, watermelon, cucumber, cantaloupe, cocklebur, and pomegranate. One other factor is the number of fruits produced per plant. The more fruits per plant and those with the greatest number of seeds per fruit have the highest biotic potential.

## Investigation 23

1. cotyledon—storage of food for embryo; embryo—responsible for growth of plant; seed coat—protect embryo and cotyledon

2. The energy source for the sprouting seed is the cotyledon.

3. These results can possibly be generalized to most or all seed plants; however, we cannot be certain because our sample was small. Not *all* seed plants were observed.

4. The energy source for adult plants is different than for seeds. Adult plants obtain energy from the sun and therefore no longer need energy stored in seeds.

5. Seeds are sources of energy consumed by animals. Some humans also use them in works of art. Some seeds may have medicinal value and some may be used in oils and spices.

6. The dependent variable was the growth of the particular plant (with/without specific seed parts). The independent variable manipulated was the degree to which the parts were attached to one another. Variables held constant include the temperature, the amount of water, the amount of light, the size of the container, and the size and type of filter paper the seeds were placed on.

7. Answers will vary.

## Investigation 24

1. Light is the source of energy for continued plant growth. Only plants grown in light showed continued growth over a period of 5 weeks.

2. Plants showed about the same rate of growth in both light and dark; however, the ones in the dark may have been growing taller faster. This faster growth may assist the plant to reach light.

3. Plants grown in the light had thicker, more upright stems and were greener than those grown in the dark. Plants grown in the dark had thin, bending stems and were more yellow in color than those grown in the light.

4. The thin, bending stems in the dark-grown plants may be due to the fact that the plant has produced a chemical that stimulates that sort of growth. The light-grown plants are greener because they have developed the pigment chlorophyll used in photosynthesis. The stems are straight in the light-grown plants because they have not produced the chemical mentioned previously.

5. The dependent variables were: the life of the plant, the color of the plant, the length of the plant, and the thickness of the stem. The independent variable tested was the amount of light.

6. Our group conducted a controlled experiment because we kept the variables such as amount of water, soil composition, amount of soil, and the amount of nutrients the same for both the plants in the dark and the plants in the light.

7. Answers will vary. A sample answer is given on the next page.

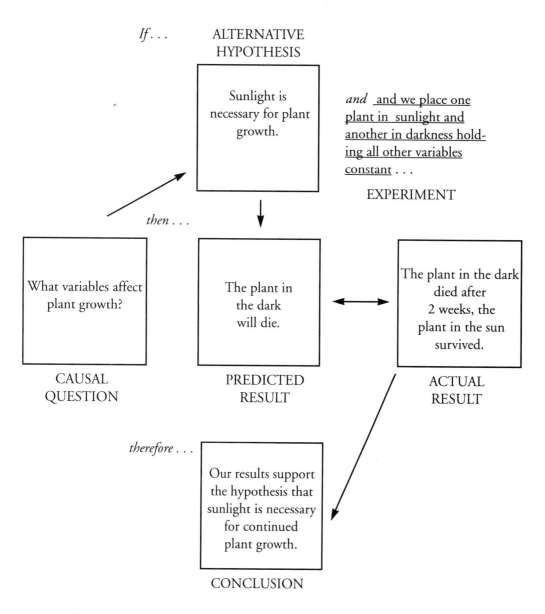

*If . . .*  ALTERNATIVE
HYPOTHESIS

Sunlight is
necessary for plant
growth.

*and*  and we place one
plant in  sunlight and
another in darkness hold-
ing all other variables
constant . . .

EXPERIMENT

*then . . .*

What variables affect
plant growth?

CAUSAL
QUESTION

The plant in
the dark
will die.

PREDICTED
RESULT

The plant in the dark
died after
2 weeks, the
plant in the sun
survived.

ACTUAL
RESULT

*therefore . . .*

Our results support
the hypothesis that
sunlight is necessary
for continued
plant growth.

CONCLUSION

## Investigation 25

1. Answers will vary.

2. Answers will vary, for example: Several things could be done to get the experimental results to match the actual results. First, the original hypothesis could be revised and new tests developed that could be then conducted to see if they match the results. Second, if you believe that the original hypothesis was correct, you should go back and double-check the materials for contaminants or defects and redo the original experiment.

3. Answers will vary. For example: Being a well-trained science student I indeed had a controlled experiment because I left all the variables except the one under investigation constant. This allowed me to conclude that the effect I observed was from the variable that was changing since everything else was the same and not changing.

4. If the experiments that were run to test the hypothesis were not controlled then the results that were obtained would be invalid because no usable data would result. It would be impossible to tell what variable was the cause of the effect noted. In addition, the result obtained from a noncontrolled experiment could not be used as support for the hypothesis and hence would also effect the answers for questions 1 and 2.

5. Plants expel $CO_2$ at night. Because this is a waste gas of human respiration people may have thought it dangerous. Also plants take in $O_2$ thus reducing the amount in the room for a patient. This seems reasonable if the room is small and is not well-ventilated and there are lots of plants.

6. Answers will vary.

## Investigation 26

1. Succulent leaves are a good adaptation in arid climates due to their increased water retention.

2. Small leaves in desert plants are advantageous due to their smaller surface area; therefore, they have less water loss.

3. Plants such as the paloverde with green bark contain chloroplasts in their stems and therefore are able to photosynthesize in dry periods after their leaves have dropped off.

4. Cacti are able to carry on photosynthesis without leaves due to the presence of chloroplasts in their stems (or trunk).

5. The loss of leaves in arid environments as the photosynthetic structure decreases the water loss of the plant and allows food production to continue year round, even in the hottest and driest times of the year when leaves would be costly and detrimental to the overall good of the plant.

6. Plant roots are not green because they are not exposed to the sun and could not carry on photosynthesis. The lack of color is due to the lack of chloroplasts and chlorophyll in the roots.

7. Green plants fade and drop leaves when not exposed to light. This may be primarily the result of the cessation of photosynthesis and loss of chlorophyll. Plants need light to sustain themselves, and without light the plant can no longer utilize all of its leaves, so it sheds them to conserve food and water.

8. Starch is merely a complex molecule of several combined sugars. The equation should not be rewritten as plants store their food (glucose) as starch and break it down for use as needed, similar to fat hydrolysis in animals.

9. In part III of the experiment, amount of light served as the independent variable. Three variables to be controlled were the $CO_2$ source, amount of moisture, and nutrient source for the plant (i.e., soil). The dependent variable measured in this experiment would be the production or lack of starch.

## Investigation 27

1. Plants do contain more than one pigment based on the chromatography that showed at least two distinct bands of color. Yes, this gives indirect evidence that plants use more than one pigment to capture light but further experiments would be needed to demon-

strate that the pigments are involved in light capture and not something else. Perhaps the pigments could be separated from each other and exposed to light. If, when placed in the dark, they gave off light, this would support the hypothesis more directly.

2. perhaps because they too contain chlorophyll molecules

3. Perhaps the other pigments seen in the chromatography are in the leaves but masked by the large excess of chlorophyll. When the leaves stop photosynthesizing in the fall, the chlorophyll degrades and is not replaced or is absorbed into stems. The remaining pigments are then visible.

4. Yes, it appeared in the chromatography as a slight orange color.

5. This was not a totally controlled experiment. There were too many independent variables that we didn't control. Independent variables included temperature, length of elodea, ambient light, whether plant was used the class period before ours, age and part of the elodea used. Dependent variables included number of bubbles produced. Variables we held constant were the distance to light source, person counting the bubbles, and criteria for counting.

## Investigation 28

1. The green color is seen in the cells inside smaller structures called *chloroplasts*.

2. The iodine test was negative in the albino plants and positive in the normal plants. This shows that the starch was produced only in the normal plants, thus supporting the hypothesis that chlorophyll is needed for the production of starch.

3. The ratio of green to white was 3:1. Yes, this shows a genetic relationship. The color differences must be due to the plant's environment or its genes. Since the environment was the same for all plants, environmental differences could not have caused the color differences.

4. The initial growth of the albino plants was probably due to the food stored in the seed (i.e., in the cotyledons).

5. The independent variable was the seed type (albino vs. normal). The dependent variable was amount of plant growth. Independent variables such as amount of water and amount of light were held constant. In this sense the experiment was controlled.

6. Answers will vary. A possible answer is given on the next page.

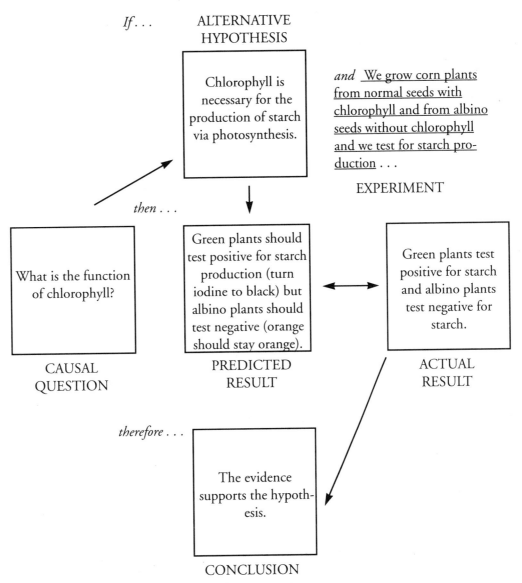

*If . . .* ALTERNATIVE HYPOTHESIS

Chlorophyll is necessary for the production of starch via photosynthesis.

*and* We grow corn plants from normal seeds with chlorophyll and from albino seeds without chlorophyll and we test for starch production . . .

EXPERIMENT

*then . . .*

What is the function of chlorophyll?

CAUSAL QUESTION

Green plants should test positive for starch production (turn iodine to black) but albino plants should test negative (orange should stay orange).

PREDICTED RESULT

Green plants test positive for starch and albino plants test negative for starch.

ACTUAL RESULT

*therefore . . .*

The evidence supports the hypothesis.

CONCLUSION

## Investigation 29

1. amount of light
   temperature
   number of leaves
   orientation of plant (upside down vs. right side up)

2. movement of water in the glass tube

3. It's improper to compare setups A and B because the difference in temperature in the setups could affect the movement of water.

4. Setups A and D could be used to test the hypothesis that light increases transpiration because the temperature is the same in both setups while the amount of light varies.

5. Setups A and C could be used to test the role of leaves because the temperature and amount of light are the same, but the number of leaves vary (leaves/ no leaves).

6. The movement could have been caused by temperature differences or amount of light, but we cannot tell which because both of these variables varied.

7. Setups A and D could be used to test the affect of light; A and C could be used to test the role of leaves in transpiration; C and E could be used to test if something in the stems (tubes, pumps, etc.) moves the water up; B and D could be used to test the effects of temperature on the rate of transpiration.

8. Answers will vary.

## Investigation 30

1. Answers will vary. For example:

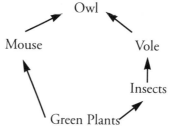

2. Answers will vary.

3. Since there were three skulls in one furry ball, and there would be 365 of these furry balls produced every year by one predator, $365 \times 3 = 1,095$ prey animals would be eaten by one predator every year.

4. The prey population would probably increase dramatically if the predator population decreased because every predator kills and eats more than 1,000 prey animals every year.

5. A smart farmer would consider predators such as owls to be beneficial because every predator would potentially kill about 1,000 mice every year. If mice eat like owls, they would consume many times their body weight in grain over time. However, larger predators like wolves or coyotes could present a serious problem to ranchers because they could kill a significant number of livestock. But on the other hand, if the rancher killed all the predators, then the deer and rabbits would multiply and compete with livestock for food.

6. Every consumer needs to eat to live, and over time much food is consumed. If an owl ate a one-year-old vole, which had in the course of its life eaten 1,000 poisoned insects, then the owl would be consuming as much as 1,000 times as much poison at one time as the vole ate in its entire life. If the owl then ate 1,000 voles over the course of a year, then it would be consuming 1 million times the quantity of toxin that a single insect was exposed to. The insects and voles collect toxins and magnify their effect many times for each successive trophic level up the food web, ending with the owl.

7. The expenditure of energy is required to capture food. As one progresses up the food chain there generally are progressively fewer predators until it gets to a point where more energy must be expended in capturing a prey than the predator obtains by eating it. Thus, the predator can not "make a living" at that level. Hence, none exist at that level.

## Investigation 31

1. Boxed strawberries spoil but an unsealed jar of jam will not because preservatives (i.e., chemicals that kill the decomposers) have been added to the jam but not to the fresh strawberries. Also the jam has been heated to kill the decomposers and sealed to keep others out.

2. Canned foods do not spoil because they have been exposed to high temperatures that

kill all or many of the microbes. If there are any microbes remaining after exposure to extreme heat they will not survive because there is not enough oxygen for them to respire. Also, if substances such as vinegar are added to the canned goods it can also kill the microbes. Finally, sealing the cans keeps other microbes out.

3. Very cold places (Alaska) with freezing conditions would inhibit the growth of microbes. Hot deserts would also inhibit growth of microbes because of lack of water or extremely high temperatures.

4. Places that have a great deal of humidity, shade, vegetation, and moderately warmer temperatures would promote decomposition. When vegetation dies it becomes susceptible to decomposition because the plant provides food for the microbes and the environment provides the shade, moisture, and proper temperature for their growth and reproduction.

5. Microbes are not always harmful. Some microbes are used to make antibiotics such as penicillin. Others are used to make cheese. There are bacteria in our bodies, such as *E. coli*, that consume undigestible food and provide us with vitamins.

6. Favorable conditions for microbial growth include moisture, darkness, food, and warm temperatures. Microbes cannot exist without moisture or food. They can survive in low levels of light and colder temperatures, but the population growth rate will be slowed.

7. Molds reproduce by binary fission.

8. Decomposers will die or become dormant when the dead organism is completely consumed.

9. Biological decomposition returns organic molecules from dead organisms to the substrate.

10. If decomposers were eliminated the plants would eventually run out of nutrients. Since plants are the source of energy for animals, animals would also cease to exist.

## Investigation 32

1. They appear similar except that the human population has yet to stop growing.

2. Answers will vary, e.g., lack of food, lack of clean air and clean water, disease, war.

3. graph

4. geometric

5. Answers will vary depending upon whether the rate of growth is projected to slow or not ($\approx$320,000,000 to 500,000,000).

6. Yes, most likely lack of food has and still is limiting the reproduction of some people. Native American Indian tribes often lacked food, as did early settlers from Europe.

7. Yes, as population increases, food supplies will have to at some point become a problem particularly if climate changes, pollution increases, crop diseases increase, and the cost of energy needed to produce the food increases.

8. Based on the prediction from question #5, there will be approximately 50% to 100% more people in the U.S. in 2050 than there are today. Recreational space will be diminished and become overcrowded. There will be a large problem of waste disposal. Rivers

will continually become more and more polluted, and possibly too contaminated (as many are already) to swim and fish. Resources that might be in short supply and might become limiting factors to U.S. population growth by the year 2050 are energy, food, water, medicine, and the ozone layer, the depletion of which may affect disease resistance. A greenhouse induced rise in temperature could disrupt the water cycle and consequently devastate the food and water supply.

9. Answers will vary.

## Investigation 33

1. graph

2. Yes, as one population varies, the other does also.

3-4. The lynx is probably the predator. In most instances its population is less than the hare population. It does not seem reasonable for the predator population to be greater than the prey population. Also the lynx population increase/decrease seems to lag behind that of the hare population as though it depends on the hare as a food source.

5. The prey is probably controlling the predator population. As soon as the prey population increases, the predators increase. And when the prey population crashes so does the predator population.

6. The predator population would increase with more food supply at an exponential rate until it started to limit the prey population size.

7. If the predators were exterminated the prey population would increase until some other factor would start killing them like disease or starvation because of lack of food. Overpopulation would result for awhile but the population might then crash or stabilize at another level.

8. The two populations appear to rise and fall somewhat together as though a reciprocal control was in effect. They appear to have achieved some level of long-term stability.

9. Interspecific competition exists when different species interact and compete for a resource, e.g., the alpine chipmunk and yellow pine chipmunk compete for living space. Intraspecific competition exists between members of the same species, e.g., two robins compete for the same worm.

## Investigation 34

1-3. Answers will vary.

4. Factors a–e reduce plant material, reduce soil moisture, reduce number of natural herbivores, reduce number and diversity of most consumers, increase pollutants.

5. The most important abiotic variables are amount of rainfall and temperature as these determine to a large extent the type and amount of vegetation in an area. The vegetation to a large extent determines the kind and number of consumers and decomposers.

## Investigation 35

1. The first organisms that appeared in the pond were autotrophic algae. Then primary consumers, which are dependent on the producers, came next. Then secondary consumers appeared that could feed on the primary consumers. Other than the site of these populations, other variables of possible consequence might have been the water temperature, the pH of the water, the presence of gases ($CO_2$, $O_2$) in the water, the amount of light needed for photosynthesis, and the accumulation of waste products in the water. All of these could affect the populations in a variety of positive or negative ways.

2. Answers will vary. For example, humans may build a dam, wiping out water for some organisms and creating opportunities for establishment of new autotrophs. We also pollute air, land, and water with chemicals that can pave the way for the death of some communities and the establishment of new communities. Heavy foresting of certain old, slow-growing trees and replacing them with fast growing, more profitable trees contributes to starting a new succession. Strip mining of coal and copper provides opportunities for some pioneer autotrophs to become established.

3. Different climax communities result primarily because of differences in climate (i.e., long-term differences in temperature and rainfall). Dry areas such as the deserts of Arizona simply do not have enough moisture for large plant communities to become established. Likewise, cold areas of Canada do not provide a long enough growing season for some plants. The permafrost under extreme northern soils also prohibits plant growth;, thus, only smaller, fast-growing, short-lived plants dominate.

## Investigation 36

1. One can learn about recent adaptations and possible phylogenetic relationships.

2. The organism has become extinct. The upper layers were not conducive to fossil formation for some reason.

3. The organism is a new product of evolution. The lower layers were not conducive to fossil formation.

4. The scarcity of fossils can be attributed to the factors required for fossilization. When organisms die, they decompose into their basic elements unless something happens to prevent decomposition. Usually the organism must be buried in a medium such as a heavy layer of silt that will prevent bacteria from acting on the dead organism.

5. That coal has been found at Antarctica suggests that at one time Antarctica had a warm climate that supported the production of a lot of plant material. This assumes that coal comes from vegetation. This assumption has recently been challenged.

6. If organisms do not change across time then the fossil record should show no change in form of organisms from layer to layer and possibly a decrease in the number of organisms in the higher layers due to extinction (if this is allowed by the theory).

7. If all organisms were created at the same time, the fossil record would show nothing in the layers before the appearance of organisms and all the organisms in the layers after the appearance. In higher layers, the number of fossil forms may decrease due to extinction.

8.

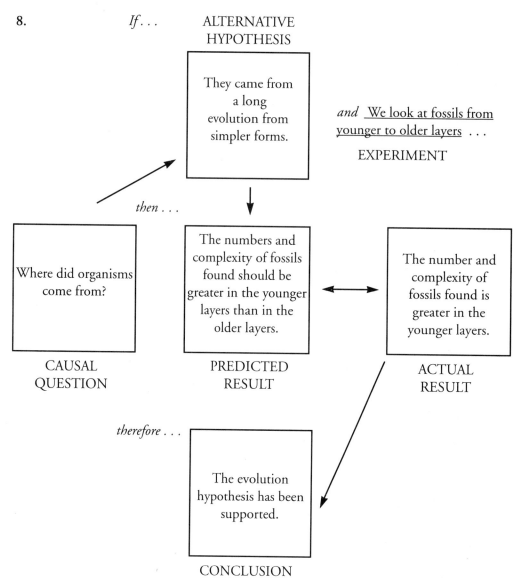

*If . . .*  ALTERNATIVE HYPOTHESIS

They came from a long evolution from simpler forms.

*and*  <u>We look at fossils from younger to older layers</u> . . .

EXPERIMENT

*then . . .*

Where did organisms come from?

CAUSAL QUESTION

The numbers and complexity of fossils found should be greater in the younger layers than in the older layers.

PREDICTED RESULT

The number and complexity of fossils found is greater in the younger layers.

ACTUAL RESULT

*therefore . . .*

The evolution hypothesis has been supported.

CONCLUSION

## Investigation 37

1. Compared to the age of Earth, humans have existed for only a relatively short time. Students will see the difficulty of even placing humans on the time line proportionally unless they construct the time line to be very long. Human historical events are so short that there will be too little space on the line to distinguish these events.

2. The first evidence used was the sequences of layers in the earth's crust showing various sediment deposits that must have taken long periods of time to build up and harden. The deeper layers must have been the earliest with subsequent layers added later. Next, fossil organisms were discovered to be simpler and smaller in size in the earlier layers and increasing in size and complexity as one moved up toward the surface. Today there are methods of dating carbon and radioactive elements that give us absolute dates of the rock and fossils that we can use in addition to relative dating.

3. Assuming the time line is 5.5 billion years (= 5,500,000,000 years), then it would be 5,500,000,000 ÷ 100 inches long (=55,000,000 inches long). There are 5,280 feet in each mile, therefore there are 5,280 × 12 = 63,360 inches in each mile, since 55,000,000 ÷ 63,360 = 868.06 miles long.

4. Charts will vary. The evidence comes from the fossil record and dating of fossils and/or rocks that contain fossils.

## Investigation 38

1. The crab population has the biotic potential to increase at a geometric rate to a large size. However, the conditions of life on the beach are limiting. Individuals in the population varied in color, some more white than others. In the struggle for existence, when the beach was white sand, the white crabs were more fit—i.e., they escaped the seagulls most often and on average produced more white offspring (color is passed from parents to off-spring) than the mostly black crabs. When the beach became black, natural selection shifted the equilibrium so that black crabs and their black offspring were more fit (i.e., the blacker ones blended in better with the sand and therefore were captured and eaten less often than the white crabs). Consequently, the more frequent color for the spotted crabs changed from white to black over a few generations.

2. **a.** NA **b.** LR **c.** NA **d.** NA **e.** LR **f.** LR

3. The process of natural selection is similar to artificial selection in that traits selected by nature gradually increase within the population. Natural selection is different in that the driving force is survival and fitness under natural conditions. In artificial selection, utility or show may drive selection (by humans) of traits that actually lead to a reduction in fitness. Natural selection is different than the idea of inheritance of acquired characteristics (Lamarck). Organisms do not acquire variations in order to survive in their environment. Natural selection acts on variation existing within the population to determine which organisms have the chance to survive and reproduce.

4. supports the theory of evolution, as indirect evidence that related species have diverged from a common ancestor (the intermediate form)